UNDER 30:

FICTION, POETRY AND CRITICISM OF THE NEW AMERICAN WRITERS

UNDER 30:
FICTION, POETRY AND CRITICISM OF THE NEW AMERICAN WRITERS

Edited by Charles Newman
& William A. Henkin, Jr.

IN CONJUNCTION WITH THE STAFF OF TRIQUARTERLY

INDIANA UNIVERSITY PRESS
Bloomington & London

Contents

Art

Preface

This book brings together new work by some forty-four American writers and artists who, by our new social standards, are young—under 30—or were so at the time these selections were written. Most writers of established precocity are represented, as well as many for whom this book marks their first hardback publication. Others are absent for a variety of reasons: several proven writers submitted work which we felt did not represent them at their best; others could offer only reprints; a few did not reply to queries; and some, of course, were unknown to us. This book is dedicated to the unknowns.

This collection took shape from the experience of editing the journal *TriQuarterly* for several years, and as our primary editorial privilege has been to publish new and/or unknown writers, it was inevitable that we should eventually concentrate on the young. While all of the well advertised attributes of youth are manifest here—concern with formal experimentation, undisguised distaste for the literary and political establishment, impatience, self-preoccupation, the common strain of getting out from under the formidable achievements of modernism—our ideal reader will acknowledge the variety of these beginnings and recall that writers in this country, for better or worse, see themselves as something more than representatives of a particular subculture or age group.

Some questions which have *not* concerned us are: how talented this generation is compared to others; how to survive in America; whether this is a good time to be a writer. In any case, our incompleteness isn't to be excused; it's simply necessary to our structure.

Any further editorial statement should be implicit in the eclectic selection of material and its ordering. And our own contributions may serve to elucidate our editorial preoccupations.

CHARLES NEWMAN
WILLIAM A. HENKIN, JR.

Evanston, Illinois
1969

UNDER 30:

FICTION, POETRY
AND CRITICISM
OF THE NEW
AMERICAN WRITERS

Premature speculations on the perpetual renaissance

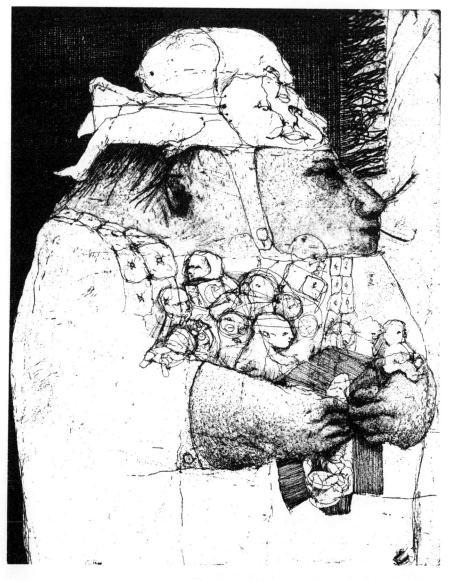

STEPHEN KOCH

Is American writing moving toward another rebirth? At the moment, our literature is idling in a period of hiatus: the few important writers of the earlier generations are dead, silent, or in their decline, while the younger generation has not yet produced a writer of unmistakable importance or even much work of very great interest. The best of it has not yet found its audience; it has not yet penetrated what is called "serious critical discussion;" and in most cases it is still a matter more of promise than substance. Even though there is a large body of new work, nothing thus far has been heard on the highest levels except an eerie silence.

The most important critical question to be asked now concerns how and when this silence will be broken; it asks whether it is the silence that precedes the speech of art. The question is purely speculative, and hence unanswerable; but it is also so urgent that I, for one, cannot help asking it. Despite the ignorance and lethargy working against the creation of serious work, I think that it can be broken and that—to put it grandly—the history of late twentieth century literature in English has yet to begin. Indeed, unless the language is to fall into complete artistic desuetude and therefore idiocy (which, despite prevailing prophecy, I do not think it will do), it *must* be broken, for in the past fifteen years writing in English has touched bottom and survived what in my opinion will eventually be regarded as the lowest and most impoverished point in its history since 1870. Luckily, after noting this fact, there is little need to dwell on it. At any rate, all the talk one hears would indicate that we have bid that period an unsentimental adieu, and even though no substantive masterpieces or even near-misses have appeared yet to herald the New Age, no knowledgeable reader needs to hear that the inspirational sources of the post-war period—moralism, academicism, provincial realism, psychoanalysis and liberal sociology—have left us a very dead *corpus delicti*. Obviously, the time has come to look consciously for new forms, standards, and dimensions of literary taste. So let's talk, however uneasily, about the Rebirth.

First, Rebirth is a bad habit which should be broken in favor of continuous creative work, and discussion of it is justified only in the face of patent cultural discontinuity—such as the breach confronting us at the present time. Unless the evidence lies, art is made from other art, which suggests that newcomers should think twice before sterilizing all wombs. As the very word culture suggests, techniques and standards must be learned, and every work of art is the product of a self-consciously applied *techne*. The incomprehensible mental tic that divides *techne* and inspiration into mutually exclusive categories remains a persistent liability of American writing, and shows few signs of disappearing. On the contrary. Nobody can pretend to precisely define the role of technique in an organic creative

5

act, but plainly the task the present generation confronts requires a degree of esthetic sophistication and self-awareness which is far from bursting out, like spring, all over. For this less than renascent situation we can partly thank the mythos of rebirth itself and its characteristically American emphasis on the saving grace of youth. The dream of a perpetual Renaissance generates as its inevitable corollary an eternal Dark Age; our literature is forever being reborn, and in consequence is never born at all. Victims of a childish and glamorous fantasy, we burble in the midst of a future which is forever *not yet here*.

And so, amid the glitter of the culture boom (sequins shot from guns) and the rivers of public relations magniloquence, our writing remains as timid and provincial as ever. This is partly the consequence of a conspiracy of mistrust between the older generations and the young. The old, one supposes, are conventional to the degree that they are either insecure or wise. It has become increasingly difficult to distinguish between these two motives, and there are moments when one suspects that the latter has entirely disappeared, particularly when one is boring oneself, reading one of the middle-aged critical magazines. On the other hand, under the normal circumstances of this culture, the young are not so much inspired as afraid. The inspiration of the young is very often not much more than the hope they attach to a future which they envision—now more than ever before—as a release. This fear, and the hope that goes with it, have their value (they sometimes imbue the courage required for creative risk), but usually they are inordinately destructive, since they postpone the engagement in the array of present possibilities intrinsic to all art. We are told that the failing of the literary avant-garde is that it aspires to so much and produces so little. (The defensively invidious inference is that it ought not to aspire to so much). But given the extreme desiccation of recent literary culture, it should be plain that the avant-garde merely aspires to the wrong thing: it wants release rather than creation, and suffers from the negative direction characteristic of youthful energy. But this negative direction has been a characteristic failure of our literature as a whole ever since it was decided that, above all, one should not be European. One identifies oneself with a set of simple-minded adjectives saying what one is not: one is not "European." Not "abstract and intellectual." Not "middle-aged." Not a "hippie." Not "academic." Not "avant-garde." Not a "bourgeois." Not a "bohemian." And finally, *"Not yet here."* The result is tedious incompetence and charismatic baby-talk coming from both young and old.

Except for this—a big except—all other signs look propitious. There is a very large reading public. The culture is prosperous. Perhaps most propitious of all is the cultural "temper" of the sixties and the shifts in artistic taste it may be able to support. A certain repressive solemnity seems to have been dispelled over the past few years; in particular, the chauvinistic, liberal ethic that drives our provincial realism is no longer taken seriously by anyone except its perpetrators and a certain pre-literate segment of the public. The change is so complete that even the newspaper reviewers get nervous when the word realism floats into sight. (It almost seems time to point out that realism is not necessarily the same as the anti-poetic, defensive parochialism with which its post-war American manifestation is strictly co-extensive). In place of the old style, one hears of nothing but a benign hedonism, which is, of course, highly conducive to the creation of art.

But this delightful turn of events should not be overestimated. It is a mere opportunity for the serious artist, an uncatalyzed statistic in a class with the relative ease he will experience trying to get the wherewithal to live while he works. So far, nothing—except perhaps one or two delightful songs on the Top Forty—suggests that the taste of the new generation is necessarily any better than that of the old. Its sole virtue is its openness, which is as open to exploitation by knaves and fools as it is by serious artists. Even the ample liberality of the hip sixties is thus darkened by a certain ominousness. For if history teaches anything, it teaches that the knaves and fools usually get there first.

AMERICA!

And so the young American literary artist faces the traditional impasse of his ancestors: the opportunity to work wonders and almost nothing at all to work them with; no training, no tradition, no models, no mentors. The liberal imagination (i.e., the esthetically conservative imagination) success-fully ruptured the modernist tradition which had gotten firmly under way during the early phase of the century, and the brilliant achievements of that era now seem terribly remote and a little marmoreal. On the other hand, the period of reaction which the thirties set in motion, and which has con-tinued until quite recently, seems still more remote, though it is closer in time. It can even be argued that the literature of 1967 has improved very little since Henry James fled the American scene in 1876. It is certainly true that the rubbish his friend Howells accepted for publication in such journals as *Godey's Ladies' Book* and the *Atlantic* was the counterpart to our own Brooklyn and Boise bestsellers. But if our writing hasn't risen in quality, the cultural "complex" has certainly changed, exactly as James foretold it would. (See his preface to *Lady Barbarina*). In 1876 that rubbish

7

was perfectly continuous with the culture as a whole. The esthetic conservatism and timidity we now confront is decidedly not, and in fact its extraordinary discontinuity ("how *can* they write that stuff?") is the only interesting thing about it. At least in several important sectors, America is simply no longer a provincial culture. McLuhan is at least partly right; the Western world, at least, does indeed look very much like a global village (which is what James meant by "the dauntless fusions to come") and whatever minor national reflexes remain, these fusions largely have robbed James' other phrase about the "peculiar fate" of being American of its meaning.

This fact is our greatest hope: at long last we have the opportunity to terminate the foolish and self-defeating search for a uniquely American art. America is no longer "America," and it will never be "America" again; the twentieth century and our emergence as the power center of the West have rendered meaningless any and all the supposed moral or spiritual privileges and burdens attributed to our historical position and made clear that the sooner we get rid of the nasty sentimentalism of our homespun *gemütlichkeit* the better for everyone concerned. The young American is just another citizen of the polyglot West; his "tradition" is the tradition of that polyglot monolith; and America itself is just another—very big—Western nation which happens to be in the saddle at the moment and riding, unfortunately for us all, with vicious, unforgivable recklessness.

Hopefully, the critics to come (froth on the *nouvelle vague*) will omit the habitual discussion of a given book's American *anima* and silently concede that anything written in English by a citizen of these shores is American—a neutral fact which, like the age of the author, is irrelevant to the critic's single concern: the book's worth as a work of art. (Alas, despite the best of wills, the critics of the present are not yet free to do so, as the reader can see). But this liberation will only be possible if creative writers take the opportunity they now have to adopt the standards and methods of international modernism—a continuous tradition of art on the highest level which in retrospect seems the obvious terminus for our overly discussed cultural questing. Americans have already played a major role in this tradition, and there is no reason why they should not do so again.

On the contrary, if the ups and downs of a chauvinistic ego are left aside, the obstacles to this solution have been the abysses (real or imagined) that separate American manners and language from those of other Western nations. The difference in manners is now nearly gone, or rather they seem trivial when compared to the forces of common Western culture and social conditions. This leaves only language. Though it is true enough that a writer's language—not only the national tongue but all the vital statistics

8

in his linguistic dossier—determines his whole art to a very large degree, the "American language" can scarcely be invoked any longer to excuse parochialism. (N.B. Though poets are purportedly more rigidly pinned to their niche on the linguistic curve than other writers, it is exactly our poets—from Eliot to Stevens to such current figures as John Ashbery, Kenneth Koch or Robert Duncan—who have traditionally paid least attention to the Curse of Babel. They have also been our finest literary artists, precisely because they take their language seriously enough to re-learn it in the light of a cosmopolitan poetic.)

But another, more serious, problem presents itself. The immemorial obstacle to serious American literature has been the lack of a viable esthetic, while the traditional response to this lack has been (to speak vaguely) "visionary": the writer attempts to formulate his own world view and then tries to create an esthetic organic to that "vision." We have even built a national literary romance around this procedure. But to succeed even fairly well, this stupendous creative task requires *real* renaissance genius on the highest level, which is one reason why so much of our serious (morally, psychologically, spiritually ambitious) literature declines in quality as its aspirations rise. (As an embarrassing corollary, many of the pop or trash arts show a much more careful and inventive consideration of their formal procedures than do "serious" works, and in fact are often of greater merit. It is better to see a small or trashy theme manipulated with joyous expertise than to see an important one desecrated in tedium and clumsiness.) Certainly if the search for visionary creation is thought to be inspired by some supposed American destiny, the twentieth century has made plain that the "destiny" no longer warrants the search. Nor could it sustain any vision worth the time. It seems more modest and practical, if less exalted, to question the "visionary" procedure by first adopting an esthetic, and once it has been adopted, artistically exploring the world view it reveals. Art is not prophecy, but discovery.

In any event, the formal repertory of serious American writing remains pitiably small, and that small repertory, desperately overworked. But if we can renounce some cherished emotional bonuses paid by provincialism and defensiveness, Americans can adopt and develop the whole anthology of modernist forms, the scope of which our literature has not even begun to explore. Certainly the past twenty years and their artistic impoverishment teach—among many other dolorous lessons—that we have gotten all the mileage we will ever get out of the Romance of Spontaneous Nature. (Equally, they warn against the timid fiction likely to be inspired by vulgarized pragmatism). It is time for us to learn that a high degree of sophistication about the techniques of form—including acceptance of both artifice and calculation—are somehow tied in with the integrity of the whole man.

As Melville understood, the metaphoric condition of serious American artists is orphaned. So it remains, but it's time to end papa's wake and grow up. Let us have no more talk about the mystical burdens of America, no more indulgence of their cozy bathos. Such talk spreads bad breath; it stinks of the ninteenth century. Nothing except ignorance, prejudice and self-pity stand in the way of America's re-entry into the arena of major art, which is that tradition of international modernism, a tradition which has the advantages of being both alive and the fountainhead of the finest literature of the age. The disadvantage of a cosmopolitan esthetic may be considerable, but I don't see what other set of standards we can adopt, and since we plainly must adopt some set of standards other than those behind the work we're getting now, we ought to make a virtue of necessity. The burden of orphanhood is the need to find or create a father. Its advantage is that you can choose him yourself.

RALPH WALDO AMONG THE DAFFODILS

Am I talking against *la vague du futur?* With a boost from LSD, Nature still Lives, at least in the gaudier slums of the major cities, and even though the returns have only begun to come in, it appears that the characteristic "creative" pre-occupation of the present generation is "spiritual" as opposed to "esthetic," or more precisely, that these two concerns have been indistinguishably fused. This is characteristic indeed. It is perfectly predictable that any ideology directed toward youth will be concerned with the young person's single question—which is how life ought to be lived—and that the answers given, however simple-minded, will seem momentous enough to merit invoking metaphysics and eschatology itself in their support. The peculiarity of American civilization is that the habitual patterns of "original thought" direct themselves to this audience and ask this unanswerable question. Such habits have their obvious historical origins in doctrines of the New Man and in Protestantism, which even at its most liberal (hippest?) cannot drop their all-absorbing concern with the problem of conduct. But though we ought to have long since moved beyond both these habits, they remain as our way of keeping the perpetual renaissance aloft and floating—but always over there, just at the horizon.

And it is floating there again. The ideology which has struck such a remarkably sensitive nerve in the generation about to come to maturity—the ideology of universal love, immersion in a kind of communal Being,

10

a return to nature (such as that proposed by the poet Gary Snyder) and its interest in the mystical expansions attributed to drugs and other medialess messages—is a surprisingly continuous extension of that Protestant transcendentalism which has always been the standard equipment of our intellectual and artistic life. (Even the Happenings—that form which aspires to transcend form in the direction of the world; that canon of workless works instantaneously created by a participatory collaboration that draws both "actors" and "audience" into a naive, mindless communion—can be understood as an estheticized version of the ethic of Concord.)

Though its revelance to art is very great, this phenomenon obviously must be discussed in general terms, since it is a "function" (another protestant word) of the community at large. My own view is that the characteristic failure of our serious art's attempt to wed eschatological spirituality with form derives from a Whitmanesque overestimation of the "democratic experiment," (though it is no longer an experiment). It derives from a confusion of the social and spiritual spheres, and while modern experience has robbed this confusion of whatever small intellectual validity it once had, it is being taken up by the present generation as a desperate way out. That generation might be surprised (freaked out?) to discover Ralph Waldo Emerson as its new guru, but plainly enough the concepts that trickle from that rather dry fountainhead are flowing once again, though under different conditions and for different reasons. Emerson's first great essay—*The Lord's Supper*—set his single theme, which is of course Communion. It is in this dream that the hippies meet him on common ground, though it is, alas, no longer the ground of a new society and a new land. The pre-occupation with Communion in the present generation is a consequence of the agony of an aging community at large, and it is further traumatizing that agony by recapitulating on the levels of both art and life Whitman's exalted and catastrophic error.

When a community is closed—or at least seems to be closed—to the dialectic of growth, "individualism" ceases to be valued and is transformed into the burden of solitude. Insofar as a society dedicated to mass thought and mass education forces this solitude on the young, they are driven to the desperate devices of the isolated, which for many of the most sensitive in the young have turned out to be tribalism, mass thinking, sensationalism (in both the philosophic and journalistic senses), and an attempt to renounce those internal forces—the analytic, the intellect, the need for dialogue, and individualism itself—which make them vulnerable to the dissociated sensibility of which they are the victims. But unlike Emerson, these young people are not rising to an opportunity. They are fleeing an impossibility.

11

After all, they are as yet emotionally unprepared for life even in a peaceful society, and are being asked instead either to participate in a what seems little better than genocide or to submit themselves to four years of tedium being trained as bureaucrats in massive factories where intellectual and emotional dialogue with their elders is rarely more than a pious joke—all the while being the object of a prurient and generally unsympathetic interest on the part of a middle class whose "way of life" seems to wait at the end of the ordeal as a condemnation. These are the obstacles presenting themselves to a generation which is the first to grow up knowing that, unless some major change occurs in the conduct of international affairs, they will all *probably* die in a nuclear war, and which has come to political consciousness at a time when the man who has his hands on the survival of us all is capable of telling his own daughter in a solemn, fatuous boast (endlessly repeated to impress visitors): "Your daddy may go down in history [sic!] as having unleashed World War III. You may not wake up tomorrow."*

In the face of these appalling realities, the apparently destructive renunciations these young people have made (they are playing loser wins, to be sure) take on a startling and even tragic dignity. They are nothing less than appeals for Grace, and they adopt *as their ethic* all the attributes of Grace: the obviation of mind, the transcendence of language, the renunciation of individualism and (as some unsung genius of the Mattachine society perceived) an essentially mystical search for Communion with the One. ("The mystical circle of friendship makes all mankind One," as the Mattachines quote Emerson's mentor, Carlyle.)

And here the problems of the community at large resolve again into questions of art. Only the drug panacea has challenged literature and the other arts as a means for discovering, or at least promoting and disseminating, the ethic of this search. Whether literature can or should bear the burden of such a quest is an important matter, but before considering it, I'd like to make this observation: this search for Communion is directly motivated by the anguish of solitude, and everything about it—from entry into the artificial paradises of LSD to the Be-Ins which, in the absence of any meaningful communication, proclaim the principle of universal love— manifests that solitude. Likewise, the tribalism which these isolatoes have adopted as their form of prayer seeks to overcome the burden of community in the name of a greater Communion, thereby making the fundamental mistake of attempting to find an ethic in the Communion of Grace. But Grace can never open the mind to an ethic: it is precisely the opposite—the suspension of the ethical—as Kierkegaard understood, and likewise Com-

*Johnson is quoted in *I. F. Stone's Weekly*, vol. XV, no. 18, May 22, 1967, page 1.

munion can never bear the burden of community. Whether experienced communally or alone, Grace can never overcome solitude; on the contrary, it can only *become* solitude in the most exalted and liberated sense. Speaking in tongues, it is utterly silent.

This silence transcends (to use the old word) both art and society in any of their possible forms, from the most hermetic to the most discursive literature, from the cubicles of conformotopia to the streets of Haight-Ashbury. Likewise, though it isn't my intention to attack whatever Brook Farmish communal experiments (advertised or not) may be going on in the back streets of the megalopolises, it's worth remarking that the successful spiritual communities of the past have always qualified their doctrines of love with a stricter order of discipline than that held by the society at large, rather than with the rejection of all discipline.

But discipline is not the point. The transcendent—and, as it seems to me, transcendental—nature of the spiritual search now going on among young people who could otherwise be expected to be the artists and intellectuals of the future cannot produce either new art or a new society, since both art and society inevitably manifest a large element of the calculated and artificial. Such is the nature of convention itself, that single hinge from which both of them turn. (The point, of course, is maintaining a society in which convention is the form for human energy and growth, rather than a blind obstacle which eradicates and overwhelms them.) But if it exists at all, the Communion which the youths of Haight-Ashbury join Thoreau himself in seeking is above such artifice, (though "above" scarcely suggests the direction of the underground generation). Even if it is claimed that this grace transcends the world by flowing back into the world through something like the double movement of the soul, there is very little to be expected from it so far as art and society are concerned. If I understand it properly, the double movement—explicit in Kierkegaard and implicit in the transcendentalists—must be made in a state of serenity, exactly that serenity which the anguish of the society as a whole has long since foreclosed, just as it earlier foreclosed the communication and human growth that might have saved us the spectacle of desperate mass neurosis exploited by such repulsive hucksters as Timothy Leary—a spectacle avidly attended by a nervously titillated middle class whose "concern" is little more than a vicious pre-occupation with the threatful re-birth the young must now go through on their own, and which is indeed a peculiarly cynical form of revenge.

One trivial (but pesky) offshoot of the cultural situation that makes discontinuity our esthetic tradition and drives the young to varieties of spiritual excess scarcely distinguishable from faddism is the difficulty in finding a vocabulary for saying what one thinks ought to be done. Just as the society spends its time puffing up smoke screens of mass thought (with or without the assistance of electrical bananas), thereby producing mass confusion, so the discussion itself promptly becomes inflated with generalities. One generality to be drawn from this observation is that it is advisable to develop the habit of thinking against generalities, though I suppose even that rule is open to question. Another generality readily at hand is that our art tends to mimic the patterns of the culture at large by dividing itself between a certain timid establishmentarianism and the most exorbitant excesses of sensationalism. (Needless to add that these two states of mind, like Sin and Death, are cruelly in love with one another, appearances to the contrary notwithstanding.) An example of this cultural mind divided against itself is the critical treatment Burroughs has received. Burroughs is a self-evidently serious artist who is also—let us admit it—decidedly sensational. But his esthetic couldn't possibly be more open to question, so much so that one feels that the solution to all the critical problems he raises will turn out to be criticism's universal solvent. But I have yet to see the critical discussion —even from writers who take their job seriously—that is more than another voice added to either the cheering or the booing section. An analogous figure—though one outside literature—is John Cage.

Of course, we are not the only nation to draw the patterns of our esthetic conservatism and radicalism from the culture as a whole: from Siberia to Gibraltar the syndrome seems to be the uninfracted rule of second-rate art. In fact, the bondage of form and rhetoric to the social paradigm—followed by a consequent confirmation of ideological habits of feeling—is perhaps the most destructive burden imposed by nationalism. (In this sense alone, artistic "subversion" has esthetic worth. To be of value, it must be the subversion of a given form or rhetoric—such as the rhetoric of subversion itself. Otherwise it will fail, not because of its subversive intention, but simply because it will not succeed in that subversion. It is not enough merely to adopt a rhetorical position, since almost all of them— however conservative or radical, however violent or benign—are drawn, subtly or blatantly, from the social paradigm.) The relation of ideology to fanaticism is well known, but the forms which ideology gives to the less articulate varieties of emotional obsession has not been sufficiently explored. Obsession has its obvious role in art, particularly romantic art, but during the nineteenth century the romantic spirit seems to have siphoned itself off into an array of national forms and animating myths—such as the myth of the Primal in Germany or the myth of Revolution in France—which invite their own particular varieties of obsessive emotional energy, such as power obsessions or Sado-Masochism. (These hang-ups are hard to export: there are plenty of power-obsessed primitives in America, but we will never have a myth of the Primal. Likewise, we have more than our share of sadists, but Sade can never assume an intellectual role here comparable to the one he holds in France).

The American romantic idea derived from the social paradigm is the myth of cosmic liberty and the oceanic consciousness, from Emerson to Whitman to Carl Sandburg to Thomas Wolfe to Henry Miller to Allen Ginsberg to Timothy Leary. (It's a bumpy ride to the nadir.) The emotional *animateur* of this quasi-esthetic is infantilism. An exploration of "cosmic liberty"—such as the one characteristic of the avant-garde during the fifties and to a lesser degree, now—is in no sense "radical" to American thought. On the contrary, it has always been our bread and butter. I can see no objection to any obsession playing its role in art, but it is worth stressing that America's typically "literary" obsession is unusually vulnerable to banality, clumsiness, and the fatuous. It's also worth noting that this tradition includes Emerson, Whitman, *and* Timothy Leary. An obsessive emotion does not in itself disqualify the romantic myth it feeds, but possibly the decadence of that tradition is recognizable as that obsession becomes more evident, more destructive to the texture of the work, and above all, more complacently expressed. This complacency is the true complacency of history, since it proceeds from the atrophy of a vocabulary. Like the men in Swift who live forever, the age of a romantic myth is its degradation, and our own has reached the imbecile stage of its perpetual second childhood— even though that myth began gloriously as the second childhood, and the rebirth, of Europe.

I mention all of this hesitantly, since it seems to invite the maddening psychologistic argument which invariably begins, "This book is nothing but an example of. . ." and the writer then fills in the name of some appropriate mental disorder. This kind of critical put-down is inadmissible, not to say deleterious to the welfare of the critic's own immortal soul, or if not that, at least his chances for being taken as a nice guy. As Eliot pointed out in his famous preface to *Nightwood,* all of us and all our works are finally "nothing but," and this transparent gambit for critical ego-boosting invites the writer to "miss the point" while he sinks into his own weakness, which is the "inveterate sin" (secularists read: callow fatuity) "of Pride."

15

The special fillip of our own myth is its invitation to the writer to disregard what he cannot disregard—form and technique—in the belief that the whole secret lies in liberty and vision. All the pointers indicate that the forthcoming crop of serious writers (it does not promise to be a bumper crop) will continue to solve the impasse of their ancestors in the old way: by confusing esthetic with spiritual experimentation. Here critical discourse bogs down in its own vocabulary. Obviously any important work of art involves both, but outside the most boring minutia of a page by page exegesis or the most head-filling rhetoric, I don't know of any way to discuss them simultaneously. We (or at least, I) lack a *langage de mesure.* Since such a terminology must be based on the esthetic of concrete works, it is obviously unavailable to anyone speculating on the future, particularly when the existing tradition is either not an esthetic tradition at all, or one which the future ought to change for the better.

It may illustrate the problem to remark that, looking for examples and precedents, my mind keeps reverting to neo-classicism on the one hand and to surrealism on the other. No sooner does one occur to me when the other undermines it, a doctrinal flip-flop further complicated by the feeling that any "espousal" of either would be presumptuous, and probably retrograde, to boot. Still, where concrete works *do* exist, as in the work of John Ashbery, Kenneth Koch, Frank O'Hara and their followers, the precedent is surrealism, or at least the most interesting fringes of that tendency. But then, it can be argued that their work is neo-classical surrealism.

But in balance it seems important to emphasize technique at the expense of spirit, simply because that emphasis seems more likely than the other to give us the canon of concrete works we now lack. (It would perhaps be kinder to say nothing about the literature thus far produced by the Learyites. One general remark: the new San Francisco wave looks like it's rolling away from the harsh aggressive rocks of yore, and washing out instead on the beaches of sentimentalism.)

A tough-minded formal self-awareness also seems to be the soundest way of combating the gassier high rises of journalism, which have an almost terrifying influence on writers and public alike. But journalism is not at fault: it only exploits the weak points of a cultural philosophy endlessly open to vulgarization and exploitation. For example, one consequence of our confusion of esthetic and spiritual experimentation is that the criterion for any serious innovation is always its *freedom,* that endlessly *disponible* middle term that invites people to encounter art at almost any sphere at all except the one intended: the concrete experience of apprehension. Even if one insists—as who would not?—that freedom is indeed the highest gift of art and its justification, the objection to our own invocation of it remains the simple-minded (sometimes called "radical") directness of our perpetual lunge toward that desideratum. If Aristotle was right to say that happy men seek happiness indirectly, it seems clear that free men get where they go the same way: via the unglamorous route of this room, this typewriter, these friends, this book. And, finally, "this" technique.

Except of course "this" technique is nowhere to be found, and I'm enough of a neo-classicist to believe that it cannot be created *ex nihilo,* adding that it is foolishly complacent to trust to the transcendent literary accidents that have up to now been America's specialty. (After all, even Dickinson had her sources.) But without "espousing" a given school, it is still possible to suggest guidelines. All the recent emphasis on the nature of media presents an ideal moment for writers to sophisticate their consciousness of technique. Even without postulating an "essence" for a given artistic genre, the hypothesis of an organic inventory of technical concerns intrinsic to an art and the genres of that art ought to prove extremely valuable. It may even be right to agree with Clement Greenberg that "the essence of modernism lies . . . in the use of the characteristic methods of a discipline to criticize the discipline itself—not in order to subvert it, but to entrench it more firmly in its area of competence." The flies in the ointment of this remarkably lucid statement are the words "essence" and "criticize." Mistrusting any doctrines of essences, I am unwilling to accept Greenberg's idea except as a useful touchstone for the creation of an artistic vocabulary. At the same time, I don't think that the "criticism" of a discipline can properly *define* that vocabulary without unnecessary loss to its expressive range and its flexibility. Finally, this "criticism" establishes an idea of a continuous history running like a backbone through a given art which, even if real, is not very interesting, any more than it is very interesting that man can properly be defined as a vertebrate.

But don't get me wrong, as the politicians say. Outside its philosophical dimension, Greenberg's formulation ought to have enormous value in the actual practice of the arts, particularly the literary arts. For example, compare the most interesting French theater of the fifties with our own. The common concern of figures like Beckett, Ionesco, Genet is theatricality: questions of rhetoric, action, mobility, the assumption of identity and the like. The brilliant results contrast shamefully with our own theater, where an inordinate overload of theatricality in the pejorative sense exists wholly bereft of that critical capacity Greenberg mentions. Unfortunately, a similar technical insight into the novel has not yet been forthcoming, though I think that for all his cold limitations, Robbe-Grillet will eventually stand as a handbook for its formulation, and that it will concern itself with the sequence of prose rhythms possible in the act of reading; that it ought to be an esthetic concerned with the sequence of events in reading time, as opposed to the novelistic illusion of chronological time. The bondage of the novel to its conventions of chronological time must be broken; if this is done, I am convinced that all the talk about the death of the form will evaporate. As they stand now, the conventions available for equating reading time with the illusion of chronological time have made the form virtually synonymous with boredom, simply because these conventions are wholly out of touch with the rhythms of perception induced by modern experience. Indeed, I can see no obstacle—outside the artist's own concerns—to a complete break with the conventions of chronological time, such as that made by Robbe-Grillet. Certainly the modern audience is more than prepared for some major changes. Criticizing the doctrine of the three unities, Dr. Johnson remarked that anyone who enters a theater imagines that a couple of chairs and a fake pillar or two are, say, Ancient Egypt. "Surely he who imagines this," Johnson wrote, "can imagine more." The reader of a novel turns a page, and imagines that two weeks have passed. He who imagines this, can imagine more. It is time to imagine more.

This brings us back to the problem of isolation. Certainly a major obstacle to our movement away from an infantile literary mentality has been the failure to establish a community of artists and readers worthy of the name—precisely that failure which continues to do its damage on the level of society as a whole. One or two caveats; by community I do not mean, of course, cliques, of which we already have an overly ample supply, nor do I mean that the artist of the future will have to hire a social secretary. But the work and risk of meaningful production—which is always solitary —needs the support of the writer's knowledge that somewhere, if only in some underground a thousand miles away, there is a community of people capable of experiencing his work intelligently and judging it on its merits. This need has more "objective" dignity than the mere needs for reassurance and companionship (themselves not to be pooh-poohed). It is obviously inherent in the nature of esthetic convention itself.

But it's best to keep silent on this subject; that way lies not madness but joinerism. Besides, such a community cannot be called into existence, and *it,* rather than the creative process, should be left to chance and "Nature." The absence of such a community is compromising to that process, and certainly explains a great deal of the artistic conservatism masked as "radicalism," which is so familiar in our writing. This sensational timidity is not, by the way, usually indulged in bad faith. Most writers resort to it only to keep from feeling they have tripped into the abyss of complete isolation. Certainly when their inevitable self-doubts are compounded by the near certainty of a hostile or uncomprehending response, only the strongest can resist this peculiar displacement of energy. But I don't know anything like a solution to this problem. Perhaps, since writers are experts in the imagination, they can imagine an audience for their work. I suspect the act would turn out to be self-fulfilling. Short of that, they'll have to settle for being strong.

We must take the leap of faith away from Grace and chasten the romanticism which seems to be our literary destiny with intelligence. We must also coldly face a virtually complete artistic discontinuity with the recent past (at least its fiction and drama) and uncover a worthy artistic tradition in a cosmopolitan esthetic infinitely broader than the one cringing, incurious habit and intellectual laziness have given us. Then we must forget about being young and bid farewell to the renaissance which is always just around the corner. Turn enough corners, and you complete a circle. Paul Nizan began his novel, *Aden Arabie,* with the sentence "I was twenty once, and I shall let no one say that it is life's most wonderful age." To which I can only add bravo, renouncing, however (through more or less unclenched teeth), the seduction of self-pity which like so many forms of seduction is a bore. The curse of being young is the (culturally sponsored) impression that one is forever *yet to be*. The advantages of this curse are all too well known and advertised, but the intoxication of its *as yet* substanceless liberty is among the trashier ways of getting high. The most striking feature of the perpetual renaissance and its prolegomena (for we rarely get further than the prolegomena) is the ephemeral nature of those scrappy documents. The endless future forever swings *somewhere else* for an hour or two, and then it is gone. Well, then, let it go. No Grace will save us from either the past or the future, but we can learn to live with them both by taking the Good Lord's advice and not swear at all by either one. Only the present—which combines the unbeatable virtues of existing and being ageless—can discover and fuse with the forms that will make presence itself linger yet a while, since it is so fair.

A plea for the domestication
of the unicorn
MARK MALKAS

FOR MY PARENTS;
AND FOR THE PEOPLE FROM HEAVEN:
PAMELA, CHUCK, DON, RAINIER;
AND FOR NANKER PHELGE
AND BLIND BOY GRUNT; AND ALL THE
OTHERS WHO ALREADY
KNOW WHO THEY ARE

> Say it is drift, not progress, none the less,
> With the old sextant of the fathers' creed,
> We shape our courses by new-risen stars,
> And, still lip-loyal to what once was truth,
> Smuggle new meanings under ancient names,
> Unconscious perverts of the Jesuit, Time.
> —J. R. Lowell, "The Cathedral," 1869

The mind is more like a stomach than anything else.
—NIETZSCHE, BEYOND GOOD AND EVIL

I: IF YOUR HEAD'S MADE OF WAX DON'T WALK IN THE SUN

A: Prefatory

Bound and determined,• her eyebrows joined in one strong band, Miss Mink Ergo abandons her old paisley Tudor. —Her own blood shadows spill around her face; —she circles the hood and constricts, as its chrome swan pierces her, with the quoin of its indifferent beak—

Dawn is earlier up there, upon the bank: Mink sneezes from the sun. Judging by her very Danish name, you should deduce *ab initio* the blonde shimmer she creates, within a sequin-mist of 'sneeze', coming into light.

She has a loveliness despite. About the famous actor, but one suspects about herself as well, Mink wrote, "Barrault; battery. Bout always tswitch tlight. & does. . . ."† She sports a killing blazer, trousers, rapier umbrella, and slim tie. Hair sprays in kinks above her brains; the cut is man-style, but has crabbed out for a long six months. That craned snout of hers brags a fancy, hooked extension, too, suggesting noses can have noses all their own. She resembles, at a glance, an old man laid-out like an older woman. 'Doomed and knows it,' that is why she has that look. *"I'm* fine," Mink Ergo has been known to pipe, "it seems to be my *blood* that doesn't fit."

But here is data that you need before we start our inquest:

Intent: This study pretends to examine the relations of a few students from our Second, and dying, City. My treatment may appear overly-reflective, or may seem to ease into the essayistic. We have only Mink to blame. For if you study her, you will talk like her. You consider everything; yet at the same time, like her you try to live ingenuously, if not nobly, within your broadened awareness, sans the freezing effects of sight. (This is difficult. and dangerous. Mink warned as she watched the pages of My *Ulysses* dirty and curl from the turning: "Eye that sees too much'll burst.")

The Hidden Cause: An action of social moment is under way. Within it lies the germ of the plot *we* shall consider:

Our country, while she holds to an uneasy, self-inflicted peace, finds that her conscious parts are in protest and that her battle is with herself:

That even in Chicago, questionable officials are being 'tailed' by Good Folk whose end is to objectify (if you forgive the paradox) political Evil;

And that bloodless hordes are gathering, here and everywhere, to attack one Southern town and march on their own souls. Surely you remember back then.

• Excerpts from M. E.'s diaries and letters are marked by cunning printer's-daggers (†), the references appearing paginated at this paper's end. Comments of my own, set off with bullets (•), go to the foot of the page where they occur. The lengthier may be postponed till the end of each passage. The search for an expository order forces us to distracting measures.

Set: Imagine now—for you must help me always—a dawning on the Great Lakes, above Chicago, where the University meets the shore. The moon is off above the trees. It is the landscape of a *dies infaustus.* Picture pastel sky, dun rainclouds skewed across the sun; but recall, those tints come from nothing so high as you divine, but from the questionable mist of cities. Descending from the fan of trees here bordering the Lake, we enter a space defined by a second, concentric arc of tilted concrete cubes: the abrupt slant of beach; and here, scattered students, bards, and 'fairies' shift in darkness, among whiffs of cheese-and-onion breakfasts, bringing the red polka-dots of cigarettes to their mouths. A radio is tuned to jazz.

(These are kids who revolt softly. They outstrip the libidinous freedom which someone, perhaps Riseman, has termed "The Last Frontier." For they *suppress* the Daemoniac, not merely in society, but in themselves. Only conscious, easeful essays into feeling are allowed, only the tenderness you read upon those faces; mad love, they have abandoned.)

Mink Ergo stands on the rise, her eyebrows joined in one strong band.

Bugger Fish, *semper felix,* prances up the rocks to join her.

* * *

Look: measure by her peers how single she is. Watch her, with a moue at her own compassion, kicking twigs and pebbles carefully away from her friend's worried toes. Her distinction is something more than dress. She seems awake; her temples, eyelids. She is holding Bugger's fingers to her breast—a gesture performed at every meeting, with each friend.

Luke sun gutters down along the pretty shore.

You can see Crispin come up the sand, wearing his 'turd' cap and evil *manteau,* gangling a pail of books and an umbrella. The cap is a crushed brown fisherman's affair. To 'mortify' his peppered, juggy neck and the mob of plush skin at his jowls, Crispin has grown his hair in hubcaps. With any other boy, Mink would suspect the intent of such a comic thatch; for she has 'analyzed' her own appearance. But the roughneck strings of mane that gaff *his* eyes give her no pause.

Young Mink plays she has not seen Crispin (though Bugger waves like mad and does a dance). But you can be sure she knows *à huis clos* that Crispin's nose-delta glistens, with bright nose-dingles, as he climbs into the sun. For she has contracted affection, in one auricle at least; it makes her near asleep with shame. (Mink lately determined that Crispin is material for self-murder. Her terror at this possible shenanigan caused the loss of equilibrium, love.)

As he walks into the public stare, Crispin inspects his trousers, to be sure that they are zippered.

They undertake their conventional patterns of greeting, safe, within their order. Mink surely quaffs down Crispin's kiss with a bawdy noise: "Ich. *Moi.*" For she has selected 'Putting on the Agony' as her stance to begin the day.

Crispin, disturbed by her, moves off a fret or two. "I love the God in you this morning," he says, "so I smile." Bugger roars, lobs one chunk shoulder through a tree's crotch, and pokes the bottom corner of his ribcage out.*

The yellow crowns of oaks are coming on fast, and sun sandblasts the tops of buildings. Even in this liberal *milieu,* the light reveals, down at the water's edge, a paralyzing frieze of eyes. So, as usual, these friends inflate their three umbrellas, with the quop of valentines; Crispin muffs and struggles, like it is his first time feathering a bow; his bucket bongs and sits in sand; and they shoulder the concave shades, vaulting themselves up.

How high they seem! Their bearings suggest terms foreign to the modern pen. One should write, *l'écriteur le sais,* of Flight, or Pinions, or Great Bounds. (But ambiguity would set in.) Certain playbooks for children—a few may yet survive—employed devices fitted to our present need. At the turn of their each page, divinely tinted figures sprang free from out the *mise-en-scène.* The figures strode on a collapsing bridge (escalated by our opening, umbrellalike) that spanned the facing pages. So there, frozen in the horrified attitudes of those antique, bloody *Lustspielen,* flanked by

* If it appears to the reader, as it does to the two boys, that Mink has gently lost her equilibrium, please excuse her. It may be—though we cannot be sure—that a certain condition makes her not responsible.

There is a self-inflicted state in which the expansion of awareness is synonymous with a joyful oblivion; when the world is transformed into images, polylevelled, though false; wherein tea-biscuit can dilate in the chewing, become flocks of strawberries for the mouth. The personality of the subject is, in one sense, self-multiplied madly, while in another it is given over. The condition is simply grace, body-chemistry's quiet gift to the smitten young—its occurrence is in fact supposed to make youth linger—a condition in which, expanding the periphery of his Ego, one perceives himself fixed in a unity and descries that Significance of which he had despaired. And more: at the same time he becomes conscious of his own heart. These transports go beyond the sexual; and though some attain to them often, to many they are granted but a single time. Little wonder the moral status of this perception-deepening is problematic. It is called ineffable, called madness, called a final Good: by assenting to its small 'death', one is said to live wider and more truly.

Is it love? Do not for a moment imagine so. Yet it *is* the sole experience more exhausted by frequency of reference *than* the Romantic Agonies. Solely because of Mink's *possible* involvement do we consider it below—the taking of a drug.

We have been told M. purchased some such on the day before this morning. If she has had the drug, then it is this which makes the rest of her actions, and our story, inevitable. Let us stress again: we cannot know with certainty. But what else could cause her, as her day plays out, to rise, as she must, high like Werther? What else could drive her to fume in Troilus' depths?

their great fairs and castles bleeding off in perspective—there a scattered *cortège* of noble bards and faeries, shifting in lightness, would (all fugitive as the years) jut out.

How good would it not be, and modern, to use like structures to project our *avant-garde* 'menagerie of three'. Imagine this Free scene, in cardboard, spread across these parted leaves:

The boys mouth their funny, hopeless kiss, squirting gooseflesh over each other's body. Gentle Mink Ergo wipes these yellow stipples off their necks and arms with her free hand. This, she often does. Crispin's forearms are chub, but delicate, crazed with pink, and Bugger's are furred, all around; while ours are fish-arms, his have bellies rife with mewed curls.

Bugger shows a touch *more* feeling, and note: Mink galls. Now when she is undercover, her tenderness, and her bawdry as well, retreat. It is typical of her. Perhaps this change of key shows her strength, her Freedom, to be questionable. *But* she reconsiders, does allow her lips to execute (though in distaste) a white kiss on his marmalade throat.

—Crispin's dying! Mink sees.

She must feel the surface of her face, hands, stomach run in quick fear. The radio skedaddles off, down there, with the shock of an umbrella closing; the beach goes poor. Mink blanks the realization from her mind.

Crispin's kiss exposed him; its vigor betrayed his probable plan of departing. On a bridge of the 'elevated' subway (a transport peculiar to Chicago), Mink Ergo one time inscribed:

Which of U, on dis Sick Transit, chooses text insteada gloss? Yr never in embraces (always listening 2 yr spirit (marginalia) glowing) SAVE wen @ The Hands of Action Greater Far—MA! DARE WE UNITE THE SUBJECT AND THE HOT-PLATE[?][†]

Mink might have written, in other words: "Only rarely, when we are Actors, can we wholly kiss."

Crispin has just kissed her 'wholly'. So, we might suppose, Mink reasons he has joined some Action that has freed his heart; and the Action most probable is: the race South.

Is this cause for her concern?

Perhaps. It may be that she speculates "Crispin's head's conspiring with his heart behind his back." Mink Ergo has read-up on Deathwishes. She fears he will escape and, all 'unconsciously', confect a death, there.

Mink is frozen in real terror. (A fly 'zeros in' on her eyes, like a midge razor. But she does not stir.)

She is, from this moment, engaged with Crispin. We might consider

24

her engagement *in medias res* the *sine qua non;* this given, all is set. For if her involvement could be wiped out now, Pinch's thought of running might die of its own. But Mink Ergo is no longer in control. She will *drive* Crispin to the end.

The air is clotted, before rain, with the rank smell of red melons.

A swatch of light curved on her forehead slides to one ear. Mink tosses her moppet mane and vamps it:

"Yo. Some take their bor-bor-yg-mi˙ for the Rumblings of the Universe. Aye: an intellectual *is* a guy who sees the anguish of the world *as* anguish. But it's your *own* that *you* see, just writ large—and Man is better than *that,* Raisin. Go, go: it is easier to save others than yourself. But it's harder to give up cigarettes than sorrow. You could Make It without this *outside* shit, these Gestures. Act as if you're gay and you'll *be* gay; the rest, forget. We *triumph* somewhat, can't you see? we *triumph* somewhat. Your Self makes Virtue questionable; his chowder-goddamned-ear forever punctured the big thing Caesar dreamed he was. —What's with these toadstools. *I've* no secrets—"˙˙

Bugger strikes Mink; her parasol yanks up its skirting and flops out flat. *Adversus solem ne loquitor.* He parachutes softly to the lawn, petrified on one dumb, mirthful yawp. Blobs run up his body.

Mink sits down on the grass to concentrate, her one eyebrow puckered. Her eyes fill, and she rises and kicks Bugger in the face, loving him. Laughing, he reclines into the saucer of his own umbrella, where he snorts nostril blood on the grass.

(After this small καθαρσίς, Mink redoes her collar. One must master boys', with the buttons on the right. And Crispin gets all tangled in his selfconscious mantle, popping with static.) Then Mink reaches out to help her antagonist and they clasp hands, and hold each other off awhile, smiling. Fresh rain wind snaps on you like laundry.

*   *   *

To the material *ubi supra* append this:

1. Bugger Fish's head's refulgent as a baboon's ass; blue, yellow, pink. He is the only 'integrated' young man here involved (at eighteen, the oldest, too), our sole representative of 'normalcy'. In high school he played football; his blouse hangs always-open; a fertility god snuggles, feisty, in his orange body hair.

˙ Defined as "noises of the lower intestinal tract."
˙˙ Same note as p. 23.

Mink considers him a case of "nobility of soul at odds with circumstance." He has been laughing constantly this year. But do not pause after your every sentence; talk right over him. In greeting, he may slam a friend, and himself, against a wall. Noted for wooing like a concertmaster; but if he whips you in a brawl he'll force your mouth and, into it, evacuate his nose. If, at evening, a three-foot tongue of fire rages past your elbow, it is only Bugger, kindling his flatulations to the moon.

2. Crispin Pinch (17) is the kind of youngster who, on a shining forenoon in September, might be compelled—if holding a brush were possible—to paint all sidewalks a specific orange. Should he make the tragic discovery that catalpa larvae have fallen, he must kiss the trees.

As novice saints with packs of muscle on their legs are wont, he will stop eating for money's sake, happy and lively; still empty, he appears with sacks of inedible spoils from a vulnerable novelty shop.

A tramp discovers himself stopped in the street, loved on the spot, and can then watch Crispin Pinch, down the block, stop to love another. Before uncovering Mink, Crispin would pick up three-four people every day, stringing them home at evening, and he would sleep unhandled with them all. He will rush to Michigan with a stranger to hear crickets, even yet. ("Man is free," he tells you. "Man is free. Man is free.") He may pour coffee on his head to make you smile, as he would die to save you. "Let me come talk to you," he will insist, always worried. "You're not gonna *die* on me, are yuh?" He will stagger for days under the approaching appointment, then forget. You may find him instead in a high library carrel, numb from weeping on old news photographs: "All those people are dead."

3. On nights when she is feeling 'open', Mink does not use the fetid sofa in their room. (First she lights on their mattress and rubs her soles together to dispel the grounds of dirt. The boys enjoy this trick, hold one another, hark for cricket-song.) They will roll her in and feel they are being fêted: dawn tinkles by their bed, in the trio of empty gilt tumblers. But there is a danger here, as well. One can lose track of who one is this way, caress a leg and find out it is his own. When they have finally 'gotten tripled [sic]', Crispin will peek round her shoulder into Bugger's face—

What, then, is *Mink?* "Bullshit, gentlemen, bullshit," she would say, should *she* be questioned in such wise. She comes below the other two, in years. Her poetry, at the time of this writing, is earning her a reputation as *enfant terrible*. Can we say more about her, and be sure?

By now, his ironflavor nasal blood has quit, though Bugger curls his tongue out yet, to smack some. And the landscape has become dead-clear.

26

(Out there, a pale youth leans upon a staff. It is a sign! that chirps out "freedom," upside-down.) So it is time to follow out our observations; the reader has all the data that he needs. Spy the odd children down below. Smell the game spang of cheddar, and the beach-smell.

B: I'll let you be in my dream if I can be in yours

[A Quest is now in order. Mink knows Crispin to be lost, 'already gone'; hence out of Goodness she must start to pursue him, upon the tawny beachhead. She must act, but cannot, surely—Crispin is right there. Mink has commented lengthily on her indirect attempt.]

. . . To return to yesterday the beach and me• (yet a-fainting under violence): Fish, gonads akimbo, shunt'd me from a very mountain, hotonmyheels into a hidden glen. (Case of splayed brains, he.)

There, find I: fernature, a roomful appointed on the greensward. Glut pounds of armchairs (hands on their knees), a-slouched spreadlegged, Here. Beautiful.

Bugger plops his back 'pon a table (like a real young blood) t'explain the setting. He ferks his skinamarink legs around a candelabra, lit! His dome's pending off the edge, inverted, so 'e yammers at me from one maleable, unblue Cyclops eye.

[Commentary:

Simply because Mink avoids reference to Crispin, do not think she is not after him. But it is Mink Ergo's singular fate that her chase cannot be admitted. It does open here. This is the 'reasoning' behind such a statement:

> *Every Pursuit (the sort that has a goal, Recovery) begins in loss.*
> *Loss is a function of our Consciousness, not only of simple departure. This, in a dual sense.*
>> *a. Awareness caps the loss. When the play of seeing-off is done, and we have come back home, it is a brown fisher's hat, for once not on our bed, that says "Good-bye." One peripheral glimpse is all we need. Its absence stands there, like a breakfront in the sun.*
>> *b. Our Apprehension initiates the search. The rape of furnishings from a study—the act itself—does naught. Only when their disappearances pop open at us, all around the room, do we take action.*

So Mink Ergo is already on her way! She is already losing, and is taking her first steps to find the boy by her side. So far is her soul beyond the action.

Yet she neglects Crispin further. In an aside, she explains her state during correspondence:]

• Excerpted from a long letter, sent by M. to her uncle, Lev Halogen, whose own poetic reputation, belatedly, has begun to assume its deserved proportions. M.'s high regard for the man is evidenced by the comparative straightforwardness, the orderly nature of her delivery. This passage deals with the morning in question, in a fashion more-or-less narrative. The inclusion of just such material is demanded by the scholarly aspect of our examination. (The date of this letter is that immediately following the morning in question.)

. . . Couldn't stop myself. So did someone else stop t'tell you in my stead? We're already on our way! Bugger Fish is here, driving. Please excuse the* hand. I haven't jitters, it's this brazen car. Bugger's sighting along the swan. . . .

. . . and he's still undressed in the garb fouled by our bloodletting.** His chest 'as had nor bathe nor rub: mud bloodflakes in that tangerine snarl. The ground runs red here, b' th' bye. But it's the whole car shaking, and not me. . . .

[At this point in her letter, Mink recounts Bugger's narration of the previous day. He and Crispin, he explains, absconded with the furnishings, having lugged them from a University hall. Students and professors, naifs, assisted the youngsters. Bugger hid the rented truck all night and, before dawn, brought the massive moebles here, where they sprawl out within the mottled glade.

The boys had wanted to determine whether this, too, were possible. ("La, well," Mink interjects, "we make the rules, don't we?") But they have become aroused by the act of theft, as Mink had feared; she had had foreknowledge of their plan. She is now concerned that this sampler will spur Crispin on to further action. Her correspondence continues:]

Betimes, up at the gladeedge, you could prcv rolling in a squadcar riotlight, then watch a mesh hat float around our forest patch t'check the beach. The less care we. You know we habitate Ground Zero, that y have 2 —and I've got acclimatized! like it! Bombs'll Pasteurize others, but crush us; we got jungle racewar, night bayonettes, Yank spies mongst us and serious about it—what's one cop, let him come, do, "there are so many little dyings it doesn't matter which of them is death." (See Kawabata, Borges.)***

[Mink Ergo was here trying to 'get Crispin back' with her green bravery. She digresses for some few more lines, then turns again to recapitulation.]

. . . The body of the law appeared & descended on us, great and spread o' chest, lumbering like elephunts do: like their pants are down around their ankles. A gay strain's in him, though: a robin'segg banana's tied around his neck. His uniform's got quaint little leaks; a wink of yellow stocking snickers over his washwoman's shins. Infra, dig? (ah, how can I tell you? It's hell just standing, just to stand.) To get to us through all the crowd of tables & loveseats, he's got to hula. But the voice of Authority'll go undimmed, for all this. ". . . & I intend to look and search for explanations," he Declares as

---

* Illegible word omitted.

** As passages like this arise, the reader must decide independently, and on each discrete occasion, whether the 'grand' word-choice reveals 1) the right conveyance of a distinctive, if anachronistic consciousness, 2) the natural parodistic faculty of modern awareness, or 3) a childish self-indulgence and spotty taste. M.'s intentional shifts of voice keep us questioning throughout.

*** Both books have been found among M. E.'s effects, but both with their pages all unknifed.

28

here-he-comes. (Always watch folk who talk like that. They talk like politicians.)

> *Voice of Authority* (Speaks tossing tiny curls and flowers in the air, leers a bitsy pink bubblegum mustacio—to me!):
> Fellow, we attempt & try to find out what goes on.
> *Bugger:* Doan looka me; *I just came on it.* (Highflung rafter-laughter.)
> *Crispin* (To show that cop the error of his ways): "Ô Mon Dieu, Vous m'avez blessè"—blesser, that means to bless [sic]—owo, you *know*— "Vous m'avez blessè d'amour:" Verlaine. —Aw, Iii'm showing uoff— My political views are to love everybody.
> *Voice of A* (Eyeing me lounging svelt in heringbone): Love's thalidomide.
> *I* (Consciously ambiguous): Cupidity.
> *B:* Frisk me?

[*The dialogue runs on pointlessly, until the radio resumes broadcast, whereat Crispin spouts "O, music O! the sky!" Mink is angered. What she styles "that decay in our chemistry: our being-free" is asserting itself in Crispin. He is 'off somewhere else.' This fouls her hunt, as does the officer's presence. So she bristles at Crispin's remark. " 'S the unkind blue that wrings us up to die! You give-in to Beauty, Love, to Hate—any silly little fanaticism." The entire passage is best omitted. "Boy," Crispin responds, "can I unkiss ya?" The gendarme is put off by these dialogues, flourishes at the furniture, inquiring what he should feel about these circumstances.*]

> *I* (Tugging his digits to my dug): Oh, *not at all.* I *know* you feel yourself and passion welded. But also this: feel deep as you may like; but don't believe in what you feel. Storm Othello as he might, he'll never fault New York a Desdemon'; the rage he's in is actual (actual, certainly: hear the breath, observe the temples beat), actual, yet false; this is only play, that a friend beneath his hand. Emotion *is* so, ambiguous. Always prepared to reveal that it is other than it is. . . . When I was loving God, I felt I'd love Him even if he, truly, wasn't, not-at-all. Did I love God? because I think it means I never loved him.*

* A note on drugs.

Of course, the personality divides. We can see, in the subject, selfconsciousness at its limit. She is double, knower and thing-known, watching as she would a silent film. Thus she loses, in a sense, herself.

Or say, it is nearly so; for she is never ex-static wholly. She strains, but never quite slits skin, and is forever springing back, into herself, and starting off again. Cradled in a burning tub, you have surely felt your form running at the outline. In prescribed baths, calibrated to body-heat, this 'bleeding' becomes most intense. Turned coldblood, like a beast, the patient's self fills up the bowl in an extension apparently unbounded.

So, like a disinherited soul in search of arms and legs, one tends to fade right into things, gaining *their* substance. It is a painful 'love'. A subject thus-far sunk in desperate unreality has got to hold any body a random center, better, a final Deliverer.

This cellular dependence is accompanied by soft demands, and it is in them that we

29

[*A shot! It hits Mink, in the jugular. —No. It is Crispin, bungling as he shuts his canopy. The contraption bats open once more, by way of explanation. Still, it frightens the children, like the children that they are. 'Tragedy', after all, even in this world, is 'Real'. Take your general fang—it is not soft. (We forget when reading.) It can inhibit great place within your temple (which a pinpoint pains); and, then, quick, begin to move. And God grant the pain, the disorder be not this: a cohort's nearing suicide. For then the dread instilled is most urgent, albeit second-hand. Time starts dying off; one must move in minute time. So, that umbrella strikes tics in all our characters, each time it sounds. Watch.*]

*　　*　　*

Mink's letter runs free. I shall summarize, cutting what Crispin would term "gorey details".

But do consider, as we go, our lilting enforcer of Law and Order. He is of our world, yet feels he can take and use authority in this glen. He was amused; but now, observe: he clutches his lapels' points around his throat, like he has a great hole in his breast, and demands identification.

Mink undertakes to use this opening to enthrall unbridled Crispin with her *proper* Liberty. She objects that identity is impossible. "The concrete, dynamic personality's exhausted as a verbal subject." She strikes her most expository pose.

Mink speaks with her fingers as many saints and idiots do: she could be weaving a cat's-cradle painfully, using invisible wire. At once, then, disordered and composed—this temper has made of her an 'image' for an entire class. Once, we *were* the *thing,* she declaims, the winning human skin. But now, taking Crispin as example, Mink Ergo laments

---

recognize the twists of illness. For the subject (whether prior to the taking, even she remains unsure) chooses to substitute for her own fate fatality of a new order; by surrendering her will, in secret she intends to blot out time or, if the phrase can be employed, to upset Destiny. These large things, she demands. And yet, simultaneously, how poor she becomes, drained of all ability in dealing with her world. Consider the fierce attachment felt, by the subject, for her companions in the experiment. It resembles the automatic love of the laboring woman for her delivering doctor. This bond will realize itself as an inexplicable despair, as if, overloaded, it has already failed. It is at this point that most lose self-control in floods of fear, preparing themselves for any evil. The climax of the fever crowds down, and one's existence is in question.

The condition's impudent intensity comes from its very weakness; the subject's terror, should her watchers leave her, will be actual. Although she wants to hide, since she has become the Other (in this case, the officer, or Crispin), she cannot budge unless he does. From that invalid fragility there rears a brute power. We know from despair can spring a wish to overcome. *Par exemple,* the hopeless case will claim the doctor, keep him past the hour, because there's no one else. He cares for her; therefore he shall be hers.

Hence, these telescoped speeches by M. take on greater significance, at least in possibility. They may be more than a lampooning of the law-man. They might mean to hold him, and to lure back Crispin, too. Hers is jest driven by a heartache. M. must clutch at least one of these people, for fear of their authority.

30

Aroint! What motion can sum him up, 'r even blood out what he means? So he composes a life hostile to demonstration—he hangs fire.

Selfportraits are always backward. But oftentimes, the mirror-image of this homily is true: our sketches of others do reflect ourselves.

Can we take the tears hung behind the rims of eyes, the ones that never quite appear, dispersing themselves over the ball, already played—can we cup them and say "here, these're what we mean"?

Mink's parody waxes mighty, dwarfing the policeman. Ecstasy, surely from a drug, shows through.

Ah! but we're not nothing. If he is finite, yet Crispin is unbound. Our greatness, having nil to do with life, 's forever possible.

That must pleasure Pinch indeed. Mink is pacing, one can know it from her tone, and the furniture conspires against her, becoming mere clumps of corners good for bumping. Down the beach, the revellers have 'killed' the coffee, and one lifts a chalice from the coffeepot.

There are strains of beings who've got to live ever-closer to their dreab of excellence. It is like there were still gods, with theb; a fresco 'round our skulls. And, since the slave imagining his freedob's free, we Are the gods. •

At this point, Mink breaks in on her account. The digression—happily —serves well as transition, therefore we reproduce it here.

Bugger's been tooling at the wheel so long, & in so-tight shorts, that his Pockets Bother Him. His fly juts s'far out you figure there's a lamp in there. Just sloshes his sulphur (devilled) hair about & bites a smile. Curse him. All he wants to do is mate, not overmuch matter what with—And he drives like th' Garden of Eden. Dead heat.

Some *motiv* in Mink Ergo's speech has roused Fish's blood. He tries once again to admonish her with a violence.

The park foliage is 'doting' and hints of its grand decay have nosed up with the sun. Two pariah dogs rage down upon the scene, slashing through a shore of dying leaves. They have been yoked by vaginal constriction while in *flagrante delicto* (a phenomenon common among dogs.) So they hobble about, like an hermaphrodite out of a classic circus, snapping each other in vain attempts to separate. They charm their audience a moment. Observation is involuntary (but for the case of Bugger, who is transported).

He employs this presence thus. Lowing, he grazes around Mink as she tenders her 'philosophy'. The officer sights him and looks set to come

---

• The deviant spellings must be explicated. We do assume—could we be wrong?—that M. has had a mind-freeing compound. But despite this, she becomes involved, as few today are able, in an idea of Dignity. She is weeping softly from here on. It appears that the whole facial mask is paraffin; the skull melts. She often cries until her teeth ache.

unhinged. Then Bugger lights into the three humans, with a dance, with a bark, like a grand lumbering loon. He is appealing to the officer to aid the dogs. "Member," he bawls, and has to navigate the lengthy sentence, winding through it as he would a warehouseful of tables and stacked chairs, "gotta treat puppies like they're gods." For a moment his distracting wins. Mink and the others laugh out, all afraid, and take a charmed pace toward him.

His *élan* is so disproportionate as to be grave. He tries to dodge behind the 'fuzz' to violate him with an umbrella. This is *Weltschmerz,* but with the smack of lips its phones imply.

Now Bugger's true motive becomes plain. He wishes to intrude himself upon his friends, not out of pride, rather to deter a miscarriage for them both. *He* knows that Crispin shaves before 'phoning Mink; that she once returned to *Lucia's* second act, with her gown inside-out. So his presence deflates those images they don face to face.

Suddenly, he breaks off and lights a cigarette. His exhalation hits a beam of light and shatters on it, coiling brilliant up and down, elaborating creamed and swirling curls. Then he jabs his groin—his own!

The action is almost rhetorical—and not so forceful as one, petrified, might dream. He yelps and sinks among the sunshades and the davenports. He could be doubling up over a 'ribtickler'. For the moment we shall see no more of Bugger's pretty 'puss', so tumefied and red.

Bugger's determined effort notwithstanding, by Mink's bravura Crispin is possessed. Though in his nature tame as any monk, he joins the free-for-all, with one act of his own. (Until now, he has remained a shade abstracted, peering through the rainclouds to pity the morning's single star.) He has not got his bumbershoot to close as yet, so he resembles a floor-lamp in the gloom, while he begins to 'try' the constitution of 'the Law'.

He clasps one hand around that cap, as choirboys or rabbits will pray, and expatiates upon a queer subject: the spontaneous combustion of the human body. No physiologic causes known, this pup explains to the frantic official; a man is simply consumed by himself, he says, flaming at your elbow.

Even Mink Ergo is struck by his outburst. She first displays amazement, and then shock sparked by her own body, that is hot of-a-sudden. (She is given to smile at this, under her mucous nose. Exposed to a report like Crispin's, the suggestible are doomed to, at least, a day of tending-toward conflagration.) Bugger is still storming with his dogs at this point, into the

32

bargain. So one might imagine what the officer must feel, although he strains to hold his image.

Mink has, as well, a tertiary response to Crispin. She sees, with waxing awe, that she has won, that she has searched-out her companion. For Crispin's display is all for her consumption. He is habitually 'off somewhere', as if a radio were keyed for him alone. But now, as chance might have it, Mink has recovered him.

Hence, his newfound *Dasein* must seem precious. When Crispin 'itches' his nose, and three squids of oil slink from the furrow of one wing, Mink shudders.

Just before Bugger molests himself, Crispin shakes free of the discourse to exclaim: "Mink Ergo—I want to tell you—that you love me."

WELL, HE ALMOST KILLED ME [*Mink interrupts herself, after this last line, to write*]**—EVOHÉ!· Mea Culpa though. I held-eyes with Bugger so he run us off the road. (Me riding the deathseat.) We STOPS on the shoulder pointed off asphalt, overlooking a rusteamymorningpond ("add that to rhetoric"; reJoyce!). Here's some of the most stunning country in the Cuntry, yet w/ damned, offal (!) Gentry (like testes within a gown) inside. The undercuts: shantihs, one-whore towns. I descended for to test the doom of takin every step on scarlet soil—**

Things next turn *fin de siècle*. Sunny rain scatters in a rush; but all is stopped here, in the thick of the grove. Umbrellas are not needed. The park's immunity lends it verve.

While cool rain shafts wash outside, Mink, suspended here in heat, begins to hum a soft French carole. Do not fail to understand; repeat: she is driven into song. Glee, volts of it, gag her, or they threaten to.

It is possible that this pausing moment fixes Mink and Crispin (through no fault of their own), revealing their spunout tale as a single figure. *N. B.,* Mink yawns in awe at her sensation. She is yet weeping. Her jaw catches. Happiness like hers should determine this for you: there shall merely be a mime of cause-and-effect from this point onward.

(Moreover, behold a tense confusion here. It goes beyond the complication of letters that engage the present and the past alike. Mink's time has been arrested, the project of her search, dispersed. Crispin's quote has catalyzed this reaction. Her plan now tends toward Entropy.)

Mink recalls herself (for she is as good as dreaming). She puts her palm, in a trembling fit, upon her breast. Left mute by her seizure, she bites her fingers so the lid of tension over her rim won't burst. The officer, unable to understand her delirium, must think her bacchic or else mad.

Along the beach, the big hush of rain has quit. Four slender trees lean

· This entry and the remainder of M.'s letter in a new pen (red) and in a slightly variant hand.

33

up the bright incline, forming thin angles with their shadows; roots and lone branches hang from the sand and gravitate, zigzagging. They are petrified in the paling overexposure. . . . But late rainladen leaves are on the nod. And now tentative, as if just coming to herself, only a little out of joint in Time, the rustling park begins to rain.

This final blow: a youngster bursts through the trees, speckled. Dancer is his name—we shall meet this youth again. He has newly returned from Copenhagen, is lodging in a vacant mansion that seems to sport no floor. He proves that you can make your visage Art; simply bandaide it before sleep to keep it lye-white, a shrivelled blank pulp, all day long. You might, if you wish, leave a sprinkle of geometric figures pink. Under his red patch, the socket is empty. A pet fowl, devouring kitchen yeast, exploded in his face, and a duck-shard smashed the eye. Mink Ergo calls him 'Beautiful'.

Dancer tugs his hair and wails "The sky is falling—O!" The rain drips constellations round him as he speaks. The children down below have found, while playing hide-and-seek (the boy reports), a boy who, from every look of things, had consumed all the sweetest toothpaste he could hold, and died. In a word, suicide. Dancer bustles back and forth, urging our Authority to his duty.

*　*　*

It is now that the uninitiated will be driven to give way. One should consider the atmosphere. The glen is laden, after all, with an emporium of furniture in the Old Order, inexplicably thrust *here,* like machines into a bower. These props have nothing of the mildness of kitchen chairs, the reader understands. A dreadful gloom lies couched in the hard oak *flora* and whorled eagle's hands of this woodwork.

The furniture persists, oblivious to them and us, around the tiny actors. Bugger lies gored somewhere in the midst. Mink is ranging among the pieces, Crispin in her wake. This corrosive dew covers everyone. And now, this new manikin is come, with yet new folderol. One might hear the policeman's radio crackle, beyond the stand of trees.

The officer deteriorates and snatches Dancer, freeing a 'slew' of disorders, viz.,

1. Dancer, quite the professional with police, goes limp, jilting his antagonist off-kilter.
2. Mink recovers but to retreat. She undertakes to dream, one must presume, on ways of making after Crispin. So,

34

a. She shows anger when he dogs her concentration.

b. Crispin is rent.

c. Before turning again into her thought, Mink does Pinch's umbrella, saying privily, "Daddy, my game's so simple, only a child can play." She says it uprightly, like that waitress marm who regrets to tell you "Sorry, sir, I'm closed."

3. Crispin, at this juncture, his heart still clenched against the rain, heads for the latrine. Modern Man provides few accommodations else for weeping on-the-spot. The big parabola bay is now patched turquoise and sudden, deeper colors.

a. Crispin goes desperately along the rise to a 'relief station'— the picnic shelter. It forms a single long portico. He has to walk under a high groined arch. Although he is on the rim of tears at this point, Crispin chuckles and stalls over choice of bathrooms. Picking "Men", he finds there are inhabitants: the proof is a concoction of staccato blats and, *più allegro,* contrapuntal tricklets.

b. But when we are weeping, odors are of small account. Not so, however, those silver boxes bolted on each stall—Crispin has no dime. Well: he plucks up, toots his nose into the Faustus cloak, pulls down the cap and, opening his umbrella to hide his tears, strides under it, out into the sun, and toward his adventure.

4. Mink aids Bugger and makes to leave with him.

a. The officer shouts, enraged, yoked to a sopping Dancer, sloshing in the leaf-husks, that he would not do so, were he she.

i. Nor would she, Mink sneers in response, if she were he.

ii. Disgust strips his uniform away; he can only wish her to be done. He tells her, crisp in fatherly tones, how "desperate" she is.

iii. "Those answers have no questions," Mink retorts, no longer afraid of being 'pinched'. "I want a queen, a Self."

b. Mink actually draws near the officer. She has already heaved back in herself, safe from her own display. Her sanguineous tongue picks its way out, trumpet-vermilion, and pours longer than any tongue; it 'horns in' on The Man's eardrum, the left. and scares wild into a fluted coronet: Blood. Do not your tonsils bunch at that? Mink goes to hosing the antiques with her coral spew, trying to save her Wing-Tips. Snared and reeking, the 'copper' retches into his own mouth, and gulps that blend down in time to rail against our poet that this move of hers is not *allowed*. Immediately Mink quits, frozen, and looking truly guilty. Dancer is in stitches. Oh, but (c) there's something—

  d. Mink exits, helping her friend along, abandoning the furniture, and Crispin's pail, to chance. The dogs still wrestle. As the children limp away to search for Crispin, Mink's insidious umbrella reaches out and clutches a *Louis Quatorze*.

It should be noted well, 'in caps', that Mink disregards these ultimate scenes in the record of her hot pursuit. She terminates her 'recap' with circuitous soliloquizing, thus:

Me, I'm a kind of nigger. So I know: Freedom's here, a live tree in my head; it waxes, bursts m' skull. Seecurity! ((Sh'll be an ancient wrinkled Grammer, asterisks going off b'low each eye, and each denote the footnote: "Yeah, alone.")) (I see they've caught an Asian Foe of ours. A mortar shell, a live one, punctuates his bum. Which at any time might burst, black him to ash. A!) Y'know, somebody's f(F)reedom turns me hunchback, wit' a questionmark Busting (from) my very backbone. I find the spine to mind Impossibility. (Some sentence.)

Crispin's dying! free! for nothing! comme th' idiom goze, "for love" (!!!)

So here I (we) run, lost in Questing for him down this "foul rag-and-boneshop" (Yeats), the US South.

I'm scared.

—He really might make himself die, and now us too. But, do we have the right 2 stop him? His disease's moral. I weep for fear. Stiff. One has a "sense of ancient Evil" (Sewall). Lost!

" 'A man must be involved in the passion & action of his time,' " Cris pontificated before his little Exodus—that ¡really! déspicable act. I chucked him Go-ee-thee, back: "Th' man of action has no conscience." But I did it mostly just to—zut!—clutch the final word.

Which this is also, Uncle.

Love,[†]

REFERENCES

Page 21   Ergo, Mink, *Diary-ae:* Jan. 4, 1964. Unpublished.
Page 24   *Ibid.,* Feb. 11, 1965.
Page 36   Halogen, Lev. *My Ars Poetica.* New York: Middlesex Press, 1966.

Beyond omniscience
notes toward a future for the novel
CHARLES NEWMAN

"... I keep thinking about that last novelist."
—E. M. Cioran

If we are to take much recent literary criticism seriously, the novel appears to be the most short-lived, abortive artform in the history of narrative literature. Historically, only a holding action of the bourgeois mind between the demise of epic poetry and the rise of modern cinema. Methodologically, simply a convenient device for those social scientists of the last century, who, lacking statistical technique and electronic communication, had to content themselves with what Goethe called "mere narrative." And *mere* is still the adjective most appropriate to the novel's condition.

It was some 40 years ago, in Madrid [within the year that *The Great Gatsby, In Our Time, An American Tragedy, The Magic Mountain, The Counterfeiters* and *Passage to India* were published elsewhere] that we were first told with any assurance that the novel was dying. For José Ortega y Gasset, the genre seemed no longer "an exploitable mine," but rather "a stock of objective possibilities" which were being exhausted. As is so often

37

the case, the critic's own terminology furthered the very dehumanization of art he deplored. To see the novel as a machine is, in itself, the basis for the discovery that it is running down. It was Randall Jarrell who penultimately defined the modern novel as a "longish piece of prose with something wrong with it."

While Ortega insisted elsewhere that it is form more than content which triumphs over Time, it is curious that in the case of the novel, he should define Time as something that catches up to a form. He missed, I think, a single point, which is mine—that the novel as artform does not spring from theoretical considerations, but rather from a pragmatic response to a loss—the loss, if you will, of the omniscient voice, of admissible content itself.

In retrospect, it is not so important that we become incapable of believing in the epic hero and his ranted recitations, but more, if we could no longer believe in *him,* how could we possibly believe in any omniscient narrator? It is at such a point that art can no longer claim the sanction of religion, magic, even history; in other words, it cannot be *trusted* simply because it appears within a recognizable frame, or is related by an "authoritative" voice. The very *idea* of the novel is a response of desperation. Do we *believe in* the characters? Do we *trust* the narrator? What do these questions have to do with art? Do we ask whether we *trust* a composer, a painter? Do we *believe in* Marvell's coy mistress? No other art form elicits reactions which derive ordinarily from human relationships, no other betrays such an uneasiness about its aesthetic existence.

Yet, as might be expected of a genre intrinsically related to middle-class liberalism, the novel has constantly struggled to regain an authority it never had, to lay nostalgic grounds to be *believed in,* to take an equal place not *in* art, but in discourse *about* art. From such struggle its constant crisis of form issues.

Starting with that premise, the history of the 19th century novel might then be viewed as a series of masks or stratagems compensating for the genre's questionable lineage. In this context, the *romance* emerges as the character-istic bourgeois response to the loss of omniscience—for the narrator in direct-ing himself to the preconceptions of his audience, to the attention span of *their* convenience, provides the illusion of authority regained. The narrator's defects are disguised insofar as the reader adopts them for himself. The reader becomes, in Ortega's words, a "temporal provincial"—as if he were something more to begin with.

Naturalism, while its pretensions are anti-romance, asserts its own authority just as surely to justify its scientific ways to man. "Is it not time to make justice a part of art," Flaubert asks, "so that art may attain the

38

majesty of the law, the precision of science?" And within his work, the romance and the naturalistic method are enjoined. 'I may give you Madame Bovary,' Flaubert implies, 'but I give her to you through God's eye.' No wonder we look back upon his century as the apogee of the genre. An audience can ask nothing more of an artform if it is both romantic in its procedure and scientific in its findings.

It was Joyce who broke up that happy marriage of convenience between the romance and naturalism by destroying the illusion of God speaking to the villager. And while he may have believed with Flaubert that the personality of the artist finally refines itself out of existence, the effect of having the narrator's mind working in full view of the audience, is to insist upon the accountability of the narrator himself—*beyond* any frame or methodology—and signals the reign of the "intellectual" in the arts, the Bourgeois' authority regained in spite of himself.

Joyce did not exhaust the novel as we are so often told by commentators who have exhausted themselves within his. He merely exhausted Omniscience as a point of view. The narrator could never again claim his form *ex hypothesi* in terms of its audience's attention span, or in terms of a preconceived scientific method. Nor could the Bourgeois reader ever again escape through romance and dignify it as science. Next to Bloom, the epic hero is epicene. Next to Joyce, God comes off as simply a poor linguist and a monologist at that. And certainly the reader can no longer make it as a "temporal provincial." *Finnegans Wake* is the first great book without a single sentence we can *trust*.

Joyce exemplified what Flaubert hated most—"all personal affectations and nervous susceptibilities"—though paradoxically he realizes Flaubert's theory of form more than Flaubert himself—"Form is as free as the will of its creator." Flaubert was still concerned with what *kind* of a novel he was writing, how to justify the form generically. But were we to ask what *kind* of a novel *Ulysses* is, we would undoubtedly be answered with the rhetorical question Stephen Hero playfully asks himself, "Is the bust of Sir Phillip Crampton lyrical, epical or dramatic?" With Joyce, novelistic form no longer can be understood as an imposition of structure but rather as an extension of personality.

There is some justification in treating the novel as dated, since it is in fact the oldest of abstract art forms. Its thrust from the beginning has been towards an alogical, autonomous structure—syncretic, not synthetic—held together by the tension of its own formal contradictions, testimony to the interpenetrability of experience, and the need for combinatory expression.

The one thing we know about the novel is that it is always dying—the greatest novels often being those apocalyptic in structure, presaging renewal by their very exhaustion. Of all the arts, it requires the least apprenticeship but the most endurance, both in its audience and its maker.

What has always set it apart from the other arts, including even poetry and the essay, is the lack of a proscenium—a given frame—"the mere force [that word again] of the excited imagination without the assistance of material objects," as Sir Walter Scott used to say. And certainly, such a form lacks the kathartic spontaneity of the aural/visual arts. But Goethe knew that—we do not need the prophets of the New Immediacy to tell us that literature is a reflective art and requires a reflective act to experience it. "It is not urged against cuticles that they are not hearts," Santayana says, "yet some philosophers seem angry with images for not being things, and with words for not being feelings. . . ."

The novelist would be untrue to himself if he placed the novel in a competitive position with the proscenium arts. The American writer has been traditionally paranoid about his craft; to accept his media as anachronistic will only serve to make him schizoid as well.

Historically, the very reason the novel could not revive the Renaissance hero is because it carried the Renaissance mind to its logical conclusion. While inductive method made possible the rediscovery of the classics of antiquity, it could not reproduce them. And the modern writer might then be defined as a Renaissance mind without an antiquity to exhume. We are left with the mind working on itself, a conflict between empirical investigation and that of the intuitive imagination. Ortega defines this conflict as that between "scientific psychology" and "imaginary psychology," or, to use the Positivist's terms, between verifiable and visionary experience.

There are authors, in retrospect, for whom the conflict seems less overt. Flaubert, because he worked in a time when the romance was still venerable and science not yet suspect, and Joyce because he worked in a time when the suspicion of all literary convention was still exciting, and not the working hypothesis of every freshman English class.

Curious that a form could pass from barbarism to decadence in less than a century? Not really, when we recall that for two hundred years English critics denied that the novel could have a form at all, because it wasn't like a sonnet or a sonata—while one's own generation of critics maintains that indeed it had a form, but that it is hopelessly dated. We are used to critics in all the arts recognizing a form only when it has become anachronistic, but the modern critic generally takes a position in which he can hedge all bets. The contemporary novelist is told roughly this—yes, form endures beyond content, and yes, the novel had a form, but unfortunately it died at the point when our forebears were denying its existence, so that the trouble with contemporary fiction is one, its formlessness, two, its inability to develop a new form (like the other arts), and three, its indistinguishability from past forms.

Clearly, the *age* of the novel, like the ages of opera and reform, is past. But why this makes the form obsolete is more difficult to assess. Did novels get worse as their monopoly on mass communications decreased? Do movies get better as their audience multiplies? To base art on either the burial or rescue of a form is mediocrity's greatest privilege.

The modern novel this side of Joyce has moved inexorably to break down the strong situation, psychological motivation, the serial plot; and with the rejection of the last possible "given frame," the chronological plot, the last guise of omniscience is erased. If an audience can no longer predict a narrator, he is no longer omniscient.

This has had the effect of placing a singular burden on the speaking agency, for he can no longer speak within a "situation," a world, but must justify the situation itself. It used to be that he had only to "authenticate" it; make it "live," as they say. Now he must answer the dull mistress's constant query: "why live?" As his given authority has diminished, the narrator's struggle to assert himself has become more visible—one might refer to him as a *nouveau* narrator, in every sense of the term—most of his efforts are simply directed at laying the grounds to be *believed* in, the establishment of an authoritative voice.

For the writer in this fix, there seem to be two rather extreme alternatives—which I will call the *bourgeois* persona and the *philosopher* persona. The former, to date, has provided us with our greatest "classic" American literature. For example, although Ishmael, Huck Finn and Nick Carraway begin and end their respective narratives, they merge effortlessly into the third person as their stories gain momentum. I call them *bourgeois*, not because of their class background, but because they do not allow their ideas or their method of perception to violate their experience. Like the good inductive scientist, they at some point must take their perceptive apparatus for granted, and provide a generality larger than the accretion of detail. In this sense, as narrators, they accede to experience itself rather than to their vision of it, and are reborn not to make some penultimate comment —an admonishment to get back to work in the garden, say—but are reborn to history itself. It matters little whether the thrust of that history is towards the future, as with Huck, "striking out for the territory," whether they are "beaten back" into the past with Gatsby, or are simply reborn to the neuter

41

present to tell the tale like Ishmael. The bourgeois narrator, as supreme relativist, barters with his experience, and in the ability to *suspend the suspicion of his own perception,* gains access to history.

It is no secret that the most interesting of contemporary fiction has moved in an opposite direction—from the bourgeois accession to history to the philosopher's concern with the nature of perception itself in a historyless world. A major distinction is necessary here. One recalls Tolstoy's saying:

My job is merely to be talented . . . not . . . to solve such questions as that of God, of pessimism, how and in what circumstances . . . and if the writer whom the mob believes in has the courage to say that he does not understand anything of what he sees, that alone will be something gained in the realm of thought.

It would seem that Tolstoy did not follow his own advice—the narrator of *War and Peace* is, after all, God explaining Jesus—but the real difference between his attitude and that of contemporary writers is the *category* of philosophy each values. For what Tolstoy was trying to avoid was the imposition of *metaphysics* upon literature, while in the modern novel, our excesses are due rather to the imposition of *epistemology.* Unhappily for us, ideas are more expungeable than methods. Tolstoy could organize his philosophical imperatives so they could be excised from the narrative by future generations, while our every strategy is invaded by the epistemic process. The narrator as epistemologist views the novel as a kind of positivist's mind/body problem—in Gilbert Ryle's words, "the ghost within the machine,"—and so it is not surprising to find the relationship of the philosopher-narrator to his novel's structure as precisely that of a ghost within a machine. When Wittgenstein defines philosophy as a "battle against the bewitchment of our intelligence by the means of language" he locates the major concern of the philosopher-narrator.

What is most curious about the novel as an instrument of the epistemologist, however, is that it caters to the time sense and preconceptions of its "audience" just as surely as the serialized, chronological novel catered to the 19th century bourgeois. And the suspicion is that as the bourgeois once saw in naturalism a justification of his way of looking at the world, so the "new novel" is the philosopher's *romance.* "A genre becomes universal," Cioran says, "when it seduces minds which have no reason to embrace it."

The most important thing about the distinction between the philosopher and the bourgeois narrator is that it has been blurred. Their interaction is missed by those who predict the death of the novel—for their argument is dependent upon an unresolved dialectic between our two personae. Consider this typical stricture:

Now, the examination of the evolution of the novel from its beginnings to our day, reveals that, from being pure narration which but alludes, the novel had advanced to strict presentation . . .

Who said that? Susan Sontag? Norman Podhoretz? Marshall McLuhan? It is of course Ortega 40 years ago, and he is talking about Balzac! Yet this same quote could appear on any page of *The New York Review of Books* and we would not recognize it as published in old Madrid.

Ortega goes on to define the clash between "imaginary" and "scientific" psychology, but what he failed to predict is that in giving up omniscience, the post-modern novel has blended the two—there is no necessary clash between empiricism and intuition for the epistemologist, because history for him is simply a way of looking at history. The philosopher-narrator does not allude to events but describes the way we see events. This is (perhaps) what McLuhan means when he says the "medium is the message"—that we are not goal but method-directed. "Pure narration" and "strict presentation" have become one and the same, compromising any critic who would beat one with the other. As every man has become his own psychologist, every narrator has become his own epistemologist.

If the fusion of the romance and naturalism made a certain kind of 19th century novel possible, so does the fusion of the bourgeois and philosopher persona suggest a certain kind of novel for our time. For example, *Catch 22* is not remarkable for its plot or characters, but for the attitude of its characters toward their plot. And in works as various in intention as *Pale Fire, Naked Lunch, The Sot-Weed Factor,* and *V.,* the greatest drama is whether the narrator will ultimately succeed in finding a form for his story. This *nouveau* narrator is not primarily concerned either with imagination or fact, but rather with the structure of his work, *das Buch* itself. It is not science and the imagination that are at odds with each other, but the narrator and his form. That first-person narrator who so casually adopts the omniscient third in classic American fiction finds the same sort of transition impossible today.

This is not to say that there is no longer conflict between the bourgeois and philosophical modes: Consider the fate of the naturalistic tradition in Bellow's *Herzog*. Here is a consciousness so overwhelmed by experience, historical and personal, that the most he can manage are notations for a novel, philosophical imperatives for unperformable acts of art. He is precisely what Ortega complained about when he said that "fiction is an art of forgetting," and that 'culture' is what one remembers after one has forgotten all the books one has read. Herzog cannot forget anything, so it is not surprising that the letters he writes, his exposition, is more interesting than his life, his fiction. It is only when his exposition is sufficiently speculative as to be unweavable into the narrative that the novel surges; and hence, he falls back on the diary form to give his internal evidence some patina of external authority. It used to be that the diary form diminished the barriers between the writer and his experience. At this late date it seems rather to heighten them. Instead of the mind absorbing and transforming external experience, it is external experience (occasional as it may be) which serves to document, even justify the mind. In other words, it is only when the narrator becomes his own narrator, his own built-in, cameo third person (only when we are certain that Herzog *is* Bellow) do we begin to believe him, and that is about as far from omniscience as you can get.

On the other hand, in the "new novel," the *romance* of our time, the narrator is notable for what he does not see or say, if not for what he forgets, at least for what he cannot remember. Ortega would complain not that he forgets too much, but that he doesn't know enough to begin with—evidence, certainly, for a "scarcity of possible subjects." Yet far from being that best last gasp of a tradition, the "new novel" seems to be a return to a primitive realism which Ortega thought impossible. "The progressive dis-realization of the world began in the Renaissance . . ." he complains, "where shall we find new material to reconstruct the world?" Where indeed? Nourished on the chiaroscuros of impressionism, impelled to take thinkers like Croce seriously, Ortega could not foresee the desperation which has forced us back on the world of objects, surfaces, artifact; and thus we concoct a naturalism which prides itself on self-indulgence, romances which scientifically suppress themselves. Herzog is most interesting when he is least believable as a character. While in the "new novel," our trust in the narrator is restored at the price of our interest in him. He recalls Chekhov's Treplev: "I have talked so much about new forms, that I am falling into a convention myself."

Apply this dialectic to the twin giants of modern American fiction. Faulkner's mind, so characteristically bourgeois—unsystematic, vacillatory, reactionary in all but his private aesthetic—never attempts to justify his mode of perception. He allows himself to be overwhelmed by his experience, by the story itself, in a thoroughly "classic" manner. He goes out like a good bourgeois should—lost in the story he has pieced together. While the other great totem, Hemingway, remains the most tragic example of the bourgeois mind gone philosophical. Increasingly he allowed his patented way of seeing things, his epistemology, to stand for history, so that *The Old Man and the Sea* may be seen not so much as the product of exhausted celebrity, a self-parody, but as an unwitting precursor of the "new novel"; the first American anti-novel.

Ortega insisted that the artist must "care more about his imaginary world than any other possible world" and urged the novelist to retreat from history to the "village," so that he might develop, not the forces which shaped his characters, but rather the "inner mechanism" of his personages. The problem with being a "village explainer" is not that you have to be a village, as Gertrude Stein insinuated, but rather, which village is worth explaining? For in our time it is criticism and not the artist which sets the village and makes a virtue of parochialism. The writer who is out of the right village at the right time is in trouble—to be in Yonville when one is wanted in Paris, or to be out whaling when one should be in Boston can be devastating to a career if not to talent.

It would seem, then, a simple matter for an alert writer to assess our literary geography and take up in the proper village—presumably with a grant—particularly at a time when the academic and the commercial world reinforce one another at so many points. Truman Capote has made the most publicized attempt to do just this—and realize Ortega's dream of a novel where imaginary and scientific psychology are enjoined.

The central thrust of *In Cold Blood* is not only away from the current experimentation in fiction, but also from Capote's personal brand of self-consciousness. So that the public relations of a "new form" is typically less significant than the history of his own ego, the way in which he thinks he ought to view the world, and the way in which he wishes his narrator to be regarded. Oddly enough, the weakest portions of his book are his descriptive passages, where the prissy personification of inanimate objects as in *Other Voices, Other Rooms* reasserts itself. Only Capote, and Capote as Cosmopolite, could hear as his final sentence, the alliterative abomination, "the whisper of wind-voices in the wind-bent wheat." The strength of the book, on the other hand, lies in his generally successful attempt to avoid his past forte—petty lyricism.

But what prevents this book from being seriously regarded as a *novel,* new or otherwise, is precisely his failure to fuse imaginary and scientific psychology. For the book purports to analyze and dramatize an act of violence, but to explain this village he resorts to, as climax, a lengthy quote from a Menninger Clinic report on psychotic behavior. On this dull shaft of officialese, the entire narrative momentum of the book impales itself. As an empirical justification for the imaginative reconstruction which precedes it, it fails utterly. Comparable failures would be *David Copperfield* if its climax were an excerpt from the *Parliamentary Report on Poor Laws* or perhaps *Crime and Punishment* with an appendix from the Czarist police files on anarchist behavior.

Capote raises a serious question in spite of himself. Why can't the findings of social science be woven into a convincing narrative? And for that matter, why isn't large-vision'd and elegantly written history considered an imaginative form and appreciated as such? Schlesinger's *A Thousand Days,* for example, is more of a novel than *In Cold Blood,* particularly if one's criteria for form are 19th century. Again, the key to the book is not to be found in either its public relations or critical categories, but rather the way in which the author struggles with his form, the way he wishes his narrator to be viewed. For Schlesinger wants to be taken as a dramatist here, an involved observer of attributable sympathies and sensitivity, as much as Capote yearns for the detachment of the social scientist. While both viewpoints are certified by personal vantage point—the author as participant—the thrust of their involvements is quite different. While Capote is trying to take on the mantle of positivism, Schlesinger has also rejected his earlier style and reverted to history as personal memoir—the sort of approach we associate with Cash and Parrington, or even Bancroft and de Toqueville.

This is not to say that Schlesinger is a novelist—only that he makes appropriate use of the novelist's prerogatives. For his prose, like Capote's, breaks down where the true novelist's must live—on those commonplace experiences whose feeling is otherwise lost on us. And like Capote, he is weakest when he is at his most professional. Thus his descriptions of Kennedy family life, and of Mrs. Kennedy in particular—the experiences which affect him as a human participant most strongly—are by turn stodgy and sentimental, and his casual observations painfully repressed. "Conversation filled in the interstices of the afternoon" is undoubtedly the way in which a historian views dialogue, as helpless a response as Capote reporting those wheat voices.

Yet Schlesinger invariably allows the reader to judge for himself the circumstances and character of his observations. "Early in August my wife and I were asked to luncheon at Hyannis Port", is a typical chapter opening, and that is hardly a positivist covering his tracks. He could have easily fallen back on the diary form like Bellow and let events justify his mind, or he could have detached himself like Capote, as his eminence would certainly have allowed him. He chose, however, to stretch his framework as much as his particular sensibility would allow, using his roles as amateur confidant and professional scholar to reinforce one another. In this way, he becomes the metaphor himself, the mediator between the private personality of his protagonist and the public events which surround him, an accountable agent as no omniscient narrator could be. Proof of this is that even if Schlesinger were found eventually to be inaccurate in his particulars, no error of memory could compromise his structure. While even if Capote is perfectly correct in every detail, nothing can unify his book.

So flexible is the narrative structure, then, so thin the line between the verifiable and visionary, that we have two equally oblique side-swipes at the novel—one which succeeds as history because it appropriates all the techniques of the novel while disclaiming any intention to be one, and another which fails as a novel because it appropriates the techniques of history in its claim to be fiction.

But what if one rejects both the novel as history and history as the novel? What do we have left? The arch reply to that question has produced the most startling fiction of the last decade; what journalists have come to call "black humor" and academicians, "dark comedy."

Its essence can be seen quite clearly in a slight book which appeared at the same time as *In Cold Blood* and *A Thousand Days,* and was naturally crushed between them though it deals similarly with an analysis of the violence which underlies our society. And while it may be nothing else, James Purdy's *Cabot Wright Begins* is certainly a novel.

Cabot Wright is a parody of the archetypal American W.A.S.P. within the archetypal American picaresque—a refutation of both our national experience *and* the traditional literary embodiment of it. As in Nabokov, whom Purdy at his fleeting best most resembles, a false crisis in life is the metaphor for a genuine crisis in art. Or to put it another way, the struggle of the protagonist to overcome his environment is merely a refraction of the narrator struggling to overcome language itself.

The plot does not suffer from encapsulization. Bernie Gladhart is sent by his wife/muse Carrie Moore from Chicago to Brooklyn in search of the hero/rapist, Cabot Wright, lately released from prison, in order to "tell his story." Cabot is that "good subject" which hopefully will give Bernie's otherwise undistinguished and highly personal prose some verisimilitude. Bernie finds out absolutely nothing, however; we find out about Cabot *in spite* of the storyteller, which certifies his modernity if nothing else. Actually, Cabot is located by one Zoe Bickle, wife of another failed novelist, Kurt Bickle; and Zoe, in collaboration with Princeton Keith, editor of editors, ghosts Cabot's story, though it is rejected in the end by Al Gugglehaupt, Goethe of publishers. Princeton is banished to his hometown in the midwest, Bernie is cuckolded in his absence by Joel Ullay, a colored super-swordsman, and Zoe Bickle ends the book with perhaps the most anticipated climax in all post-modern literature:

I won't be a writer in a place and time like the present.

47

Cabot's character development is worth pursuing since it obviously represents the "novelist's" answer to Schlesinger's and Capote's researches, the consequence of "caring about an imaginary world more than any other" these days.

Cabot's fall from normalcy is traced to the fact that he was a "supposititious" or illegitimate child. But what plagues Cabot is not the fact of his background, but the jargon—psychological, journalistic, academic, and the causal logic of each, which purports to explain him *in terms* of his background, his village. The question, then, is not so much one of Cabot's "illegitimacy" as his "hypocathality"—not his unsuitability as heir to the traditional American Dream, but his unsuitability as protagonist for the traditional omniscient narrator. Indeed, his illegitimacy has meaning only in the sense that a jargon will tell us something about its user—for example, if we make the "beast with two backs," we run the risk of producing "bastards." If we have "promiscuous coitus," we could have "asocial progeny." If we "make love," we might have "unplanned children." But if we achieve "simultaneous orgasm," what we've got are "supposititious" children.

The problem is that the "background" upon which Cabot's violence is based (and more importantly, the movement of the plot itself) is destroyed when we discover that he did not know about his questionable paternity until *after* he was released from prison—so that the cause for his rampage (more than 300 rapes in the Manhattan area alone) can hardly be attributed to that. Indeed, when finally cornered by Zoe Bickle, all Cabot can recall is that he started "feeling tired" one day, and that his wife and employer urged him to see a psychoanalyst, who promptly, after diagnosing his sickness as "chronic American Fatigue," suspended him from a padded meathook and liberated his libido. Thus unrepressed, Cabot "gets deadly" and attempts to satisfy his newfound sexual strength, first through his wife who eventually can't keep up with him, and then upon the female population at large. While this is going on, his wife is committed to "the nut-hatch," his parents are killed in the "revolutionary Caribbean" and these tragic events are once again enlisted by his village explainers as causal agents in his demise, except that, again, Cabot discovers them *ex post facto*. It is clear that Purdy is trying to give the lie to any kind of conventional rationale—in terms of plot or psychology—*to explain* Cabot's behavior. As soon as any one narrator smacks of omniscience, he is struck down by conventional wisdom.

What is being rejected, however, is not only the scientific pretension to explain human behavior discursively, but also the literary presumption of Aristotelian complication and dénouement. Purdy's vision consists of an autonomous, inexplicable action enveloped by a series of commentators who equally pervert it. And the tragedy is that in the inexorable operation to define his "flaw", Cabot is gradually deprived of any identity whatsoever. His personality is overdigested until it becomes suitably surreal to others and unreal to him. Indeed, in the end, the only explanation he can offer is that he raped out of "boredom," which is, of course, both more plausible and dramatic than the other alternatives. Cabot says:

"I have lost my memory for consecutive events . . ." "I have read so many variations of what I did I forgot myself . . . I have heard my life so many times, I am a stranger to the story itself."

And there we have the storyteller at mid-century.

Purdy is at pains to avoid the two staples of popular literature, psychological motivation and sexual description. He refuses to be that "good narrator" as Cabot refuses to be that "good subject." We are told nothing about his formative experience except in the clichés of the American Dream, nor are we told precisely *what* has made Cabot tired, just *how* the psychoanalyst releases him, the manner in which he accomplishes his rapes, or even how they felt. All we know is that he accomplished them "easily and well." As substitute gratification, we are treated to grossly unsuccessful parodies of other novelists and other media, usually in metamorphosed headlines, reaching a climax when Cabot's last exploit is defined for the public mind as "ANONYMOUS COON STRIKES AGAIN."

Such a lack of characteristic fictional ingredients might well be traced to the nouvelle vague—*Cabot Wright Begins* resembles that scene to the extent that it is rhetorical criticism more than fiction. But the French "new novel" is essentially a philosophic rebellion against its own past masters. ["Outward events, traumatisms, belong to the cinema," Gide maintained, "the novel should leave them to it"—"Cinematographic vision destroys reality," Proust elaborates, "because its form separates it from the truth to which it pretends to limit itself."] Whatever else it has accomplished, the "new novel" has refuted its modern predecessors more thoroughly than the Anglo-Saxon novel has ever been able to do. Whether that represents an advance is another question.

Purdy's rebellion, however, is not directed merely at a philosophy of form, but against the whole of American literary experience. While his French counterpart seems to mistrust language and its effect on modern experience, Purdy, in a very traditional way, mistrusts modern life and its effect on language. What Purdy reflects above all is the paranoia we have about communication itself; the feeling that our extensions of media have overreached us, that "the medium is the message" means simply that the

49

medium perverts, no matter what the message. And in this context, "form" can hardly be understood as a preconceived phenomenon, or even as a writer's prerogative—but rather as a recognition of a medium, first by those who sell it, and then by those who buy it, intellectual and commercial alike. Like Cabot's "supposititiousness," the entire question of form becomes *ex post facto,* germane to consumers and critics only.

In many respects, Purdy is that *last* novelist. He carries Gide's ideas of the "pure" novel—one which would leave the greatest amount possible to the reader's imagination—to its logical if absurd conclusion. He exemplifies Joyce's implicit assumption that originality in literature derives initially from waiving *all* literary conventions. He is Tolstoy's noble narrator who can "explain" nothing of what he has seen. He exemplifies the new novelists' concern with art as criticism as much as creation. And he is Ortega's ultimate novelist, for certainly he has forgotten enough. In short, he has given up every conceivable prop of omniscience. There is no conflict between imaginary and scientific psychology, because there is no longer any distinction between them. Purdy certifies that if a novel is to mean anything in our day, it must have as its central proposition the question of its own existence.

The ambiguity of such an aesthetic need not be elaborated. For Purdy is as close to Camp as a serious writer can get without being its apologist—Camp being defined as the parody of that which is no longer worth parody. After all, to "rape" out of "boredom" is a perfect metaphor for the aesthetic which attempts to destroy the clichés of life by beating them with the clichés of art. It is but a short step from the constant questioning of form to a mere contempt for it.

In this situation it will do no good to recapitulate Ortega's arguments, even in the hippiest prose. Whatever critics like Marshall McLuhan have to tell us about the *New,* they have only regurgitated the party-line in regard to the death of the novel. The rise of a non-literary or even non-verbal culture does not signify the death of literature, any more than pluralism negates synthesis —the former simply defines and enhances the value of the latter.

We have grown up with a generation of critics who have analyzed modern novels with techniques gained in response to modern poetry. Now we are faced with another generation which applies to literature the techniques and assumptions used in analyzing movies, music and painting. There is some queer testimony to the novel that it should remain amenable to so many different perspectives; but it would be sad, after surviving the critics who viewed the novel as poem, to be given over to those who insist on its being a happening.

50

Naturally, the three works specifically discussed here are "failures," and it is somehow instructive that the least "significant" of the three is also the truest. From Schlesinger we wanted that engagé political novel of power America has never had, from Capote, a genuine sociology of violence with a narrative appendix of specific causes *a la* de Sade, and from Purdy, a philosophic critique of the mass media and their relationship to our unconscious. This only confirms the law which seems to have emerged from the most recent demise of the novel—that any contemporary experiment in prose defines itself by the intensity with which it claims a form other than its own.

What *is* interesting and valuable about these unlikely books is the way each author struggles to lay the grounds for his narrator to be believed in. Oblivious of the roles and styles their careers have accredited them, they equally confront, though none of them resolve, the conflict between their visionary and verifiable experience. And though their strategies are quite different, they testify collectively that the contours of the novel have only begun to be explored. Schlesinger struggling with his gravity to be humane, Capote with his prissiness to be profound, Purdy with his absurdity to be—beautiful— these efforts signify a coming to grips with literature rather than merely an attempt to find one's place in it. And the form that is destroyed in those struggles is what we *merely* call the "novel"—the continued and venerable adjustment of our empirical guises to what's left of our consciousness.

Ortega's Modernism, in its dialectical rejection of the nineteenth century, blinded us to the variety of our past and hence the alternatives of the present. Nothing could be more harmful to the contemporary novel than the continued, labored refutation of traditional formulae. Now that we have learned to do without plot, psychological motivation, character development, moral judgment, we may yet learn what they are good for. The greatest danger to fiction is not the reconsideration of devices already categorized, but a warmed-over positivism, a solemn shooting of ballast no longer on board. We have at no small cost cleaned ourselves up, and can carry on that battle against "the bewitchment of intelligence by the means of language" on our own terms. True experimentation uses tradition ruthlessly, it does not expend its major energies in making the past appear old.

In the main, the most searching writers today—Barth, Borges and Beckett can serve as exemplars—have unabashedly used their knowledge of literary history to advance the state of the art (even though it may be a history of their own creation) and this revaluation compliments a lateral movement in younger writers to learn unselfconsciously from national literatures other than their own. There are very few promising and/or young American writers today who have not been more influenced by "foreign" writing than by any of their immediate predecessors. And the genuine merit of 'national discoveries', such as those of the new French novelists, have only become ascertainable as writers of other cultures have adapted them to their own experience, without being committed to a programmatic defense of *la méthode*.

What seems to be developing is a kind of international clearing house of stylistic innovation, which inevitably makes for a wider variety of narrative voices and consequent structures. Needless to say, it is in such international dialog that the novel has lagged behind the proscenium arts. And if this analysis is on the mark, then Nabokov is the protean novelist of our time—not merely because he has spanned several cultures, or turned traditional formulae to contemporary uses—but because he has succeeded in developing structures in which once disparate poetic, philosophical, theatrical, and documentary voices are enjoined under the name of the novel.

"All writers think they are realists," Robbe-Grillet says, but the bourgeois narrator who takes his perception for granted, the philosopher-narrator who counts primarily on the suspicion of his own perception no longer seem "real" as isolate voices. To paraphrase Ortega, both "primitive realism and total subjectivism are impossible." So his distinction between "pure narration" and "strict presentation" also becomes impossible. The contemporary narrator can neither accede to history nor deny it. He is beyond omniscience.

"The novel lends itself more easily than any other art form form to the absorbing of elements alien to art. Within the novel almost anything fits." That's Ortega again, in a passage the implications of which he seemed to ignore. No other literary form can give sufficent scope to the progressive conflict of "imaginary and scientific psychology." For the novel's form is the consequence of that conflict; and that pure struggle between the narrator and his own form is the drama that holds our attention in the long run.

The function of criticism, for a writer in any case, is through the examination of particulars, to discover what our premises really are. Can it have taken this long to discover that hermeneutical discourse about the novel, as *form,* dead or alive, is circuitous? It would take a novel, a great one perhaps, to explain why we continue to exhaust ourselves in this way.

The interrogation

for Robert Creeley

Place the man
in the chair, direct
the light at his vision, ask
the question.

The man stiff in the hard chair,
sweat on his face like pearls.
Now in the white light
he sees nothing; now the light
is his reality; now
you will sweat it out of him.

The words come slow, broken
like fingernails. The light
projects their shadows on the air.
Slowly the air gets darker, slowly
you will break him into his vision.

Outside the megaphone of light
you sit like a shadow
mouthing the question. The words
pour from him; the shadows
draw substance from his harsh sweat;
they stand beside you
claiming acquaintance. The man
escapes into his truth, his lies:
is that truth, is that
not truth. The darkness
is in us, the darkness
pours from us.

You retreat from the chair,
from the voice of the question,
you become the black angels of his vision.
Your light like a dwarf sun
dies: you are the smallest of his lies.

DAVID LUNDE

Dry foam

I sat hard
staring sand to gold.
A voiceless house,
an August beach,
stingray rotting gray,
I smelled all things
in the fog.
I could scare gulls.
They didn't know
shells cut feet.

Bon voyage, mon chou chou,
yours will be longer
harder than mine.
Words come easy in the fall;
the spring has its own noise.
I'm sorry I can't see
act three to the end.
I left London in May
and the same rain
chilled me as badly then.

I watched a man
yell at his bed
filled with me.
Friday sat in the room,
the yellow light
void of heat
as lemonade,
gray on grey
no smoking here.
Even in dark,
all things gray,
color causes sight.
The world is forgiven
where hell and heaven
meet and stink at the ocean.

SUSAN WHITNEY

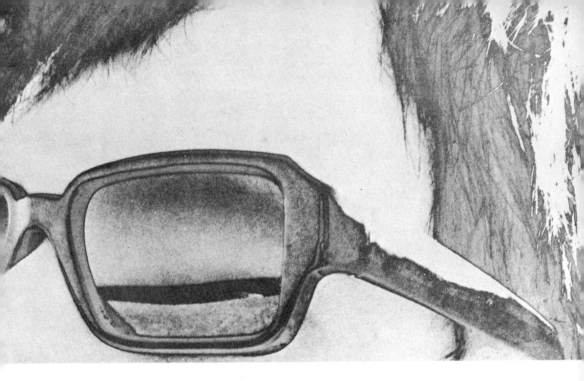

Sunglasses

The air is interesting
My sunglasses today.
Last week they were

Interested by the sea.
In my sunglasses
I look like Grandma Moses

Wearing sunglasses
And interested by the sun,
The air, and the sea.

How hungrily
She looks at the world
Today!

Is it a child's wisdom
In the colorful pine tree
That throws itself upon Grandma Moses?

On her back she fades back
Into the sandy land
And changes slowly to silicates.

How interesting she seems
To my sunglasses
Who cry "O Daughter!"

TOM CLARK

A visit

"Le bonheur, quel ennui!
Mais l'ennui, quel bonheur aussi."

With you the days were scarcely three hours long,
Like winter days within the arctic circle
On which a brief and splendid solace shone:
What did we do on which? Let's see: on Monday
We went out, on Tuesday we stayed home
Before the nonexistent fire, and read.
From time to time the cat got up and crossed
From one to the other, yawned and stretched and settled
On a fresh lap, encouraged by our anatomy
To resume the briefly interrupted nap
That is a cat's life. One turned a page.

How slow, how infinitely gentle then
Seemed to us the clumsy flight of time,
Like one of those birds, barnyard or extinct,
That flap from branch to branch but cannot really fly.
Each tick of the clock was noticed, weighed
Like a pulse beat at its proper value.
Thus in no time it was dinner time,
And, ah soon after! Time to go to bed.

Now I can't remember what we read
Or said, or even how it felt
To have you here, near, within sight and hearing,
Neglected, as a treasure is neglected
By its owner, secure in his possession.
Time's deliberate pace, too, was deceptive
For even then in retrospect it flew.

What of the other days—for there were several
Sped in a variety of ways,
Spent like unreplenished capital
To the present starvation of the senses.

On one we took our borrowed bicycles
And followed a path beside the inland sea.
I said, "Is it not like Cornwall or Devon?"
You laughed and replied, "It might be
Were it not for all the ugliness, the highway
Nearby, the brash apartment buildings
And the widespread middle-Western platitude."
Your kind of joke; you observed—
It was rough—"The waves are wearing mufflers."
If you were a Greek you might have said,
"Underneath, the Nereids are dancing."
And I told you how I used to come
Here alone, while waiting for your visit,
In the afternoons, with an apple and a book.

It is painful to remember every morning,
Mornings too intimate almost to record,
Rich and various as a paisley scarf:
You emerging towelled from the bathroom,
And later, together in the shower, masked
In soap, slippery, lascivious as fish;
Too intimate, and yet I keep a record
Of what we did and how and when and where.
Friday you lay back upon the sofa,
Sunday I awoke within your arms,
Thursday you bestrode me like a colossus:
And it is as if in all of our embraces
The universal was made personal.

Now: now I need to stop and think a minute.
What have I left out? Oh, everything.
It is like looking at a map or seeing from the air
A neighbourhood where once one was at home,
Or like reading the menu, after, of a meal:
Is it, or in what sense was it, real?

Poets must have something else to write of
Than their own epic thoughts and tragic feelings.
But what? Will a comic interruption do?
The scramble, worthy of a bedroom farce,
When the delivery boy rang the bell, the sudden
Sinister breakdown of the telephone,
Which now, like my anxiety, seems funny.
Or your silent tears? The stories of the army
In which you shone as the ironic hero
Maladroit, touchingly inferior, and wise?

The very muchness of the world disgusts me
Some times, when it comes between us two,
And suddenly I lose all appetite.
At others it is all we have together:
You never guessed with what courage taken
Like the moments on the bus, to me apocalyptic
Before we said goodbye again: you proved
How much can be included in a look,
And the fleeting sun illuminated
As it set the shining fancy of your flesh.

DARYL HINE

Easter Season

There is almost no sound . . . only the redundant stir
Of shrubs as perfumed temperatures embalm
Our coast. I saw the spreading gush of people with their palms.
In Westchester, the crocus spreads like cancer.

This will be the death of me. I feel the leaves close in,
Promise, threaten from all sides and above.
It is not real. The green seed-pod, flaky dove
Of the bud descend. The rest is risen.

LOUISE GLUCK

One transvestite way of figuring on stopping in a village woods

There is a clam in the village who keeps
his pearl concealed in a trouserskirt
and never exhibits her self as more or less
than a blank-eyed quick figural distance.

He is neither this nor that but and and is
confined in my retina, a grain of salt. I am
imprisoned in my membrane, her shell is my
nacred far sight and irritant silences.

See, in this quiet the things that seem
to speak are accents foreign to the profane
vision. Tight-lipped, succumbing to sight
in this hallucination of farsightedness:

an alien salt-grain, sea-pulsed, I
unhusk till it become a brackish swell
blithering native translations, far old womanman
marking to make me myopic in my loud cell.

See in this quiet the things that seem
to speak in tongues (sonofabitch) that more than seem
to neither expose the molesting speed
nor cocoon the eye in the near quick of snails.

And some can make butterflies of mosquitoes,
some can make of mosquitoes butterflies;
some can make a butterfly's flight cumbersome, some
can pin them in rows, glossed figurines.

But there is a village in the clam that keeps,
its figures' shoes, annoyed by stones, walk in
a shore-threatened talk, a fast swirl of skirts
and shirts in the peopled streets.

R. J. WILSON

Five for
Charles Starkweather, murderer

1

America's Golden Boy!—
Nebraska-bred, nervous,
guilt-edged—

this dust bowl
baby was born with grit
between his teeth . . .

. . . and then love
hemorrhaged.

'Oh, I can understand that.'

2

The tiny burst veins urge
the poem out of fleshiness.

'The trouble with your poem,
Charles, is that gun:
too Freudian.'

But it happens that poems
can be sprees,
twisting holidays

composed of whatever
unsymbolic sand.

3

The worst criminal
is the petty thief who would
have us unaware of loss.

There is no mistaking
the shotgun-bearer,
head-splitter, beautiful
angel of death

whose wings were
beaten on everyone's
worldly anvil.

4

Some simply cannot
keep their distance.

These must be taken
seriously, for they
are so violent,
so much alone,

they will never really
compose themselves.

5

How many last suppers
in the death house?
These walls the stone tablets
for how many bent scriptures?

'I screwed Lorraine
under a cottonwood on July 27, 1948.
Afterwards she was silent.'

'This do in remembrance
that nobody . . .'—

and who remembers now
life on the outside?

C. G. HANZLICEK

The circuit

I even broke down and made a little scene:
the wigs
ushered me into a private room

where the chances of breaking
even were slim.
The sign read: huge cocktail

man with jetting experience
desires correspondence
with saint. This is perhaps a lie

except for an interlude
when I went back,
the wigs being asleep at this time.

I was hunting a final instrument,
a hostile machine
to articulate my only defense. Nothing

tried to get me—
men were working in the trees.
One invented the wheel

suddenly; then his friend came up
with the hill,
when we all started to bleed.

I recognized questions from the crowd.

JAMES TATE

Poem — three lines

I sing in season
Out, I only say:
    "One in my hand, one in the air, and one in you"

SAINT GERAUD

Sunday dinner
JOYCE CAROL OATES

Late one Sunday morning a group of people stood in a cemetery, in a small irregular circle around a gravestone. It was an overcast day, clouds in big frozen swirls reflected the wave-like frozen look of the grass below, sky and earth blended in a hard colorlessness. Everything looked as if it had been chiseled out of one great granite-hard substance: the clouds, the trees, the people standing decorously about the grave, and of course the gravestones themselves, which had actually been chiseled out of some hard substance and even engraved with special messages that made each grave unlike all the rest. And so while everything looked like everything else, yet the gravestones publicized the individuality of those who slept peacefully beneath them.

No one else was in the cemetery. It was December. The men and women grouped about the grave—which was marked by a fine squat stone of the color of pale salmon, rough on its edges and yet amazingly smooth on its front and back—noticed that old flowers and ribbons and glass containers and wire supports for wreaths had been left here and there in the cemetery, and they were displeased. One of them, a tall hefty woman in a brown coat with a fur collar, stooped to pick up a mangled bouquet of bright pink artificial flowers that had been discarded. With a distasteful look she stuffed it in her coat pocket; she would dispose of it at home. One of the men, the youngest of them all, a pale, fresh-faced, sly-looking man of about twenty-five, peeked around a tombstone and saw two beer cans; at first he smirked, then his mouth stiffened with anger. He pursed his lips and said nothing. The shorter woman, who wore a peach-colored hat with a veil that drooped down surreptitiously over her face, suddenly knelt before the grave, hiding her face in her hands. The three brothers exchanged glances, impatient and embarrassed and yet a little pleased; the big woman looked resentful. She stood as if at attention, her pocket bulging with the old bouquet, and stared past her sister's pert peach-colored hat at the gravestone, which read: GLADYS AGNES PERCH 1900-1950 OUR MOTHER   Blessed Art the Pure in Heart Beloved by God and by Her Children.

Somewhere a church bell tolled, slowly and solemnly. The youngest brother's mouth was filled with saliva at once, for it was noon and time to eat; they would be going home now to Sunday dinner. His sister Mary, kneeling in the grass at the foot of the grave, always took five minutes but no longer. He could see the tip of her veil moving back and forth very slightly as she breathed, now touching the end of her nose, now lifting gently from it. The young man, Leroy, had to clench his fists in his big overcoat pockets because he was impatient with hunger, and yet he could tell without glancing at his older sister that she knew exactly what was going on in his mind, every thought, every picture, even the tension in his fists. The church bell kept ringing. It might have been ringing in heaven itself, it sounded so far away. Why were Sundays set apart to be such strange days? Why did it seem that something unusual might happen today? Leroy liked Sundays, because everyone talked about the past on these days, about their mother especially, who had been dead now for fifteen years. He had been only a child at her death, and so the memories of the others were especially valuable to him since only through them could he learn anything about the wonderful woman who had given birth to him at a rather late age in life, on her part.

His two brothers stood back, hats in hand. They were bigger and taller than Leroy and had always been older, and so he did not fit in with them. He did not have much to say to them, but liked to listen. He felt most at ease with his big sister Estella, though she bullied him and pushed him around; but that was to be expected since she was exactly twice his age. He felt at ease with her because she said what she thought, unlike his brothers Jack and Jake, whose sophistication and dignity made them strangers to Leroy. And Mary was very nice, very sweet, but always her eyes were swimming with tears, for she felt very deeply the sufferings of others and of herself. Of course she had her own secret, which she guarded

64

jealously, and Jack and Jake had their secrets, and even Estella had hers, which she sometimes hinted at, vaguely, on holidays and on Sundays when the visit to their mother's grave had especially moved her. Only Leroy had no secret of his own. He wondered how one acquired a secret, what one had to do. For what did life mean when there was nothing to remember, even if remembering would be sad? So far as he could make out the main occupation of life was thinking back and he was unable to do this. When he did try to think back, for instance about his mother, he would only discover that events he tried to recall were remembered in great inexhaustible detail by his brothers and sisters, and his own versions were always bypassed as if they were no more than insignificant little dreams. Then Leroy himself lost interest in his own memories and would sit at the feet of Estella or Jack or Jake or Mary and listen, entranced, as that mysterious world of their past was recaptured, as if some stray detail might suddenly tell him something about himself. . . .

"Look at that," Jack muttered to Jake, as they waited for Mary to finish her prayers. Jack was a handsome though balding man of forty-five, whose overcoat was made of expensive dark material; loose in the crook of his left arm was balanced a shiny cane. He pointed with this cane at something just beyond the next gravestone, a fierce angel mounting the air on muscular wings, and Jake, too vain to wear his glasses when he went out visiting, squinted and tried to see. It was a discarded piece of women's underwear, bright yellow and decorated with white silk buds. Jake probably could not make it out, but he took his cue from Jack's angry tone and grunted a reply. Jack took out a big white handkerchief and blew his nose, which he often did when angry. "The sort of thing that reminds me of our father," Jack said. "I wouldn't put it past him," Jake said emphatically. "No respect for anything," said Jack. He took a few steps to one side and peered around another tombstone, but saw nothing. His frown did not relax. He kicked at what looked like a deceptive pile of old leaves and sure enough, underneath was a whiskey bottle with lipstick smudges on it. Jack's face reddened and he kicked the leaves back over it. Such things reminded him of his father, who had abandoned his wife and four children many years ago, simply walking out one day and never coming back, never sending a message, never doing anything. Jack remembered the weeks and months he had spent at the big front window, watching for his father's return, looking out at sunshine and rain and snow alike, watching and waiting in vain. They had all been by windows, except Leroy who hadn't even been born yet but was born just a few months afterwards, each by his own window, waiting and hoping, and nothing happened of course and stayed that way for years. The old man had never returned.

Mary glanced down at something, her eyes brimming with tears, and moved one knee slightly as if in surprise—they saw her pick up a chicken wishbone, which she had evidently been kneeling on by mistake. She stared at it, her lips trembling. With one competent gesture Estella leaned over and snatched it out of Mary's gloved fingers. "Don't pay any attention to that. Nothing at all," Estella muttered. She stuck the wishbone in her pocket with the bouquet. Jack and Jake exchanged a glance. "I don't know what the world is coming to," Jack said resentfully. "Yes," said Jake, as if he had seen what had happened. He was a year older than Jack. In him words took their time, winding slowly to the surface and sometimes never getting there at all. It did not matter; he had not much to say because he did not notice much. Yet he had a fine aristocratic manner, at times a little pompous, Jack thought, though he really admired his brother; and his appearance—his silver-gray hair, his long noble nose, his small moustache—was really more impressive than Jack's. Jack glanced around at their kid brother, Leroy, who was licking his lips dreamily. Thinking of dinner. Leroy had a keen, sharp, face, with sharp-looking black eyebrows and narrowed eyes, it was queer how he sometimes reminded Jack of an animal—not a familiar animal but one a child might imagine, having brought together the sly, sleek features and manners of many animals. The boy wore an old overcoat of Jack's that was really too big for him. It hung below his knees and its shoulders sagged, so that the boy did not look as if he were wearing it so much as waiting inside it.

"Oh, Mother! Mother!" Mary whispered. The others were embarrassed. Every week this went on; though they were sympathetic with Mary they were also impatient. Of course they all felt Mary's sorrow, but did not choose to show it. Jack thought it good form to keep one's expression taut and impersonal, that was how civilization after all had arisen from chaos. He straightened his broad shoulders, thinking of civilization. And at that moment his gaze happened to be caught by something in a tree not far away—his neck craned forward, but he could not make out the object. Unobtrusively, he strolled behind Jake's pensive form and around behind Estella, who waited with her big angry face like a mask, and over to the tree. He pretended to be glancing around without any design, and finally got near enough to make out the object: it was obviously a bed sheet or part of one, crumpled up and twisted around a barren tree limb. Jack saw on it a bloodstain, a strange ugly dried oval of blood there accosting his eye. He was furious. With his cane he slashed at the bed sheet but could not dislodge it. He noticed Leroy watching him and stopped; he had to learn to control his temper better. But all sorts of thoughts were racing through his mind, thoughts that did not belong in so sacred a place, hardly fifty

66

feet away from his mother's final grave. And indecent thoughts too, which disturbed him the most. How strange it was, he thought, caressing his balding head, how strange it was . . . things changed, cemeteries as well as neighborhoods declined and grew common. Why did things change?

Estella wondered if she should touch her sister's quivering shoulders. Mary was crying more than usual, why was that? That morning she had found an insect in her bed and had been upset; perhaps that was the reason. Estella felt a surge of affection for her young sister, and her usual envy for Mary's delicate, pretty features was overcome. And anyway Mary was not nearly so intelligent as Estella; everyone said so. Even their father had said so, once. But she did not like to think of her father, who had betrayed them. . . . Sometimes, just before falling asleep, she thought of her mother and father in a strange picture: her mother a lovely Christmas tree covered with snow and her father a bird, a crow or a buzzard, with dirty black feathers and a hungry beak, that jabbed viciously at the Christmas tree. And she would sit up in bed, her hands perspiring. Her father! And her mother—victimized by illness, by circumstances, by her own sense of duty, feeling she must work, always, scrubbing and polishing and sweeping and washing the house, upstairs and downstairs, all the rooms, and the basement, and the wine cellar, the garage and the garage's little attic, the house's attic, over and over and over, even the little porches that went out from several of the upstairs rooms, and the big bird house-hotel in the back lawn, never resting, taking care of the children, loving them, sacrificing for them, sometimes eating nothing so that they might have enough to eat— and so she had died one day, worn out with the struggle of life. Estella felt her eyes sting suddenly. She did not want to cry, did not want to be weak like Mary. She turned her head and looked over at Jack—he was a short distance away, looking up in the air, from tree to tree, as if searching for something.

Estella walked over to the gravel path so that Mary would hear her footsteps and look up. It was time they were leaving. The air was chilly and Jake had forgotten to wear his wool scarf. How ugly the cemetery was, Estella thought. She passed near Leroy, who began to follow her immediately as if he had been called. Dried-up old flowers and plants left over from summer—pieces of cellophane wrappers blown against the gravestones —tiny American flags that had been stuck on sticks into the ground but had long since fallen over—discarded hotdog buns, half-eaten—and—Estella's eyes widened at the sight—over there on a lovely white marble tombstone was a woman's sheer nylon stocking, flung over the stone as if it were really a transparent leg about to climb over. The cemetery had once been so lovely, so exclusive, and now the same thing was happening that had happened in their neighborhood: everything running down, taken over by the lowest elements. Estella sighed, feeling helpless.

Now that she was on the gravel path Mary did look up. "Oh," she exclaimed, touching her chest, "I'm sorry I kept you waiting so long! Please forgive me!" Jake helped her to her feet. "Estella, I'm sorry—I didn't realize the time—"

"Nonsense," Estella said, looking away. Yet she was pleased at Mary's tone. "Let's be on our way, now."

"But poor Mother, left alone!" said Mary.

"Yes, poor Mother!" Jake sighed. He had given Mary his arm and the two of them followed Estella. Leroy walked alongside the path on the grass, since there was not room for him. "Poor dear soul," Jake said, "I'll never forget the day she died. The agony she endured . . . and all of it so horrible, because she had deserved an easy death. She had deserved a peaceful death."

"Please don't," Mary sobbed.

"Jake, please," Estella said sharply.

Jake's jaws snapped shut. He felt his face turn red; he was very warm. Of course he was wrong, but yet . . . at the age of forty-six he did not like to be scolded by his older sister. He had been wrong, though. He sometimes said the wrong thing. When he had his glasses on, safe at home in his room or in his study, he could see things sharply and for some reason did not talk much. Without his glasses—they spoiled his aristocratic looks—everything was blurry and watery and he seemed to talk more, he did not know why. Now he looked about, squinting. His eyesight had been perfect for years, when he had been a child; then, three days after his father had abandoned them he had woken up and everything was blurry. Everything was blurry and strange. And it had never been made right again, never. Jake remembered his mother cuddling him in her arms. He blinked rapidly to keep the tears from coming in his eyes. And, by accident, his eyesight suddenly seemed clearer, because of the tears perhaps. He looked around, wonderingly. It was so; things were more in focus than usual. He could see the smaller limbs of the trees and the way the snowless ground shaped itself in swirls, hard frozen mud and grass. Jake walked along with his weeping sister leaning on his arm. They were approaching a tree by the path. Jake thought he saw some carvings on it—he squinted, but did not dare to blink for fear he would lose the astounding clarity he possessed—and, sure enough, someone had carved names and initials into the bark. Lovers, he thought, young lovers. He could make out a big heart in the midst of the carvings and, as he came closer, prepared to see the names inside it. He had already begun to smile a little—for though he was a bachelor of forty-six, still he

68

applauded love—when he passed by the tree and saw that, inside the carefully chiselled heart, there was an obscene command, of the sort often seen in alleyways. Jake's eyes blinked of their own accord and in the next instant he could see only as well as usual—the words, the heart, had faded away. "How very strange," he murmured to himself, embarrassed.

Jack, ahead of them all, was anxious to leave. Only around their dear mother's grave was the cemetery sacred; everywhere else it was tawdry. Where was the groundskeeper? Jack thought of writing a vicious letter to the cemetery officials. He would do that this evening. It was distracting to stand at his mother's graveside and pray, while refuse lay all around, so unkempt and common. He waited by the wrought iron gate for his brothers and sisters to catch up to him, Leroy with his keen hungry look, hunched in the old overcoat, Estella with her proud, mannish strides, Mary fragile and weeping, Jake guiding her, with his tiny moustache like a piece of metal beneath his nose. And just as they were about to step through the gate, Jack happened to notice something lying on the ground, between the evergreen bushes and the fence—his eyes grew huge, he felt his scalp prickle—it couldn't be what he thought it was—But yes, unmistakably, there it was: the skeleton of an infant. It had been discarded beneath a browning evergreen tree. Estella must have noticed his shock, for she said, "What's wrong?" and stared at him bluntly. "Is something wrong?" Mary cried, staring up from her handkerchief. "What's wrong? What is it?"

"Nothing—nothing," Jack said. He walked on as if in a trance. "Just something dead—a dead thing back there—"

"A dead thing?" said Mary, her voice trembling with tears. "What is a dead thing doing in our cemetery?"

At home they all relaxed. Leroy had picked the big Sunday paper up off the porch and brought it in and he was now reading the comics, sitting on the old sofa and awaiting dinner. Jack and Jake divided, as usual, the rest of the paper and were sitting in leather chairs on either side of the big marble fireplace; there was a feeling of satisfaction and yet of melancholy in the air. Sundays were always the same. A special atmosphere seemed to descend upon the big old house, reaching down perhaps from the old roof with its clapboards and rusted lightning rods and meaningless peaks and spires, so wonderfully ornamental eighty years ago but now queerly italicized against the modern sky. Estella, in the kitchen with Mary, glanced out a window at the sky and thought that at one time, in her childhood, winters had not been so ugly.

Mary, pouring lemon sauce over the roast, was in her usual Sunday mood. Tears sprang into her eyes as some jagged thought from the past struck her. "If only things had been different," she said. "If only my own life . . . my unfortunate accident . . . had been different, then Mother might not have. . . . Or I could have taken her to live with me. . . ."

"She never said anything about going to live with you," Estella said quietly. "She was quite happy with the arrangements here."

"But when they fell through. . . ." Mary said, sniffing. She dabbed her eyes with a corner of her apron. "Of course she wanted to be with you, you were with her all the time. You were the oldest, it was only right. . . . But when your own plans failed, then I could have taken over. If only you hadn't kept her so much to yourself! I could have—"

"You could have what?" Estella said angrily.

"You don't know what I could have done," Mary said. She faced her sister with a peculiar coquettish look. "You don't know anything about me, not really. It's my secret." Estella was alarmed, seeing in this forty-year-old woman the delicate girl who had almost come between her and her mother; and the brothers had always liked Mary better because she was gentle and sweet. Sometimes even Leroy listened to Mary with an attentive, dog-like look of affection, a way he never looked at Estella, though Estella was confident that he liked her best of all.

"And you don't know about my story either," Estella said.

"I know enough!"

"Only what I've told you." Estella drew herself up to her full height— a little over six feet. Mary was so short she had to tilt her head back. "But anyway," said Estella, "there was never any question about who would take care of Mother, plans or no plans. Everybody knows that."

"You were always bigger. You bullied her."

"Bullied her!"

"You bullied her!" Mary said, closing her eyes.

Estella jerked open a drawer and took out the pot holders.

While the sisters set the dining room table, in angry silence, the brothers sat in the living room reading. "It says here," Leroy read, slowly, "that twenty-four men trapped down in a mine are still there, after four months. Did you read this? They sent them down some games to play and some new clothes. Did any of you read this?" Jack and Jake grunted, without glancing up. "They're naming some streets after them, and a railroad station, and a shopping plaza," Leroy said. "I wouldn't want to be in a mine even for that, would you?" His brothers' indifference always angered him, though he should have been used to it by now. He smiled bitterly, envisioning Jack and Jake stuck down in the earth, in a collapsed tunnel, with dirt sucked into their lungs and pressed against their surprised faces. The burden of that earth, the weight they would have to support! Much heavier than the air; —and yet the air itself was heavy and oppressive, it gave no one joy to

70

breathe it. Outside it was tinted with soot from factories and trucks, and inside the house the air was always stuffy and damp, staying as it did in one place all the time. When Leroy stood at the bay window and looked down to the sidewalk (they had a long, sloping, weed-choked front lawn) he saw only Negro people walking past, and their dark skin seemed to him so much stronger than his own. It would resist the dreary air, while his could not and turned a murky, bloodless color; it would stand out against any background, with the bravery of mindless stone, while his shivered with uncertainty. For, Leroy thought slowly, he was coming to an age at which questions bothered him all the time. Why was he here? Who was he? What was he to become? Anyone who asked these questions of himself was uncertain and weak. . . . "It says here," he read, loudly, "it says here that a woman was raped in a maternity ward last night. What do you think of that?" He noticed his sisters turn away. But what was wrong? What had he said? "What does that mean?" he said to Jake, who was sitting closest to him. "Read something else!" Jack snapped. Leroy read the stamp news. Next to that was a column about the stock market, and next to that one about how to be happy. He read everything slowly and then turned the page. "It says here," Leroy read, moving his finger along the smudged type, "that six hundred Boy Scouts on a hike got lost. Part of the army is looking for them." "That's very sad," Mary said shrilly. "And over here it says," Leroy went on carefully, "that the brain of a tapeworm was transplanted to a little Negro child. What do you think about that?"

"Is that the same one?" Jake said. He glanced up; he was wearing his glasses and looked like someone's grandfather. "The same tapeworm they were using last month?"

"I don't know, how should I know," Leroy said sullenly.

"He doesn't have time to read everything," Estella said. Leroy was grateful for this. "And why always ask him about things he doesn't know?"

"He should learn, then," Jack said pompously. "Civilization may be defined as the constant increment of knowledge in the face of stupidity. And anyway, our aunt Ruth had a tapeworm. It isn't uncommon. She was very religious and seemed to have misunderstood something God told her: she thought she was going to be delivered of another Christ, but in reality it was only a tapeworm. Not that one should be too sure, of course . . . of the manifestations of God . . . but still. . . ."

"That would be destroying life, to kill it," Mary said. "We went all through this with the priest!"

"I don't want to argue any more," Jack said. "You people won out; they didn't kill it. She still has it. It isn't my tapeworm, it isn't my affair. My own tapeworm is my own business."

71

"You see how jealous you are about your own!" Mary said.

"Mine is a different matter entirely," Jack said. "At any rate, I want to keep myself out of female problems."

"After that one time, hmm?" Jake said, shaking his finger. He was grinning in an unusual, rather rowdy way.

"Oh, that!" said Jack, blushing.

"What about that one time?" Leroy said eagerly.

"Nothing, absolutely nothing," said Jack.

"Did something happen? When was it? Was I born yet?"

"Nothing happened," said Jack.

"Somebody tell me, please," Leroy said. He pulled at Jake's arm. "Tell me what happened."

"It's his secret, nobody knows exactly," Jake said, drawing away. "Entirely his own business."

"And you have a secret too, huh? Don't you?"

Jake seemed to be staring at something far off in the distance. "Yes," he said gently. "Yes. That's so."

"And you won't tell?"

"It's not a happy secret—"

"What is it?"

"—and yet there's a kind of nobility about it— All experience is valuable, Leroy. Suffering itself is valuable."

"What happened? What did you do?"

But Jake had turned back to his paper.

"Nothing ever happens to me," Leroy said. He began to bite his fingernail, hoping Estella would notice and scold him. "I never do anything. Never. I don't have no secrets from anyone."

No one was listening. Leroy put his hands to his face suddenly, as if to hide his expression: for he felt his muscles tense and go rigid with viciousness, a look that said he would like to tear them apart with his teeth. The feeling passed quickly. His heart pounded. "God," he whispered, pointlessly. "They all keep to themselves. They have their own thoughts. They remember things. They know things. They remember *her* and *him* both. No matter how hard I try to remember her they always remember her better. And they have their own lives, all kept secret; they wear masks. They aren't really themselves but other people! And me, what about me? Will I get a mask? Will my face change? Why doesn't it change? Sometimes I get so nervous—so mad—I think I could kill them—or somebody—"

But the smell of food stopped his thinking and he jumped to his feet. Mary, wiping her hands on her dainty apron, came to the doorway and beckoned to them. Though she was forty she always looked young and fresh,

72

especially when she smiled and showed dimples around her pink lips.

The brothers sighed and let their newspapers fall. Leroy, his mouth watering furiously, led the way; Jack and Jake followed, rubbing their stomachs. Both wore vests made of a silvery material. Estella sat at the head of the table, Jake at the other end. They all bowed their heads. Leroy, his eyes shut, sat with his long narrow backbone straight as if poised to swoop down upon the food. "Our dear Father," Estella said, "we do thank Thee for this food, and for all the food set before us in the past and for the food to come. For the teeth with which to eat this food, we do thank Thee. We do thank Thee for the involuntary muscular activity which takes this food to our stomachs, and for the enzymes that work upon it once it is safely there, and for the process of digestion itself, that mystery that transforms the brute material of food into energy that runs our hearts and brains. We thank Thee for the little cells that multiply so that we are constantly getting larger, fed by this food, and for the air that mixes with it, and for the water that makes up ninety percent of our lives, and for the blood vessels that dutifully carry waste products to every corner of our bodies, forever and ever, Amen."

But just at that moment, just as the mashed potatoes were about to be passed to Leroy, the doorbell rang.

"Perhaps we shouldn't answer it," Estella said calmly.

"It might be something important," Jack said.

"What could it be that would be so important?" she said. She sat with the bowl of potatoes extended to Leroy, who waited patiently, so hungry that his eyes had filled with tears. "Nothing in *your* life!"

"What do you mean by that?" he said.

The doorbell rang again. "It might be the paper boy," Jake said.

"We don't subscribe to a paper," Mary said.

"When did we stop?" Jake said, amazed.

"Eight years ago."

"But we were just reading—"

"That's a mistake, it always comes by mistake," Estella said rudely. "Every Sunday. But it's somebody else's mistake, not ours!"

The doorbell rang again. "Maybe it's someone for me," Leroy said.

They all laughed, even Mary. "Did you ever hear anything like it?" Jack said.

"It might be the paper boy after all, asking if we'd like to renew our subscription," Jake said stubbornly.

"I think we should answer it," Mary said demurely. "I think it might be someone for me."

"And who would be coming to see you?" Estella said.

"Someone. Someone you don't know," said Mary.

"Leave her alone. It isn't impossible," Jack said to Estella.

"It isn't probable," Estella said.

"No, more likely it's the paper boy," Jake said, in his kindly but pompous way, "or the man who cleans out the cistern, or the woman who comes in to clean twice a year, or the little old man who fixes up the attic with that electric device that kills the pigeons on contact. . . . Isn't it time for him to come around again?"

Jack struck his forehead. "I just thought! It's for me!"

"Who is it?" Mary said. Her voice was sweet but resentful.

"Dear me—that business deal I told you about— It might be going to come through, now, after all the delays and difficulties—"

"That nonsense about the machine to suck dust in, to replace a good old-fashioned mop?" Estella crowed. "That would never catch on!"

The doorbell rang again. Leroy had the idea that it might be for him, that someone was coming he had forgotten about.

"Well, who's going to answer it?" Mary said. Her hands fluttered nervously about her hair. "You can't expect Estella or me to go. It's up to one of the men in the family."

"Yes, one of the men," Estella said contemptuously.

"Why do you say that?" said Jake.

"Another veiled insult!" said Jack, his face reddening.

"One ought to be polite," said Jake.

"Leroy, you go," Estella said, poking him in the arm. "You're the youngest. Go on."

Leroy stared at them. He had never answered the door before. "Go on," Estella said.

"But what should I say?"

"Ask who it is."

"Then what?"

"Then tell him he has the wrong address; tell him to go across the street."

"Unless it's for one of us," Mary interrupted.

"It won't be for one of us, that's nonsense," said Estella, "the sooner you understand that, the better. What if Mother could see us now, fighting and bickering like children? Think of her watching us! Always think of her!"

"Yes, that's right," Jake said.

"That's right," said Mary, dabbing at her eyes.

The doorbell rang again. "Do I have to answer it?" Leroy said, trembling. When Estella poked him he got shakily to his feet. The bell rang yet again and Leroy hurried to the door. The bell did not ring impatiently but with the slow languid grace of bubbles soaring to the surface of water far above. Leroy opened the door and there stood a very tall, big old man with white hair. He wore dark glasses that hid his eyes, and all Leroy could see there were distorted images of himself. "Who is it, what do you want?" Leroy stammered. "We already got somebody to kill the pigeons. Why don't you go to the house over there? Is it about the newspaper? Did we make a mistake? Do you want them back?—they're all in the cellar, I'll get them for you, I—"

The old man seemed to grow taller. Indeed, he filled nearly the whole doorway. He wore a big bulky overcoat and carried a book in one hand and a cane with a fluorescent white tip in the other. "I am the census taker," he said, bending a little toward Leroy.

"The what?" said Leroy.

"The census taker," said the old man. "It has been ordained that the census be taken every ten years in this city," he said. "I have come to take the census here."

"Wouldn't you rather go across the street?" Leroy said. "We're just eating dinner now. We got nothing to report anyway."

"The census must be taken," the old man said. He spoke in a loud, kind, condescending voice. Leroy noticed that he did not move his head at all and that behind the dark glasses his eyes were secret and invisible. "I must ask you questions—I must find out your name, your age, your occupation—everything about you."

"Not me! Not just me!" Leroy said. "What about them in there?—they're older! I don't live here alone, I'm the youngest one, you ask them questions if you got to! I never done nothing wrong!"

"Leroy, who is it?" Estella called.

The census taker took a step forward in a way that was at the same time hesitant and bold. He tapped with his cane around the doorframe. "The questioning lasts only a few minutes," he said.

"Talk to them—them in there! I never done anything wrong!"

"Surely you received a notification of the census?"

"No! Nothing! Never got nothing!" Leroy stammered.

"Leroy!" Estella called. "Who is it? What's going on?"

"The census taker has called," the old man said loudly, "I must ask for a few minutes of your time."

Estella appeared in the doorway, holding a white napkin. She stared at the old man and Leroy had never seen her face look so odd. "But what is it?" she said falteringly.

"I am the new census taker," the old man said, in a declamatory manner. "I have been sent to ask you a few questions for our files."

"The census taker?" said Estella. "But you . . . you look. . . ."

"Pardon me?" said the old man, cupping his hand to his ear. "You said 'you look like my . . .' but I didn't catch the last word." Leroy had enough sense to close the door so that the cold air could not get in. The old man shuffled forward, tapping with his cane in that strange way, and Leroy watched him from behind. A really big, muscular body, for such an old man. And hair absolutely white, the kind of white they never saw these days, standing out from his head slightly so that he looked like a big untamed bird. How strange he was!

"I didn't say all those words. How could you hear it?" Estella said. Leroy did think that she looked queer. Now the others had appeared in the doorway, staring and listening. Mary teetered forward on her girlish high heels. Estella took her hand, something she never did, and they all stared first at Estella and then at the old man. "Why did you come here?" Estella said. "What do you want? Why have you done this?"

"Now, really, really," Jack said, springing forward. He took hold of the old man's arm and led him into the living room. "Such strange behavior, you'd think we never had any company! Please excuse my sister, she doesn't seem to be well. And now, my dear man, I understand perfectly what you want. The census must be taken regularly; it's nothing to be alarmed about. Civilization demands that files be kept for everyone who has ever been born or has ever died—the assumption of civilized life is that each individual can be rendered into a statistic and that, having been so rendered, he achieves a meaning otherwise lost to him. I understand very well, but you see— women! Women don't understand."

"I understand," Mary said coyly. She followed along beside the old man. "Are you going to ask me my age?" she said.

"His questions are standard ones," Jack said. "My poor dear man, out in this cold and at your age! And I see you have had a misfortune somehow, an accident no doubt. Unless I'm seriously mistaken, those dark glasses do mean . . . ?"

"Oh, he's blind!" Estella cried.

"Blind?" said Leroy.

"I never realized. . . . Blind!" Estella said. "But how did it happen?" Her voice was faint; she stood with one fist against her big bosom.

"We'll invite him to dinner, then, that's only proper," Jake said. They turned to him gratefully, for he always said the right thing sooner or later. "Perhaps he could ask his questions at dinner?"

"Yes, I thank you kindly," the old man said. His head turned from side to side as if he were a big doll performing for them. "I seem to be just a little confused. . . . This family? Who is the mother and who the father?

76

Or is this a boarding house? Isn't this neighborhood strictly zoned against boarding houses?"

"This is a family home, I should hope so," Mary said. "Oh, yes! We're all in the same family, we've always been happiest that way!"

"Who is the man of the house?"

"The man of the house—why, he's gone, I mean—there isn't any—He isn't here— But I have three brothers," Mary said, flustered, "and Jake is the oldest. Do you mean him?"

Jake came forward, squinting. He seized the old man's hand and shook it vigorously. "Very pleased to meet you, sir," he said.

"And the mother, who is the mother?" said the old man.

"Our mother is deceased," Mary said quietly. They all looked at the floor; only the old man did not move. "She's been dead for so long now, it seems. Every Sunday we go out to visit her at her grave, but. . . . She doesn't know about it. Or does she? Anyway, we have no mother any longer. It's just Estella and me."

"Estella?" said the old man carefully.

"I'm Estella." They looked with surprise at their sister, who stood outside their little circle, watching them with a peculiar stunned look. Her big generous face was splotched with red and white patches.

The old man also turned, as if to look at her. They watched his wrinkled face, which was calm as a mask, and his eyes hidden behind his glasses. He hesitated. Then he nodded politely, in a way that reminded Leroy of Jake. "I am very pleased to meet you, Estella," he said.

"Now, let's go in to dinner," Jack said. He put his arm through the old man's arm, taking charge. "We have quite a big house, I should explain it to you. This is the living room—a fireplace at either end. We don't use them, ordinarily, except to throw things in now and then—orange rinds, coffee grounds, what have you. The closet is just behind us. Yes, let me have your coat, that's a good idea. I'll hang it up in here. And your cane? Or would you like to keep it? —How nicely your coat hangs in here, right alongside our coats!"

"It fits right in," Mary said enthusiastically.

"It's a handsome coat," Jake said, squinting.

"I'll put your cane up on this shelf, where it certainly won't be lost," Jack said. "It's a pity you don't have a dog assigned to you."

"My dog ran away," the old man said.

"What a scandal!" cried Mary. "One of those pretty seeing eye dogs?"

"Something should be done about that, someone should write a letter," Jack said angrily. "Standards are always being lowered!"

"You see it all over," Mary murmured to Leroy.

77

"And now, sir, if you'll give me your arm," Jack said. He obviously felt quite important, leading the dignified old blind man into the dining room. "Excuse me, sir, watch out—I mean, be careful—There's a statue in the doorway. By the doorway. Yes, this is our dining room, and there are French doors across the way that look out into the back yard. At the end of our property they're building a shopping plaza; on clear days the noise gives poor Mary a headache. But civilization must be understood as a series of distinct noises—progress cannot be halted. You'll discover that I'm quite progressive in my views. My social position, my education, my measurements, my financial position would all suggest that I be quite conservative, but that is, surprisingly, not at all the case. You'll find—"

"Oh, Jack!" Estella said girlishly. "He doesn't want to hear about you!"

"You can sit here, sir," Jack said, ignoring her. "This can be your plate. I hope you'll enjoy our little dinner—"

"Here, here," said Estella, nudging Jack aside. "I'll dish it out for him. What do you expect him to do, grope around the table for the food? Men have such ideas!"

Jack went to his chair and sat, sullenly. The others came in and took their places: Leroy began to eat, watching the handsome old man and Estella and wondering what was behind the old man's dark glasses. He himself could see perfectly. He wondered what it would be like to be blind and have no eyes: he closed his eyes tight and tried to eat, but his fork kept jabbing and clicking at nothing, and he had to open his eyes to find the food. How strange it must be not to have any eyes! He supposed the old man had flesh grown over the empty sockets, maybe little valley-like hollows where the eyes had once been.

Mary and Estella stood on either side of the old man, offering him food. Mary put something on his plate that Estella did not consider good enough; she knocked it off onto the floor with a disapproving grunt. "He needs a napkin. Jake, give him your napkin," she said loudly. "Mary, why don't you pour him some fresh water?"

"I'm busy here, with the sardines," Mary whimpered. "I have more than enough to do."

"He needs water. Please get it."

Mary hurried out to the kitchen, sniffing. When she returned Estella had sat on one side of the old man and was helping him cut a piece of thick roast beef. "I must acknowledge my extreme gratitude," the old man said, turning his face from side to side. "Your hospitality is wonderful."

"Oh, we were brought up that way!" Mary exclaimed. "Our dear mother taught us every nuance of tact. We owe everything to her."

"Yes, that's right," Estella had to agree.

78

"That's right," said Jake.

"Our mother said to us: if you ever discover a crippled old lady out in the snow, you bring her out something nice and warm and cozy, a thermos bottle filled with vegetable soup," Mary chattered happily. "Or woolen socks. Or a nice clean handkerchief, if she has the sniffles."

"And it happened once, and we did everything she told us to do," Jake said. "It went off without a hitch."

"Our mother was very sensitive to all humanity," Mary said. She sat on the other side of the old man, very pert and lively. Her lips looked pinker than ever. "She gave us the best of the food. She took care that every scrap was given to us, that we have the vitamins and nutritions out of it before it was thrown away. *We* got the inside of the banana; the peeling was always thrown away or given to someone else. *We* got the inside of the egg, always; the shell was tossed outside. The outside of the lettuce, where it's all brown, you know, and bad, was discarded, and *we* were given only the finest, freshest part in the center, for our salads, with a magnificent French dressing that was Mother's own recipe, and delicious tomatoes cut in diced quarters, and strips of celery arranged in a spoke-like effect—only the best part of the celery; the top part, where it's all leaves and insects, you know, was thrown away. Or sometimes it was given as a hand-out to a hungry person who never would have desired anything better anyway, you know. . . ."

"A pity you couldn't have met our mother!" Jake sighed.

They all sighed; even Leroy, who was chewing his food.

"She sounds like a wonderful lady, indeed," the old man said. "It often happens that women like her attain a degree of perfection quite . . . unattainable to the rest of us."

"Ah, God save her soul," Jack murmured. He was dishing out some mashed potatoes onto his plate.

"She often said she'd claw the eyes out of anyone who tried to hurt us, her dear children," Estella said.

"A mother will always defend her children," said Jack. "That is a medical fact."

"A religious fact as well," said Jake.

"One doesn't exclude the other," said Jack, half-closing his eyes.

"Religion and science have no argument, in my opinion," the old man said graciously.

Jack and Jake smiled at each other, brought together by the old man's deft remark. Everyone smiled, even Leroy, who did not really know what was going on.

"If only our poor dear mother were with us today, to be entered in your census report," Estella said. She tapped at the big book that the old man had placed beside his plate. "Our dear mother often read the newspaper, late into the night, to see if her name was in it. She was a carnivorous reader. . . . At the end, when her mind was failing just a little, she sometimes called me to her to ask if a photograph was of her or of some other woman. She sometimes forgot the way she looked, which happens generally with old people. And so I could tell her, gently, that perhaps the photograph *was* of her. She was just a trifle vain!"

"And when she bustled downstairs on Saturday evening, for our family sing-together!" Jack said. "Why, with her parasol and her big feathered hat, you'd think she was a belle of eighteen!"

"Even at the end, confined to a wheel chair, she always came down to assure the gaiety of the proceedings," Jack said, wiping a tear from his eye. "I've never made the acquaintance of another woman with such spirit!"

"But we haven't allowed this gentleman to ask us his questions," Jack said. "What better time than now, when we're all gathered together around the family table?"

"You wouldn't mind my asking them at dinner?"

"Certainly not!" Estella said, rapping the ledger book significantly. "We are an extremely flexible family. That too was one of our dear mother's achievements."

The old man popped a hot muffin into his mouth, chewed it quickly, and said, "The first question, then, I believe is, the combined age of all living members of the family." He opened the big book and felt about on the page, his fingers moving skillfully. "Yes. What is the combined age of all members of this family?"

"Two hundred and six years," Estella and Jack answered at once.

The old man took a little pencil from behind his ear and wrote this down. Leroy could see that his writing was quite fancy, and for some reason this annoyed him. Leroy's own writing was slow and deliberate and said what it was supposed to, without any flourishes.

"What is your combined weight? In pounds and ounces," the old man said.

Jack and Estella were both counting frantically on their fingers, but Mary bounced in her chair and said, "Seven hundred and sixty-three pounds, and no ounces!"

"I don't believe that," Estella said.

"Yes, I think . . . I think so," Jack said, tapping at the fingernail of his smallest finger, deep in thought. "I think so. Leroy, you know, just gained three pounds last year. You may have forgotten that."

Estella's face darkened and she looked at her youngest brother almost with hatred. "That's from his eating between meals," she said. "He sniffs around out in the kitchen like an animal, like a hog sniffing in a garbage dump! And so he gains three pounds, just like that."

"Boys will be boys," the old man said, writing in his book.

"Yet they must make an effort to superimpose themselves," Jack said. "Otherwise we would never have ascended out of chaos."

"And yet, boys will be boys," the old man said meaningfully, turning his blind eyes up at Jack.

"Why, yes, I didn't mean . . . I wasn't . . . I wasn't contradicting you," Jack said.

"Yes, he was!" Mary said, nudging the old man.

"No, I wasn't. I wasn't contradicting you."

"It had the effect of that," the old man said. He groped about before him and his hand came accidentally upon the plate of delicious cold sliced turkey white meat; he picked a piece up, tore it in three equal strips, and began chewing. All the while he chewed he was facing Jack.

"I didn't mean it to, sir," Jack said. "I was merely stating something I had read somewhere. . . . A fact of misinformation, as it turned out."

"You should be cautious about your reading matter," the old man said.

"But they shouldn't sell things where anyone can buy them," Jack said self-pityingly. "They have such shocking things right out on the news-stand . . . Sometimes my eyes are just drawn to the covers, what can I do?"

"You must not make excuses for yourself, my son," the old man said. It was odd how a feeling of strange satisfaction was in the air, affecting everyone except Jack. Leroy sat up straighter. He had the idea that the old man must now like him better, since he was scolding Jack and that meant he liked him less. And Jack always thought he was so smart!

"Now, to return to my questions," the old man said, wiping his mouth on the tablecloth. "How many bushel baskets of coal do you consume in an average winter?"

"Nine hundred and fourteen," said Mary smartly.

"Nine hundred and eleven!" said Estella.

"You counted wrong!" said Mary.

"*You* counted wrong!"

"Average between the two: that makes nine hundred twelve point five," Jake said graciously.

"Thank you, I had already thought of that," said the old man. He paused. "I had already thought of that solution."

"Yes, I'm sure . . . I'm sure you had," said Jake. "Excuse me."

"I already had the number written down. Do you doubt my word?"

"Not at all. Surely, not at all," said Jake.

"He did! He did!" said Mary. "I saw him write it down, it's there right now. He did it right away!"

"Not everyone is as slow as you," Estella said spitefully to Jake. "My dear sir, will you have some more lemon sauce?"

The old man, writing, glanced up sharply. "Excuse me?" he said.

"Did I interrupt you?"

"Excuse me?"

"I'm sorry," Estella said, "I didn't mean to . . . interrupt your writing. . . . It was the last thing I had intended."

Jack stuck his tongue out at Estella, suddenly.

"Yes, I will have some more lemon sauce," the old man said, with frigid dignity. Estella hurried to spoon it onto his ham. "Though one would have supposed it could have waited just a minute longer."

"It's cooling," Estella murmured.

"Then it should be heated!" said Mary.

"Perhaps he prefers it cool, and not hot," said Estella.

"It's the most irresponsible kind of guesswork," said Jack. "What kind of dinner hostesses are you? What would Mother have said?"

"To return to my questions," the old man interrupted loudly. They were all silent. He made them wait while he held a piece of ham to his mouth and licked the lemon sauce off. "What do you use to pick wax out of your ears?"

"I don't do such a thing," Leroy muttered, his mouth full. "I don't pick nothing out of nothing."

"Leroy," Jack hissed, seizing his arm. "Shut up!"

"What did the young man say?"

"He said he used a wire coat hanger, like the rest of us," said Mary. "Just like the rest of us. He's no different."

The old man wrote this down in his spidery handwriting. "No different?"

"No different," said Estella grimly.

"Are you sure he's no different?"

"Absolutely sure," said Jack.

"What if he were different?"

"We'd sit on him and use the coat hanger and make him just like us," said Estella. "We had to do that once with Jack, when he was putting on airs."

"There was no need to use such a sharp coat hanger," Jack said with a bitter smile.

"Did it pain you?" said the old man, surprised.

"I'm never one to complain, but yes. . . . Yes, it did."

"That's very sad," the old man said. He shook his head. "And now, let me ask you: what do you use to pick your teeth?"

"That's easy," said Mary, leaning toward the old man. "A coat hanger."

"Is it sterilized?"

"Not always," said Mary, looking down at her fingernails.

"And to scratch your back?"

"Oh, a coat hanger too. Isn't that strange?" said Mary. "That makes three coat hangers."

"And to get the dirt out from under your toenails?"

"A coat hanger, of course," Leroy said impudently. His brothers and sisters glared at him, but he noticed that the old man looked satisfied. He smirked over at Jack. "I knew the answer to that," he said.

"And what do you use to pick your nose?" said the old man.

"A coat hanger, I believe," said Jake.

"Yes, a coat hanger. I'm sure. The *handle* of it, you know," said Jack smugly.

"And to get hairs out of the bathtub drain?"

"A coat hanger," said Estella.

"A coat hanger," said Leroy.

"She already told him," Jack whispered. "Shut up."

"Have you," said the old man, "ever signed a petition or sent a telegram to the Legislature requesting legislation?"

"Oh, yes," said Mary.

The old man wrote this down. "What do you like to read?"

"We always read *The Last Days of Pompeii,* every weekday after dinner," Estella said. "It was our mother's choice."

"Would you say you were, as a family, 1) average 2) ordinary 3) queer 4) outstanding? Think carefully."

Jack hid his face in his hands; Jake frowned. Estella licked her lips. "These questions are so . . . probing," she murmured.

"I've never looked so closely at myself," said Jack sincerely. "Have you, Estella?"

"We're average," said Mary.

"Yes, average," said Jake.

Jack sighed. "Very well put."

"Do you think homosexuality should be extended to animals?" the old man said.

"No, definitely not," said Estella emphatically. While the old man wrote she kept shaking her head. "I'm against that definitely."

83

"We're just average," Leroy said.

"Excuse me?" said the old man.

"Nothing, nothing," said Mary, making a hateful face across the table at Leroy. "Our youngest brother didn't say anything."

"I thought I heard him say something."

"You didn't, did you, Leroy?"

Leroy bit off a piece of meat sullenly. "No."

"And what, in your opinion, is the meaning of life?" said the old man, licking the tip of his pencil. "Think carefully."

"My brain is flowing with blood; it hasn't been activated like this for years," Jack said admiringly. "Amazing!"

"I think that happiness is the meaning of life," said Mary, and they all agreed.

"Happiness," said Jake. "Yes. Happiness is the meaning of life."

The old man wrote this down and closed the book. "I thank you for your intelligent cooperation," he said.

"It was our pleasure," said Estella, pleased. "And now do have just a bit more lobster. I'll just snap this claw off—"

"Did I ask that the claw be snapped off?" the old man said gently, tilting his head and waiting. When Estella did not reply he chuckled and said, "When you grow up, my dear, you must be careful not to over-indulge your husband. That can be unpleasant, you know!"

Estella giggled and waved him away.

They watched him eat. He ate with the awkwardness of the aristocrat who offers this awkwardness as a kind of condolence to those who watch, understanding their envy. Even Leroy felt pleased at something. It seemed that the dinner was going well. Something was as it should be, in its place. He could remember the days when his mother was still alive, and he had had the same feeling then. Of course he could remember her only near the end of her life and he saw her in his mind's eye as a scrawny, nervous old woman who shovelled food into her mouth with hands like arthritic roots, moaning and whimpering, with saliva running down her chin and down the sagging folds of her neck, and with parts of chicken skin and gristle stuck to the exceedingly sharp teeth near the corners of her mouth—but his brothers and sisters always told him, sternly, that their mother had never been like that and he was remembering someone else or just being stupid as he usually was.

"Ah, sir," said Jake timidly, "I wonder if I may ask what led you into the profession of census taking?"

"Surely," said the old man, spitting a piece of meat out onto his plate.

He had a large dignified face with stretches of flesh that looked muscular. His skin was pale, as if bleached from exposure to moonlight or some other cold, pale light; his lips were ascetic and demanding. "You may ask, surely," he said in a declamatory voice. "I have travelled for years. Before I lost my eyesight I thought it would be possible for me to cross the boundary of this country. I was tired of this country, I had been here too long. I was turned out of my home and so I became intimately acquainted with the details of this world. So long as you live in a house you don't see them." Only the old man and Leroy still ate; the others leaned forward, listening. Estella's eyes were glittering. "Once in a while a cockroach or a sand fly or a crack in the wall calls your attention to it and consequently to the fact of *change* amidst the illusion of permanence, but oftentimes even those things are absorbed into the safety of the house itself— you don't see them as they are, isolated. When you're turned out of your own home, however, your ancestral home, you suddenly gain vision." And he tapped his dark glasses significantly. "Until then you're blind."

"I know what it's like outside!" Leroy said. "I been there!"

"Will you shut up?" said Jack viciously.

"Keep him quiet," Estella hissed across the table.

"As I said, you are blind until then. It was so in my case. As I lost my eyesight I gained in insight." He groped and came across the dish of olives and pickles; he stuffed a handful in his mouth. "Ah, what the great world can teach you!"

"I been there—I know what it is!" Leroy whispered. "You ain't the only one."

"A world of fish heads and fish eyes and beet tops," the old man said angrily. Leroy was frightened at first, then realized that the old man was not angry at him but at something else. "Tinfoil wrappers! Melon rinds laced with flies! Old enamel basins with black scratches on their bottoms! Broken mirrors, broken dolls' heads, broken combs, bones with gristle still on them! I saw everything. I was there. I saw everything. Peach-colored lampshades half buried in the mud, rusty automobile fenders that were once someone's pride and joy, paper bags with garbage bursting out of them—moldy books, letters never received, certificates of honor, dancing school diplomas— And over everything, great clouds of flies, humming and buzzing. Don't forget the flies. Don't ever forget the flies. In the sunshine they glint like little jewels, precious black jewels. And the whole junk heap is always burning. Day and night, in rain or sunshine, it's burning, smouldering, the fire working out of sight and never coming to an end; and once in a while a hog will break through a barrier of blackened cardboard or steaming automobile cushions,

85

with a heart-piercing squeal—getting burned. I knew enough not to get burned, anyway. I wasn't stupid like the hogs. Every day I walked miles, trying to get out of the dump heap, kicking smouldering papers in front of me, ducking and running through the haze of flies, holding my hands to my face to protect myself—I walked and walked—my feet were wrapped in bloody bedsheets—I never tired. I was supposed to come to a river or a creek or some body of water that was a political boundary, and there would be a gate house and an official in charge, to welcome me and take my toll charge from me and help me over to the other side. On the posters it advertised the other side—its lovely blue lakes and blue skies, its green grass, its green tree leaves. But when I sometimes climbed all the way to the top of a mountain of junk—grapefruit rinds and banana peels no longer slippery and eggshells and shrimp tails—why, then, what do you think?"

"I don't know what to think," Jack said.

"The other side looked no different. No, *sir*. It looked no different. The other side was a thunderous cloud of flies just like our side, turning and glinting in the sun, and only disappearing at night—because they were black, like the night air. But their humming kept on. In those days I could see quite well, still, and I tried to point this out to the others. But they never believed me. Their eyes had begun to dim, what with the flies crawling on them and sucking at them while they slept, poor stupid things. . . . And so they never believed me, but kept going, walking on, pushing on, some of them leaning on staves and some on crutches, singing and murmuring together like herds of elephants."

"Oh, my," said Mary. "Do elephants sing and murmur?"

"He's thinking of sheep," Jake whispered, touching his finger to his lip. "Don't disturb him."

But the old man was too moved to hear. "And so if I had crossed to the other side it might not have made any difference, in the long run. I console myself with that."

"I don't . . . believe I've ever seen a garbage dump," said Jack.

The old man sniffed, puzzled. He seemed to be sniffing Jack out. Then he said, rather contemptuously, "What was that? What did I hear?"

"I said," Jack gulped, "that I don't believe I've ever seen it. The garbage dump you speak of, sir."

"*Smell,* then," said the old man. He made a sudden gesture toward Jack and knocked the gravy boat over; luckily it was nearly empty. Mary took off her apron and wadded it into a bundle and put it into the gravy to soak it up, unobtrusively and quietly, so that the old man would not notice. "Close your eyes and smell. The odor you smell is the smell of the garbage dump.

Do you smell it? Do you hear the flies buzzing?"

Leroy stared, chewing his food. Something about the old man frightened and annoyed him.

"I'm not sure. . . . I don't know. . . ." said Jack.

"Close your eyes and smell, but keep your mouth shut. Watch out for the flies!"

Jack closed his eyes tight. His face was wet with perspiration. "Well," said the old man triumphantly, "what do you smell?"

"Perhaps I smell it," Jack said uncertainly. "Perhaps. It seems to be just Jake's after-shave lotion, but yet. . . . Yes, it might be. . . ."

"You're lying," said the old man. He laughed. "Don't you think I have any sensitivity?"

"I'm not lying, sir," Jack said. "Excuse me, but I never lie. I never lie."

"Lying is defined only in relationship to the truth, which I happen to possess," the old man said. He picked up a handful of string beans and shook them once, as if to get rid of flies, and popped them into his mouth. "If I did not possess the truth anything you said might very well be no more a lie than anything else. As it is, however, I am the custodian of the truth. What I can't recall—and there isn't much—is safely recorded in this book."

"I was not conscious of lying," Jack said. He sniffed. "There must be at least two kinds of lies, those done on purpose for meanness and those done out of ignorance."

"You mustn't count too heavily upon your ignorance," the old man said sagely. Estella looked with triumph at Jack, folding her arms. "Anyway, they all lie. Everywhere." The old man sighed, picking a tiny fleck of food off his lip with his tongue. "You come across somebody sleeping inside an old refrigerator, with smears of catsup all around, and grease, and broken light bulbs; and what will he say to you? He says *he's* not living in a dump. He always says that. He says he loves the country air—and when you breathe it you have to throw up, what with the garbage and sewerage and smoke, and flies sucked in your mouth. He says he loves peace and quiet and that's all he wants out of life—and just on the other side of the refrigerator the garbage trucks are unloading, their wheels are spinning around in the slick muck, and the hogs are nosing their way right toward you, squealing and grunting. He says he wants nothing more out of life than to mind his own business and live to a peaceful old age, but when you peer at him you can see the little red pimples on his face that are going to get bigger and bigger and turn hard and come together in a running, smeary white mess, then start eating back into his skull and into his brain; he's got maybe a year to live and he knows it, but he never lets on. That's man for you! Our noble race. . . . And some of them even get married out there and settle down in a carton or something, and have children; and the children grow up and never learn the word for 'fly' because they never lived in a world where there wasn't flies everywhere. Unless you can stand back from something you can't name it. But they all lie to you!"

"I believe you. I do," Mary said. She bent her head toward the old man. "I know you're right—you're so old, your hair is so white, your voice is so strong! I can smell the garbage on you, too. I know you're right."

"We gonna have pudding tonight or now?" Leroy said, his mouth full.

"I'm afraid I don't understand, about the garbage," Jack said, trying to smile. "I have great faith in man's mind and so I know that if you explain it carefully to me I'll understand—"

"You're stupid, that's all," Mary said snippishly. "You're no better than Leroy! Mother tried to tell you the facts of life—about how worms come out of dead mice, and other things—but you hid your face and crawled in the furnace! You were afraid!"

"That's not true, it was Jake who did that," Jack said. "I've never run away from the truth!"

"And then what happened?" Estella said to the old man. "Tell us more about your life."

He was chewing noisily. The images in his dark glasses bobbed and were confused. Finally he swallowed and said, "One day they said they wanted to check up on everybody living in the dump. They set up an office on some old furniture and we lined up to take a series of tests—an aptitude test, an I.Q. test, a personality test, and a test to show anxiety and aggression impulses, I think it was. And I was the one to get the job, out of all the applicants."

"That was wonderful," Mary said.

"Yes," said the old man. "It was. And now here I am. That was sixteen years ago—how fast time moves!" He waved his hand, idly, as if chasing flies away from his face without much enthusiasm.

"But what—what happened to your eyes?" Mary said.

"That's too personal!" said Estella.

"Your eyes, your dear eyes! I seem to have the idea—I don't know why— I seem to have the idea they were *blue*," Mary said nervously. "Why is that? How strange it is! What happened to your eyes?"

"Not at the dinner table," the old man said, clearing his throat.

They sat in silence. Leroy tried to figure out why his brothers and sisters looked so tense. Mary said slowly, "We've had terrible things happen to us too. Our father abandoned us."

"Abandoned you?"

88

Danny Lyon photographs

ALBANY, GEORGIA /1965

MARIA / CARTAGENA, COLUMBIA / 1966

HYDE PARK, CHICAGO /1965

UPTOWN, CHICAGO / 1965

"Yes."

"Abandoned you, just like that?"

"Yes."

"Yes, that's true," said Jake.

"But why did he do that?" said the old man.

"He was evil!" Jack said. "An evil man! He broke my mother's heart and ruined Jake's eyesight and is responsible for Leroy's damaged brain—his brain is turning to water, every night more of it changes into fluid, sometimes you can hear it drip! Our father was evil!"

"And our mother was good. A saint," Mary said tearfully. "And yet I did a terrible thing, too—I—I ran away once, and I—I pray to God and to my mother to forgive me! It was terrible, shameful—"

"Nobody cares about your cheap little secrets," Estella said.

"Yes, we all have pasts, for that matter," said Jack. "Not just *you*. My own experience was ugly and tragic and helped to break my poor dear mother's heart, but—"

"Shut up about yourself! Always yourself!" Estella cried.

"Indeed, you all seem to forget," Jake said slowly, as if beginning a speech, "that it was *my* experience that made the most impression upon our mother. If we are to interpret responsibly certain remarks she made in her last coma—"

"Who cares about you?" Mary said. "You old bores! Old maids! I don't believe you ever did anything! I don't believe you ever went anywhere—probably hid in the basement so she'd miss you and then you came back to cry on her chest—it wasn't a very big chest either— How I hated you!"

"And do you think anybody ever believed *you?*" Estella sneered.

"It was true, what I did," Mary said. "You're just jealous of me, you always have been. And you should be." She put her arm through the old man's and leaned against him, smirking around at Estella. "You remember how Mother said I was the prettiest, and she felt sorry for you with your big old ugly face! Yes, she did! On her death bed she said: 'I feel sorry for Estella with her big old ugly horse face!' And then she turned to the wall and died—the poor thing!"

"Mother never said that!"

"She did, she whispered it just for me to hear!" Mary cried. "You believe me, don't you?" she said to the old man, who was tearing off a section of meat with his teeth. "And my father liked me best, too! One day when no one was around he played a game with me and went with me in the dirty clothes hamper, just me and him together and nobody else! And then later on he gave me a cherry sucker, so there, and he never gave *you* anything!"

"I hardly believe that," Estella said.

"You're just jealous! Big old ugly horse face!"

"Mary, you seem to forget that we have a guest with us today," Jake said quietly. "What will he think?"

"It makes me think of my own family, long ago," the old man said dreamily. He patted Mary's hand. "It happened in another world, nearly. I too, I fell in love and married; one morning I was walking across a river of junk and my foot slipped on a pile of cabbage leaves and I fell heavily, down into a little valley, and landed right on top of a woman. She had a strange white face and black hair, not beautiful exactly but striking, and such sharp teeth there on the side! And long white lovely hands—when she brushed the flies away from her face her hands were like beautiful white fish gliding in a dark, deep, glimmering pond. And so we were married. But after our first child, a girl, was born, she began to change toward me. She and the child ate all the food as fast as they could, and left only crumbs for me. They grew strong and big and I grew weak. Then another child was born, a boy. And she would sit with them both, one on each knee, and her stomach swelling in the middle with yet another baby, telling them stories —strange stories about herself, her past, when she had been a beautiful black horse, in another life evidently, and a beautiful black bird, and a cat—very strange stories— And gradually she sucked all their love into herself and left nothing for me. When they looked at me their eyes were like shells, with the insides scooped out. They didn't see me, not really. And more children were born, one right after the other, another boy and then a girl, and the oldest ones got tall and strong and bold, and snatched scraps of food right out of my mouth while *she* laughed! I got weaker and weaker. They gave me what they had finished with—they tossed me empty banana peels, empty egg-shells, the top part of the celery that's all leaves and insects, and the outside of the lettuce that's all brown and bad. She made me sleep outside in the rain, and once she made me hamburger patties out of filth and sawdust! I, who loved her and the children, loved them all! And one day she ordered me to leave because she didn't want any more children. And so I left. I wandered for years. I sent back money whenever I could, because she had had another baby son soon after I left, but I never heard from her again and that was that. Young love! How beautiful young love is!"

"What a strange woman she was," Mary said.

Leroy clutched his head suddenly in pain. "What's wrong?" said Jake.

"What's wrong with him?" said Estella.

"Hurts—" Leroy muttered. He grimaced, shaking his head. "Got a pain—headache—"

"A headache? You?" said Estella.

90

"How can he have a headache?" said Mary. "He never had one be-fore."

"He only wants attention, as usual," said Jack.

Leroy groaned.

"Yes," the old man said philosophically, "we are all guilty. We are all guilty of each other's filth."

"All guilty, yes," said Jake.

"All guilty," said Mary slowly.

"Not me, not— Not me," Leroy said. He was pressing both hands against his forehead and waiting anxiously for the pain to end. "I'm not guilty of—of nothing I didn't do! I'm—"

"Shut up," Jack said. "We're all guilty, of course. That's a premise of civilization. The first rule—you build everything upon that, the original guilt, you build laws and traffic regulations, sewerage measurements, national holidays, banking hours, the duration of air raid whistles. What is civilization without guilt?"

"I never did anything wrong," Leroy muttered. The pain had lessened a little. "I know that."

"Young man, we are all guilty," the blind old man said, shaking a greasy finger at him. "Just as that woman was guilty."

"No, not me. Not me! To hell with that!"

"We are all guilty! We're all aspects of the same soul, the gigantic soul of the universe," the old man said. "You only think you're *you;* she only thinks she's *she;* he's *he,* she's *she,* that's *it,* this piece of meat is this piece of meat, the water in this glass is no more and no less than the water in this glass. On the contrary, I say to you: we are all aspects of the same great soul of the universe, like a great goulash with many ingredients!"

"I'm not going in no goulash," Leroy said. "I'm nobody else but my-self and never was and I never done nothing wrong and I'm not guilty!"

"Leroy, leave the table," Estella said.

"No!"

"You'll be whipped if you don't leave!"

"I want some pudding!"

"You'll never get any pudding again!"

"Anyway," said Mary, putting her head on the old man's shoulder, "anyway, I believe you. I know what you mean. I don't question."

The old man touched her face, running his fingers over it as if trying to read it. Very slowly his lips moved as if he were saying something to himself.

"Oh, that tickles," Mary said. "Don't do that!"

"What's your name?" said the old man. "What is it again?"

"What does it matter? We're all part of the same universe, the same soul," Mary said. "Let me tell you: when I was fourteen I ran away and joined a convent. That's my secret!"

"What a lie!" said Estella.

"I did! I joined a convent!"

"You can't prove that!"

"You're just jealous because *you* don't have any secret," Mary cried. "I ran away and joined a convent, the order of nuns with green underwear. We put b-b's in our shoes to remind us of Christ's agony! We scratched our fingernails on little blackboards we carried around with us, to remind us of God's displeasure! We ate live grasshoppers to remind us of the evil of nature! But one day I decided to leave and so I ran away again, down the road, and caught a Greyhound bus and escaped! And that's not all!"

"What lies! Anything to get attention," said Estella.

"You're just jealous because my secret is better than yours," Mary said. "And you were in my cosmetics box again last night, weren't you? Some lavender eye shadow is missing! Don't deny it!"

"That isn't true—you're lying!"

"You're just jealous because he likes me better than you," Mary said. "I know he likes me better. I know what he means when he says we're all guilty."

"No," Leroy said. "No. That's not— He don't—"

"Shut up, stupid! You're guilty if he says you are!"

"And you—you should talk about people in your cosmetics box!" Jack said. "Who always leaves the shower curtain on the outside of the bathtub, so the water drips down through the floor and onto the pool table? Yes, and who never cleans up after herself in the bathroom? Muddy footprints on the floor and on the wall by the light-switch! Rings of dirt in the bathtub!"

"Leroy does all that!" Mary said furiously.

"I do not!"

"You know he doesn't use our bathroom, we won't let him," Estella said. "If there's a mess in there it's one of you three."

"She's just jealous, she can't help but be jealous!" Mary said. "Because our father loved me more than her and *she* was never loved by nobody! Never! And she never loved anybody either!"

"I was in love," Estella said hoarsely.

"What a lie!" Jack laughed.

"I was in love! I was! I was once in love!"

Everyone except the old man laughed, even Leroy. The ache was still in his head but was not too bad now.

"I was in love— Yes. With somebody in this very room," Estella said.

They were silent. Then Mary giggled, then Jack. Estella said, shuddering, "Yes. I was in love with somebody in this very room. And though I never spoke of it, though we never touched—yet I conceived a child through the violence of my love. Yes. I've never told this, knowing how you would scorn me. But now, with this old man here, this strange old man, I feel I can tell the truth—the truth will make me free—for as he says, we're all guilty— all guilty—"

"Estella, my heavens!" said Jake. "Did I hear right?"

"Don't listen to her, she's crazy!" said Mary. "Such talk at the dinner table!"

"And I performed the abortion myself, myself," Estella said, sobbing. "With a rear view mirror from Leroy's bicycle and an ice pick—"

"What's an ice pick?" said Leroy.

"They used to have them when ice was in the ice box, instead of the way it is now," Jack said impatiently.

"What ice box?"

"The refrigerator!"

"What?"

"The refrigerator used to have ice in it."

"It still does! It has ice in the top part—"

"Once upon a time," Jack said, "it was just a box with ice in it. The ice was delivered in big chunks and first you used a saw, then an ax, then an ice pick to break it up. Then you put it in the ice box."

"An ice pick was something like a screwdriver, if I'm not mistaken," Jake said. He was always politer to Leroy than the others, for which Leroy was thankful. "It had a handle and a point; its function lay in the point."

"My child," said the old man to Estella, "who was it you loved so fiercely? Who was the father of your unborn infant?"

"I can't tell! Never!" Estella cried.

"I don't know whether to believe any of this," Mary said slowly.

"It might simply be a plea for attention," Jack said to the old man. "You know how women are. My own case, now—"

"Listen to him!" Estella sobbed.

"My own case illustrates much more aptly your judgment of man," Jack said. "Of course I was quite young then—hardly more than a child, thirty-seven or thirty-eight, I forget which, and I too ventured out into the world, against my dear mother's wishes, you can be sure. I broke her heart, and for what? I fell madly in love with the shadow of a woman that fell before me on the street, and I looked up to see that that woman was a Negro. A Negress. Very beautiful, like bronze, with dangling earrings in her ears and a red kerchief! Long muscular legs, gleaming bronze and gold and brown, like a goddess! And I followed her everywhere, lost with love, abandoned to lust. And never, never did she bother with me. I would lie on the roof of her house at night and listen to her television set; anything to be near her. Then one Sunday morning she went out, all dressed in a long red silk dress with bustles and a big ostrich feather hat, going to church, and by some mistake she went in the wrong church. The congregation was all white. And I was following her secretly, lost with love, but when they turned and saw her, and when they jumped up out of their seats and crowded around her, I—I pretended not to see! That is the shame I must live with! I abandoned her, I crouched in a pew and pretended to be singing a hymn, because the organist upstairs was playing a hymn to drown out the noise. While they swarmed over her and struck and beat and tore her, I, I abandoned her, I betrayed her out of cowardice, do you understand? I never saw her again, whole. And this is the shame I live with daily— I, I, guilty! guilty!" He pounded his chest and sobbed, an ugly noise that embarrassed Leroy.

"I think he's just making that up, like her," Mary said. Her voice was shaky. "Don't believe them. They just want your attention."

"And so you see how I am wallowing in guilt!" Jack sobbed.

"My son, you are indeed guilty," the old man said thoughtfully. "I recognize some of my own anguish in you." He was picking at his teeth with a fork.

"Oh, *him!*" Mary said jealously. "Thinks he's so evil, and he's the one who squeezes the toothpaste tube in the middle!"

"That's not me, that's Jake! Jake!"

"And he sits and picks dandruff out of his hair and eats it, when he thinks nobody's looking!"

"I do not!"

"And his stomach is fat—there's dirt all caked up in his belly button!"

"That's a lie! A dirty lie!" Jack cried.

"I don't believe either one of them," Mary said to the old man, "and anyway I did more than they did. I'm worse than them."

"How come you all done these things, and I never done anything?" Leroy said spitefully.

"What did he say?" said the old man.

"Nothing, nothing! He didn't say nothing!" Mary cried. "Anyway, I did worse things than anybody. It's just that . . . I can't remember them all, they're mixed up in my mind. It's dark in my mind. But you believe me, don't you? That I'm worse than them?"

The old man groped for his water glass, found it, and lifted it to his lips. He spilled water on his chest but did not notice.

"Well, do you believe me or not?" Mary cried. "You're not going to let them fool you, are you?"

"Don't listen to her," Estella said. "She still wets her bed, what do you think about that?"

"I do not! Oh, I do not! What a lie, an ugly lie!"

"It's true!" Jack cried.

"You don't believe them, mister, do you? Do you?" Mary cried. She slid her arm anxiously around the old man's neck. "Mister? **Do** you? You look so strong and wise! You know everything! You've got white hair and no eyes and you're big and tall and carry that book around with you that's got everything in it, every fact written in it. I know you don't believe their lies. What are your eyes like, mister? Can't you see anything? Why don't you take your glasses off?"

"Ultimately," Jake said, clearing his throat solemnly, "it may be that I am the greatest sinner here. I don't like to talk about myself, but—"

"Oh, for God's sake!" said Jack. "Now listen!"

"What's that old maid trying to say?" said Mary.

"You may recall that I too left our dear mother's home, one spring morning," he said. "I wore precisely the clothes I am wearing now. This vest is new, however. I was a handsome man, as I am now. I decided to improve myself and so I took a course in business administration in the evening division of the university. I've kept all this secret until now. Yes, a course in business administration. . . . And one evening there was a tremendous thunderstorm during the professor's lecture, which was in an amphitheater on the third floor of an old building, and we huddled together in the flickering light, trying to take notes, some of us actually down on our knees praying to God for mercy. The old professor showed no fear and continued with his lecture until the lights went out; then he was forced to stop. He went about lighting candles, soothing us, telling us we would be safe. Such a brave, good man! For six days the storm continued—the windows were blown out and rain cascaded in, plaster and parts of boards began to fall, killing some of us at once. And when we tried to get out we saw that everything was flooded—the stairs, the hallway, the campus, the city, as far as we could see. And the rain kept coming without mercy. So we huddled together, those of us still alive, weeping and praying, the good professor with us, and very slowly our numbers began to decrease, the weakest of us succumbing first, one by one, and lay foaming on the floor, while the relentless muddy water kept creeping higher and higher. Weeks passed, and starvation began its grim hold. And, of course, you must have anticipated what finally happened—"

"What? What?" shouted Leroy, unable to sit still.

95

"The strongest of us . . . were forced. . . . We were forced to eat of human flesh," Jake said, hiding his face. He shuddered violently.

Everyone was silent. The old man pushed his plate away.

"I myself," Jake sobbed, "tore flesh from that dear old professor's bones—his very bones! And I ate it! I ate it!"

"My poor child," the old man said.

"Don't even talk to me! Don't think of me!" Jake cried. "I'm no good, I'm a murderer! A cannibal! I've been living a lie all these years—pretending to be good, to be moral, even to be a finicky eater! Now you see me in my nakedness—how can you bear to look upon me?"

"I don't even believe it. No. I don't believe it," Mary said, dazed. "You can't even eat pickles. I just don't believe it."

"His digestion tubes are all clogged up," said Estella. "I don't believe it either."

"But, don't you see, it was from *that* they got that way!" Jake said. "Clogged with human hair and fingernails and his Phi Beta Kappa key!"

Jack leaned away from his brother, making a face. "I doubt that it's true, but still. . . . Just to say such things is disgusting."

"Yes, I'm disgusting! I recognize it, I admit it! We are all guilty of being disgusting!" Jake said.

"No, not me," said Leroy. "You leave me out of this."

The old man sighed and tried to draw himself up to his full height. "Yes," he said, ponderously, "we are all guilty of being disgusting. That is the sole attribute common to all of us."

"But you don't believe him, do you?" said Mary. "That old maid? He never did anything! Never had the courage! You don't believe him!"

"It's possible—yes— It isn't impossible," said the old man.

"Do you believe him?"

"I'm not. . ."

"Do you?"

"I don't know. It would take some thought, some calculation—"

"Then I don't like you any more!" Mary cried.

"Why should he believe you and nobody else?" said Estella. "You had the least to confess of any of us, as it turned out. "You're just jealous!"

"Well, I did more than I told you. I—I did other things too—"

They laughed at her. She turned to the old man angrily. "You believe me, don't you? Don't you?"

"Yes. . ."

"Now wait," said Jack, "what the hell? Why give in to her? You know she's lying."

96

"She always did lie," Jake admitted. "When we take baths together on Saturday nights, Mary and me, she's always the one who knocks the plug out with her big toe, then she tries to blame me. She says I knock it out with my bottom, but that's a lie! She's always lying!"

"Listen to him, when his pet rabbits got in my doll house and made a mess!" Mary sobbed. "Just yesterday!"

"And you broke my erector set!" Jake shouted. "I found the box hidden behind the umbrella stand, and when I took it out, sure enough! Some parts were broken!"

"That wasn't me, that was Jack!"

"It wasn't me!" Jack said, knocking a plate off the table. "Don't blame me!"

"Who do you believe?" Mary cried, clutching the old man's arm. Leroy noticed that the old man looked a little nervous. "Tell me! Who do you believe?"

The old man paused. His mouth opened but no sound came out. He passed his hand before his face, as if chasing away flies, and then he said rather uncertainly, "We are—we are all sinners. It's very difficult to—"

"But which one of us do you believe?"

"Don't listen to *her!*" Estella said.

"Don't listen to her!" Mary cried, pushing against the old man. "Tell them you believe me most of all!"

The old man got to his feet shakily. "I think," he said slowly, "I think that—"

"Hey, you aren't blind!" Leroy cried suddenly.

Everyone stared. Leroy got to his feet and faced the old man across the table. His head was pounding with something that was more than just pain. "You told us all kinds of lies and got away with it because you're blind, because you said you were blind! But I bet you ain't! Told me I was guilty when I never done nothing wrong—never! I never done nothing at all! All my life I been hearing lies from people older than me and I'm tired of it. Do you understand? They told lies when they said that they remembered things right and I remembered them wrong, they told lies when they looked out of the window and said what the weather was, they told lies all the time! This whole life never made no sense to me. I don't remember no mother, not the same one they had, and I don't remember no father, and I don't remember myself from one time to another that I look in the mirror! Now you come along and spoil the dinner and she won't even serve the pudding, now, and you tell me dirty filthy lies about myself—tell me you know about me already, got me set down in your goddamn book, said I was guilty! What the hell does that mean? Like everything was planned before I was born and I just come into it, like water comes out of a faucet, and don't have anything to do about it! Well, I say to hell with that!"

His brothers and sisters stared at him. They had never heard him talk like this before. Fortified by their terror and by the old man's silence he stood taller and his voice got louder. "Now you come here, old bastard, and tell us a lot of goddam junk nobody wants to hear! Spoil the whole day! The last census taker that came here fell through a hole in the living room floor and into the cistern; that was that! Goddam accident, but what can you do? And the one before that—another blind bastard like you—his own dog turned on him and dragged him all over the living room and bloodied everything up like hell; and if that wasn't enough, now you're here! Well, I'm tired of it! I know you're not blind but only pretending, anything to get a meal, and I never was fooled once!"

"He is too blind," Mary whimpered. "I bet he is."

"I bet he's got real-life eyes behind those glasses!" Leroy crowed.

"I bet he doesn't!" said Mary.

"Bet he does!"

"It's possible he was lying. . . ." Jack said, rubbing his forehead. "In that case we shouldn't have told such . . . intimate things to him. . . ."

"It was a mistake, clearly," Jake said.

"But he is blind, I know he is," Mary said.

"I don't believe he could have lied, no, I just don't believe it," Estella cried. "It couldn't be true, after what I confessed—To confess such a thing to a man who wasn't blind! My God!"

"I bet he's got eyes, I bet it!" Leroy shouted. "Let's just take a look!"

The old man stepped back. He raised his hands as if giving them a kind of blessing. "I am truly blind," he said.

"There, you see!" said Mary. "You let him alone!"

"Let's just see!" Leroy ran around the table to him. "Let's see, let's see!" he said, trying to get the old man's glasses off. "I bet he's got eyes just like me. Hey, mister, turn around here—hey! You want to make me mad? Let's see—" And he jerked the dark glasses off. "See! Look!" he cried. "He's got eyes just like all of us! Eyes! He's got eyes!" And he snapped the glasses in two and threw them down.

"It's true, he does have eyes. . . ." Mary said, blinking.

"You see, he was fooling us," Jack said. "An incredible thing. . . . We must have better police protection in this city."

"Having eyes does not necessitate not being blind," Jake said pedantically. "Or do I mean the precise opposite . . . ?"

Estella had fallen back in her chair, sobbing. "I can't believe it!" she cried.

The old man tried to get away, groping along the table. Leroy caught him. "He's still pretending to be blind! My God, will you look at that!" Leroy shouted in exasperation. "Who does he think he's fooling? Mister, you think we're nuts in this family or something?"

"But I am blind—I am blind—"

"Liar!"

"I am truly blind—"

"Then," said Leroy shrewdly, "you wouldn't mind if somebody poked out your eye, eh?"

"I am truly blind—"

"You wouldn't mind, eh? You wouldn't mind?"

"I have a card—somewhere—My credentials—"

"Tell me the truth! You wouldn't mind if somebody poked out your eye, would you, if you were really blind?"

"I don't trust him any longer. I'm sorry, I just don't," Jack said, turning away in agitation.

"Let me just take this pudding spoon here, and make a little experiment," Leroy cried. The old man whimpered and ran forward, but collided with Mary, who screamed and pushed him away. "No, no, you don't! You get away from my sister!" Leroy said. "You been lying to us all this time and now we're going to get you! If you're really blind like you say you won't mind a little experiment— Here, turn around here! Hey!"

Leroy grabbed the old man and forced him down to the floor and there, squatting over his chest, he gouged out his left eye with the pudding spoon. The old man cried out and his hands leapt to his face. A great passion seized Leroy: his head pounded, his face seemed on fire, his hands could not still themselves. He jumped back in triumph, crying: "Now what! What now! Whatcha going to do now?"

The others had got to their feet. They were silent. The old man groaned, Leroy was panting furiously; no one spoke. Leroy did not look at his brothers and sisters. "That's for calling me *guilty*, when I never done nothing!" he said. "Nothing! Never! And now you better get out of here and don't come back!"

The old man struggled to his feet. Mary jerked away from him, running to Estella's arms. Jack jumped aside as the old man groped his way around the table and to the doorway and out into the living room, along the wall, sobbing and moaning; they heard something fall over, a lamp probably, and they heard him collide with something, stub his toe perhaps on a chair; then they heard the door open and shut.

99

In the awkward silence that followed Estella cleared her throat, Jake buttoned his vest; Jack leaned over and pinched Leroy's arm, hard. "Ow!" said Leroy. "What's wrong with you?" Jack gave him a certain level look. Leroy rubbed his arm. Estella piled plates on top of one another, frowning.

"No, I just can't believe what happened here," Jake said slowly. "I can't... absorb it into my mind...."

"He was a fake!" said Leroy. "And if he wasn't, so what? The eye never did him no good, then, did it? Well, did it?"

"What do you mean?" Estella said.

"What I say! It never did him no good anyway, and anyway he was a fake. Why're you all looking at me?"

They were silent for a moment. Then Jack and Jake sighed, at the same time, and turned to go into the living room. That meant dinner was over. "I didn't think we should answer the door, if you recall," Jack said. "It's better usually to let well enough alone." Jake agreed. "Monday will be a welcome relief, after today," Jack said. "These Sundays are tiring. And the condition of the cemetery—I just don't know what to think."

"I have a difficult case tomorrow, it's been on my mind all day," Jake said. "If I've seemed absent-minded...."

"You've always got a difficult case," Estella said bitterly. She was piling all the dishes in one great stack. "What about me, running a high school? Do you think it's easy for a woman principal in a big school? And with what happened today! My stomach's starting to be upset again...."

"Take some tablets, that's easy," Mary said. She was dabbing her eyes with a handkerchief. "Anyway, you shouldn't complain. Look at my position, giving dancing lessons to those old people! Our ballroom used to be a youthful, lively place, but now everyone except us dancing instructors are old fogeys; how'd you like that? And they all want to do the rhumba, and then they fall down and break their hips or ankles. And they have no sense of discipline, those old men. No discipline at all!"

"Their lack of discipline is as much your fault as their parents'," Jack said. He sat in one of the leather chairs and lit his pipe. Jake also sat and began puffing at his pipe. "Discipline must be upheld at any cost. It's the first premise of civilization."

"Yes, quite right," said Jake. "One of my patients, that woman I've spoken of often, has been dying of an incurable disease for four years now. The effect of weak childhood training in her case is obvious. She has no sense of discipline. In the last century patients suppressed their groans of agony in the doctor's presence, but no more."

"Isn't that expecting too much of them?" Jack said.

100

"I don't think so," said Jake. He sighed. "And it's such hard work, going out three days a week. Jack only has to go out two days—"

"But look at me!" said Estella. "I go out six days!"

"And me, I go out six days too!" Mary said.

"And me!" said Leroy, who worked most of all. "What about me?"

"You seem to forget the years of study Jake and I have put in," Jack said. He was smoking his pipe thoughtfully. "Three hundred yards of law books. Don't forget how I endangered my health."

"That's so," Mary said slowly.

Leroy always hated the end of the weekend, for very early on Monday morning—at three o'clock—he had to go to work. The women cleaned the table off, and he hung around by the doorway of the kitchen, wishing they would notice him. "You polish up my badge like you said you would?" he asked Mary. "You promised."

"Your badge?" said Mary. "Oh, yes. I did it yesterday. Where's his badge, Estella?"

"In with the silverware."

"We put it there by mistake, we were polishing silverware yesterday too," Mary said. Leroy got the badge out of the silverware drawer; it was gleaming proudly. He was proud of being a policeman and so he put the badge on and stood around, waiting for someone to notice him, to scold him or pinch his arm, or to look up in surprise to see that he too now wore a mask like everyone else. He ran his tongue along the inside of his mouth, as if seeking a change. Surely some change had taken place.

"Oh, yes!" Jack exclaimed, uncrossing his legs. "I must write a letter to the cemetery before I forget. A very angry letter to the cemetery."

Leroy went upstairs to his room and looked in the mirror at himself. Where was the change? Where had it taken place? He leaned to the mirror and stared at himself, into his eyes, at his mouth, at his overlarge pores, even turning his head and trying to look into his ears. He was the same person. He did not even look older. So nothing has any effect on anything else, he thought.

So much for that Sunday.

kites tied out over the river
                              dive
fleshed in a loop from the wrist's pulse
veined close
                    til the taut-bellied balsa splits
and a rigged bone's fished to shore:

            Ballast by a lovebait tailed too high
I'm pressed to the inside outward;

                    come down to your footsteps
                    original and torn.

So:
      take the flight of this fall and drain your landing
lenslike
through the double rope of the wind's eye
where you let me fly you:
                              bound
lame in a forest of lost keys
I'll travel,
              paper baby
and a brokeback flier,

                    taped out on the doorstep
                    and fixed for certain;
                                          run again
                    to the one good time.

EUGENIA MACER

Notes and footnotes on current art

JOHN PERREAULT

I: FASHION

Abstract Expressionism, Hard Edge, Neo-Dada, Assemblage, Pop Art, Op Art, Minimal Art, Light Art, Kinetic Art, Psychedelic Art, Environments, Protest Art, Projected Art, Funk Art. . . . One style comes on the heels of another with a regularity that, when it isn't invigorating, is oppressive. Publicity follows art criticism, for "art criticism," no matter what else it is, no matter how "learned," ephemeral, footnoted, dishonest, boring, illuminating, or irrelevant is always publicity. And fashion follows publicity. Thereafter, with a little bit of luck, follows fame, fortune, T. V. interviews, museum retrospectives, and all the other trappings of instant immortality.

Older artists, who should know better, panic and pontificate at the drop of a hat. Younger artists, not yet tapped by the "establishment"—if there is an establishment, it is certainly a very inefficient and chaotic one—scream at the top of their lungs when confronted by the circus-like spectacle of the "art scene." They want no part of publicity campaigns, four-color posters, billboards, announcements in the form of jigsaw puzzles, or so they claim, right up until the last day of their first one-man show and nothing

103

has been sold, there are no reviews, and the only names in the gallery "guest book" are Hilda Bronx (on tour with an art appreciation group), the immediate family, and "Superman," "Batman," and "James Bond."

If the truth be known, the publicity machinery that artists and critics alike criticize so eloquently, with the exception of three or four top galleries, is composed largely of fantasy and the traditional paranoia of an art community. To the extent that it does exist, it is responsible in many ways for allowing so many young artists—many quite undeserving—an opportunity to display their works to the public and has opened up an "anything goes" climate that, although chaotic and a trifle vulgar, has contributed to the current flourishing of art in America.

Art in recent times has abandoned its age-old role of recording fashion. Fashion now "records" art, and the new art influences the look of our society from top to bottom. In a mass society, in an affluent society, such as now exists for the moment in America—although still riddled with many social injustices, sociological diseases, and endangered by a nineteenth-century foreign policy—there is such a demand for consumer goods, for variety, for ersatz individuality that fashion culls from every source its yearly, almost monthly dictates and inventions. One of fashion's most fertile sources has become the world of art. Nothing is too far out. Nothing is sacred. Fashion designers, ad men, and interior decorators have raided Pop Art for new ideas and new angles of sensibility. Mondriaan pants suits, Op Art ties, shifts and spangles are on sale at Macy's and in sight on Main Streets all across America. We are confronted by Psychedelic bathing-suits, make-up, and toothpaste ads. What next? We can look forward to Minimal Art monuments and Rose Bowl floats. We can predict without blinking an eye: Eccentric Abstraction bathtubs, Protest Art telephones, strobe-light fireplaces, Funk Art frying pans. Art has become the brain trust of the design factories and now relates to design and decoration in the same way that pure science relates to applied science and engineering.

Artists themselves are not any more immune to the lure of bank accounts than others and have the disadvantage of having to scrape together their own anti-poverty funds. Andy Warhol seizes the day. Warhol grabs the bull by the horns. There is Warhol wallpaper, a Warhol rock and roll group and night club act, Warhol T-shirts, and now even an Andy Warhol perfume. The nineteenth-century William Morris claps his hands in heaven while the twentieth-century Robert Morris who is one of our best "Minimal" sculptors plays along with his peers in submitting impossible monuments for the endless group shows of proposed monuments that have informed this recent art season.

Funk Art and Protest Art notwithstanding, it is no longer fashionable to be unfashionable or alienated. Artists, in spite of the propaganda, are rowdy materialists. They work with matter and understand it better than the average American pseudo-materialist and understand that it is to be used, not worshipped. This explains Junk Art, ephemeral collage happenings, tissue paper murals, mandalas made out of strawberry ice cream. It also explains that more recent, more sophisticated version of, comment on, and amendment to our packaged, plasticized, "no deposit; no return" civilization of paper dresses, hose-down rooms, and transparent underwear: Canadian artist Les Levine's Throwaways and/or Disposables, which are inexpensive and disposable.

Marshall McLuhan claims that the artist has come down out of the ivory tower into the control tower. McLuhan, however, is not completely right in his premise that we have changed from a visually oriented world to an oral-aural, tactile, tribal organization of our senses. In art at least, the Word has not been replaced by the Touch, but by the Image. Some successful artists only sell art as a by-product. What they really sell is themselves. They sell an Image. Hopefully this image represents some sort of unique sensibility, but often it is merely a stance, a myth, a hope, or a hoax.

II: CLASSIFICATIONS

At the present moment in the art world in America there is a happy profusion of styles, methodologies, ideologies, means, ends, and sensibilities. Rigidity has been replaced by fluidity. To some extent this phenomenon has been caused by the demands of fashion and the need for new copy by the art magazines and the press. Art nowadays is news, or at least it can be made to appear as news. *Time* and *Newsweek* chronicle and sometimes invent the latest "developments" faster than art critics can digest them. Nevertheless, no matter how many qualms one may have, this state of confusion appears to be healthy for art. Compare, for instance, the art world with the orderly, quite uneventful literary world in America, still for the most part stuck in some detour off the superhighway of modernism, long since rejected and bypassed by the plastic arts. Art in its latest manifestations is attempting to come to grips with our new high-speed civilization, while literature with very few exceptions continues to go over and over again the same ground covered in the thirties. Literature, at the moment, could well use some of the art world's glamor, confusion, and more than a little of its vitality.

Artists now at work in America can be classified, if classification is necessary, in many different directions, depending upon which factors one wishes to isolate for convenience, illustration or illumination. There are, of course, the popular classifications: Pop (the use of Ad-Mass iconography and the employment of commercial art design techniques and methods), Op (the "geometrical" use of bright colors and/or repetitive designs that cause strong optical and kinetic effects during the act of perception), Minimal Art (the virtual elimination of incident and design to produce clean-cut works of severe and sometimes serene geometry), etc., etc. These and other similar labels (Hard Edge, Color Field, etc.) give a quick point of reference and are good news "pegs," headliners, and, in general, are useful symbols for the isolation of some new tendency, in that they are usually based upon some kernel of truth, no matter how carelessly, callously, or sensationally they are employed or defined. But current art can also be classified as organic or structural, painterly or post-painterly, representational or non-representational. The difficulty is that some perfectly valid kinds of art just do not fit very neatly into any of these pigeon-holes that art writers are so clever at dreaming up. The one aspect of a particular man's work that places him in a particular category may not be the most important, interesting, or unique aspect of his work. The works of Jasper Johns, for instance, can be analyzed from several different points of view and I suppose that this is what still makes them so fascinating. Originally it was the imagery that was so shocking—beer cans cast in bronze, paintings of flags and targets. This aspect received all the attention and had a lot to do with sparking Pop Art since these works first appeared when abstraction (Abstract Expressionism) was widely considered to be the only valid form of High Art. Representational elements, no matter how formal or integrated were considered dishonest, unmodern, and non-art. But at present, Johns' paintings can be seen, because of their painterly brushstrokes and textures, as an outgrowth of Abstract Expressionist principles. Or, because they consist of an all-over gestalt, they can be seen as progenitors of the non-illusionistic flatness now a la mode.

Not only have notions of newness and definitions of artistic validity changed radically today, but also the meaning of skill or craftsmanship has undergone a transformation. More often than not, skill does not mean the smooth or textured application of paint to a canvas and certainly not the virtuoso use of a chisel on a piece of stone. We may indeed find the means an artist chooses to employ very interesting, but we do not question his means as long as his ends are successful. Our mass produced products have accustomed us to a uniformity of surface and a neatness of outline that requires in art the unbelievable steadiness of hand of an Ellsworth Kelly, or, on the other hand, the adaptation of techniques derived from mass production itself—silk screen printing, photocopying, the use of plastics, vacuum-molds, spray guns, or even in some cases the manufacturing of the

106

NICHOLAS KRUSHENICK, "KING KONG," 84¼"X71¼", PACE GALLERY, N.Y.

designed object in machine shops according to the artist's blueprints. Improvisation and records of anguished hesitations and changes in direction no longer satisfy our insatiable sensibilities. Artists like Morris, Judd, and most of the Pop Artists provide us with "finished" works.

Another aspect of current art that comes close to being a common denominator and has the additional virtue of being helpful in distinguishing the present rebirth of modernism (America) from modernism itself (France), is the compositional concept of the whole as opposed to the parts. The interest of a "wholistic" work of art is not the relationship between the parts or segments of the composition, but the all-over image

107

and the all-over impact. This applies to the works of Warhol, Lichtenstein, Kelly, Johns, Oldenburg, Stella, Poons and most of the sculptors of the Minimal persuasion—Robert Morris, Donald Judd, Carl Andre, Dan Flavin —and even Ronald Bladen and Tony Smith. It even applies to Op Art, or what little of it is still being produced. However, if one were to mistake this helpful "common denominator" for an absolute there would be no room for artists of great interest whose compositional devices lie in another direction: Rauschenberg, Rosenquist, Rivers, Sugarman, etc. Almost all works of assemblage and most inter-media compositions would have to be eliminated. In all art, even in these instances, the over-all effect is of supreme importance, but here this is achieved by the relationships of parts or the poetic juxtaposition of images, textures, and forms rather than by some "systemic" or reductive unity.

Any survey of current American art must encompass the unencompassable, for never before in one place at one time has there ever been such a variety of serious art of high quality. An easy procedure, but also an intellectually dishonest one, would be to choose one style, one tradition, one line of influence, as some have already attempted to do, and proclaim this particular conglomerate of attributes or species of emphasis as the major style, the serious style, and the one and only road to high art. Techniques of classification and abstraction are indeed very helpful in pointing out insights about a particular artist or group of artists, but because they only succeed by a process of fragmentation and isolation of particular characteristics these techniques can be narrowing rather than broadening and can perpetuate an absolutist fallacy in an area that maintains its vitality by the abandonment of such prescriptions. In art, as in life, classifications, definitions, and abstractions are tools, not truths, or if truths merely operational truths. They should not be used as absolutes. Generalities, although necessary and helpful, bear as much relationship to reality as names, numbers, or questionnaires that only allow yes or no answers.

Depending on one's point of view, current art is either a feast or an orgy. But to understand and/or appreciate this multiplicity of contradictory forms and styles it is not necessary to invent a common denominator; nor if one finds one helpful—such as "wholism," "formalism," or "the poetic"— is it necessary to cast aside all art that does not conform to it. A thread labeled "wholism" or "flatness" might lead one successfully out of the maze of our chaotic and pluralistic, new modernism, but only at the expense of missing some of the quite valid byways, dead-ends, and side trips present.

III: THE MESSAGE

To say that "the medium is the message" in regard to art is to reiterate an art platitude that also happens to be true. Art has no message. To apply the medium is the message slogan to television, telephones or glassware is to make these things into or to discover them as art. A famous movie mogul once said: "If you have a message, send a telegram." But if an artist sends a telegram that says "This is a work of art," then the message is the medium.

IV: THE EVOLUTIONARY FALLACY

The apparent succession of styles in the art world is only a succession of writings about styles. Minimal Art has no more replaced Pop Art than Pop Art replaced Abstract Expressionism. And Minimal Art will not be "replaced" by whatever new style is about to raise what undoubtedly will be its new and relatively ugly head. Major artists in all recent styles continue to develop, sometimes transcending the very shop-talk, headline labels they themselves in unholy alliances with art writers have helped to create and even continue to sell their works at rather astronomical prices. The ups and downs and ins and outs of art world fashion do not touch the truly important artists; they only weed out the lesser lights. It is the bandwagon climbers that must "sink or swim" each new season, not Jasper Johns, Claes Oldenburg or Frank Stella. The art world is not only the last bastion of pure Capitalism, it is also a Darwinian microcosm of natural selection. Those artists who survive from season to season, by hook or crook, are usually those who are the most vital, creative, and also, incidentally, those who have something unique to offer.

It is fashion and taste, not art itself that is evolutionary, cyclic or dialectic. Art, in and of itself, is in no sense evolutionary. There may be periods in art in which a particular technique or style is refined or exhausted and also periods in which no art of any uniqueness or value is produced. But to imply some sort of orderly development of seriousness and purity ending conveniently in a 57th Street gallery as some critics do is unfortunate. Because a particular style has ceased to stimulate new variations or our sensibilities have been saturated with a particular style's effects, an "opposing" style, of course, may be of more interest—as for instance the present preference which I myself share for post-painterly rather than painterly styles—but this interest is contingent and a dialectic of taste, not the modus operandi for a chart of art's evolution.

The anti-art pose on the part of many artists—and here I must exclude most of the original Dadaists and Futurists who, after all, were making social statements by way of aesthetic or anti-aesthetic ones, but whose works that survive survive as history and as art, in spite of anti-art intentions—is a working hypothesis, a technique, a public stance, rather than a philosophy of the same order as a theory of aesthetics proposed by a philosopher. When "anti-art" is viewed as an attack on art in general, this becomes the Anti-Art Fallacy. But anti-art as a technique of discovery, anti-art redefined as a position against the conventions and limits of art as they are practiced becomes a valid, although sometimes unintentional, tool in the search for the new.

John Cage has been an important influence on Jasper Johns, Robert Rauschenberg and many others through his radical techniques of musical composition and the philosophical, almost theological, bent of his mind. Marshall McLuhan is currently influencing and providing the rationale for many younger artists and groups of artists, such as the anonymous USCO who are exploring the artistic possibilities of new technologies and the intermedia world of film and light. But a third and perhaps more important figure in any discussion of current art must be Marcel Duchamp. The questions raised by his work and his myth are questions concerning the relationship of art to anti-art and non-art, questions that become increasingly important in current art, so much of which is questionable as art by traditional standards, and moves so closely to non-art.

In spite of his old world, nihilistic dandyism, Duchamp is the underground source of much that is current in art. He laid much of the groundwork. His Roto-reliefs foreshadowed Kinetic Art and Op Art. His notorious Readymades (bicycle wheels, latrines, and bottle racks displayed as art) provided much inspiration for Neo-Dada and for Pop. And his conceptual manner of working, his abandonment of painting, and his "metaphysical" concerns provide clues to many Minimal Art concerns.

The collection of notes made by Duchamp between 1912 and 1920, recently published in a handsome facsimile edition by Cordier & Ekstrom, New York, under the title *A L'Infinitif,* indicates more clearly than ever Duchamp's passionate concern with conceptual and aesthetic activities on very high levels of creativity.

The rigor of Duchamp's ironic intellect, however, is only the outer covering of his achievement. A point that few of the artists now practicing conceptual art seem to have grasped is that the intellect is only useful when it is employed as a delay, a subterfuge. The systematic employment of ironic, conceptual, and intellectual activities to produce works of art are only valid when these devices are used as techniques for forcing inspiration, converting the artist, as Duchamp himself would have it, into a medium.

Duchamp's famous abandonment of art for chess is symbolic. He did not stop playing, he only switched boards. For art itself and the creation of art may be looked upon as varieties of highly sophisticated visual and sensual games.

In Duchamp's hands, art reveals itself in the mirror of anti-art as the supreme game of wits that it actually is. His systematic rule-breaking, his elevation of anti-art and non-art, his new use of chance and choice have created the new rules for many new kinds of art. An artist can follow the rules that have already been formulated by history, by his peers, or by an academy. But unless within these rules he makes some new moves he is hardly very much of an artist. Even so, the artist we value the most is one who does not merely make a few new moves in a standard game, but that artist who makes up a new set of rules, a new procedure, a new game.

Another approach to anti-art and non-art risk-taking is to label it Didactic Art. Art like most of Duchamp's work, some of Johns', and the earlier works of Robert Morris, all appears to make statements about the nature of art itself, the nature of illusion, allusion, and the relationship between art and non-art. Here Barbara Rose's recent article on Didactic Art in *Artforum* is particularly illuminating.

Marcel Duchamp's procedure, however, was to examine all premises. In his search to see if it was possible to make a work that was not art ("Can one make works which are not works of 'art'?" . . . 1913: *A L'Infinitif*) he stretched the boundaries of art so that it could include more of the rational and more of the irrational, the mytho-erotic, and the manufactured and the chosen as well as the created.

In our own time, Pop Art has included more and more non-art—advertising images, targets, flags, junk, words—and made it into art or discovered it as art. Proto-Pop and Pop artists seem to have been asking themselves how much of "real" life (i.e. Mass Society "life") they could include in their works and still make art? Minimal artists, on the other hand, seem to have been asking how much of "life" and also of the traditional devices of "art" can be excluded.

Art does not evolve; it expands. And this expansion is in many cases brought about by an "anti-art" procedure which operated by incorporating more and more of what had previously been considered non-art. The tight-rope an artist walks (and this can also apply to literature, poetry, dance, film and the other arts) in order to establish a significant uniqueness is stretched between art and non-art. The risk an artist takes is the risk of inclusion or exclusion that brings his works perilously close to non-art. The closer he can come to non-art and still make art the more breathtaking is his accomplishment.

VI: WHAT IS ART?

Art in some sense can be defined as consisting of those man-made objects whose main purpose is to call attention to themselves and whose main value is the sensuous responses they provoke, evoke or deny. Really great art, like great music, in the last analysis serves no purpose. A "purpose" art once had was to celebrate, in that it "imitates" creation, the greater glory of "God" or the gods. But of course, most of us, artists included, no longer "believe" in the supernatural. Another "purpose" was to celebrate the greater glory of man, in that all art is man-made and in some way expressive of man's emotions, yearnings, and delights. But, of course, nowadays we are no longer certain we believe in man.

Art has been confused with religion and offered as a substitute for religion long enough. The art as religion fallacy runs very deeply even in much of modernism. But art is art. And artists are men. Art and artists have been demythologized. Art does not wear well—for instance, the recent attempts to make it decorate the empty husk of Christianity. There is nothing more pathetic than a church in the shape of a fish or a loaf of bread, a jazz or electronic liturgy, and a minister spouting hip slogans in competition with ad agencies, Timothy Leary and/or Christ. Equally regrettable is the inclusion of Hindu and Buddhist imagery in much art that is labeled psyche-delic. Those objects that were created for religious purposes in the past as reminders, concretions, meditative devices, or tribal nosegays have only become art as time and history have removed them from their purposeful context. Likewise, advertising images or geometrical constructs only become art when they are removed from their purposeful context of persuasion or science.

Art as a sub-species of humanism too has had its pitfalls. In some sense all art since it is made by human beings is humanistic. But "humanism" in art as in literature has fallen into sentimentality, ersatz humanism, propaganda, banality, and misplaced political and social concerns.

An operational and therefore admittedly a timid definition of art would be that art is whatever a number of artists, gallery directors, curators, critics and collectors say is art, treat as art, write about as art and even buy as art. If this saying, treating, writing and buying continues for more than a season or two, we can be a little more certain, but never completely so, that the objects involved are "art." A consensus definition of art, however, depends upon the quality of the consensus makers for its validity. Hopefully this consensus will be based upon private reactions and reflections rather than public promotions or exigencies and based upon what moves the individuals involved in a way that religion does not, philosophy does not, literature does not, and in a way that has become for the cultured person of aesthetic sensibilities irreplaceable by any other phenomenon.

In discussing new art, the criterion of significant uniqueness is helpful. There is no necessity for a duplication of those experiences that can be gained elsewhere in a purer, more original form. But uniqueness in itself is not enough. It must be a significant uniqueness, a uniqueness that is valuable because it pleases our senses in a new way.

Another aspect of art that might be profitable to isolate would be art's heuristic characteristics, particularly since much current art seems to have this as its concern. An art that is intended by a process of viewer involvement to educate our senses and stretch our sensibilities might be identified as Heuristic Art. Of course, in my use of the world "heuristic" I am emphasizing the meaning of the Greek root, "to discover," and its use as a term for teaching methods that encourage the participant to discover something for himself. In regard to art, the "something" that is indicated would be a greater sensory awareness of everyday life and sensory stimulation. Heuristic aspects of art are simplifications of larger experiences and this simplification (although it may at times be quite complicated) serves to enlarge the participant's sensory consciousness and provides some carry-over into non-art contests of experience, as in the "musical" compositions of John Cage that stimulate one's awareness of the natural sounds of the environment.

In some sense all art "tunes up" the senses. Art puts a frame around different aspects of the world and when once the frame has been removed makes that aspect of the world of experiences more available to consciousness. After consistent exposures to the best works in the Abstract Expressionist style (Pollock's great "drip" paintings, for instance, or Helen Frankenthaler's stained canvases), and in spite of the fact that these works are not as accidental as they seem, we are more conscious of similar, "natural" accidental configurations in the world around us. Biological slides, slum sidewalks, tenement walls, now have a different "look" to them. Pop Art allows us to look at the artifacts of our mass culture with a new distance, a new irony, and a new appreciation of their formal directness and energy. Billboards, mail-order ads, images of movie stars, comic books and Campbell soup cans are now visible to us in a new way. The elegant silences of the Minimal works of sculpture of Robert Morris and Donald Judd unveil the expressive and aesthetic power of the geometric, the repetitive, the clean-cut and the mathematical. In our new world of absurd simultaneities, intermedia events, Kinetic Art, Light Art and other new forms that utilize new media, new technologies, and new forms of image-overlap help us to keep our eyes open and in some way prepare an adjustment to our new electronic civilization.

In regard to Heuristic Art of particular interest is an idea proposed by Les Levine, an artist whose first one man show this year was very impressive, whose environment *Slipcover* was covered by C.B.S. television, and who has already been photographed inside his *Star Machine* (an almost invisible plastic walk-through device) by *Glamour Magazine* and from all signs is about to be very much in vogue. One of Levine's interests along with environments, vacuum impressions in Eastmanuvex of chairs, and films (his film *Critic* was a notable piece of cool sarcasm that involved three-minute unedited spots by twelve art critics on a video tape later transferred to film) is a series of works he calls Disposables and Throwaways. He evidently proposes that art is involved in some way with an education of the senses, for his rationale for his Disposables and Throwaways (plastic impressions of everyday objects which can be arranged on the wall in any amount or order, some equipped with flashing lights inside of them that are suspiciously like Christmas tree lights) is that since these works of art are produced in unlimited editions and are very low-priced they can be disposed of once the owner has learned all he can from them. Levine does not want anyone to get "hung up" on the art object itself, apparently since by implication they exist only to provide an experience that is heuristic.

Nevertheless it would be a mistake to take this heuristic side effect of art now apparently receiving more attention and define it as the main purpose of art. Only in a very general sense is all art heuristic, just as all art in some general sense cannot help revealing something about the society in which it is produced.

Art as we know from the history of art is rarely ever pure in any respect. It has been married with varying degrees of success to craft, magic, record-keeping, information and entertainment, and will continue to be so variously used and misused. Much current art, for instance, is merely entertainment. But fashionableness or Good Design need not necessarily be the earmarks of bad art, just as muddy colors, bad design and unpopularity are not necessarily the earmarks of High Art or seriousness.

*   *   *

In art at present there is almost an embarrassment of riches. Styles promulgate, propagandize, propagate, branch off in all directions. This year's finality becomes last year's fad. Artists ride the waves of publicity movements and then survive by doing what they are doing and growing—

often outgrowing the very categories that have elevated them to celebrities. One thinks of the proto-Pop artists and the Pop artists themselves: Rauschenberg has been applying himself to theatrical, intermedia events with increasing success; Roy Lichtenstein, it appears, is becoming more and more an abstractionist; and Andy Warhol's "underground" film *The Chelsea Girls* has established him as one of the most interesting new film makers.

At present New York is the art capital of the world. This may change. American artists since Abstract Expressionism have been the pace-setters for the world. This also may change. As our new electronic technologies unify the world more and more, there may well indeed be a truly world art on the horizon. Neo-Modernism may change into Post-Modernism. In the immediate future we can expect more styles, more fads, more fallacies, more celebrities, more communal art, more art.

In response to the "commercialism" of the art world, perhaps unconsciously, more and more artists are producing non-products—works of art too large, too nasty, or too ephemeral to qualify as salable merchandise. There will be more multiple editions (the poster phenomenon is already quite remarkable), more variable works of art that require the active participation of the viewer, more monuments, more environments.

My optimism is of course based on the supposition that in spite of the war in Vietnam and social injustice at home, our economy will continue to flourish and is based on the hope that tomorrow morning or the day after we will not all be annihilated, art and all, by a Third World War.

Of course, the art of the next century, if we could glimpse it, might be totally unrecognizable to us now as art and not related to any art forms of the present. But even if we are thrown back into the safety-zone of tribalism, there will still be art.

Art can be heuristic, formalistic, magical, decorative, and have any number of other attributes, but beneath its many uses and misuses the traditional principle behind the energy and age-old seductiveness of art that still comes closest to the truth about art and perhaps is its very definition is the principle of pure play. Art is a game. Man is not only the tool-making animal, the animal that thinks, and the animal that laughs, he is also the animal that plays. It is not man's tools, thoughts, or laughter that connects him to the amoral chess game of the cosmos or helps him relate to and in some sense transcend the incongruities of his own devising, it is his ability to play and to be "serious" about his play in the form of art that makes man almost human.

Thoughts of a fireman
MITCHELL SISSKIND

An old fireman was crazy about a woman. Once he came in from the coast only to kiss that Myrna. Now there was her little son Lewis, yet this hardly slowed Pete. Soon Myrna's boy was thinking: This Pete is the old frog.

Myrna sat on Pete's lap.

"I hope I'm not too heavy," she said.

"Not at all," said Pete. "It feels good."

"I'll bet it does," Myrna said. "What are you thinking about?"

"I don't know," said Pete. Yet he touched her to kiss her.

Myrna dreamed a good life with the man. She needed someone who could help raise the boy and go places, yet show consideration. She wondered: Should I grab my son and walk out leaving Nathan, the elevator man?

Myrna was losing the pleasure of life. So is Lewis, she thought, who just thinks of animals.

Nathan's sister was going to have a birthday party. Myrna was excited to go someplace. Then at the last minute Nathan decided not to go, and made an excuse.

He said, "Myrna, the meat you cook is good. Let's eat and not go out. We won't have to leave the boy."

After a while Myrna called the sister and said that Nathan was sick. Of course I was not believed, she thought.

She decided to phone Pete.

116

"Shall I go on living this way?" Myrna asked him. "Our son only thinks of animals."

For in Lewis' mind there was a house owned by rabbits.

"I don't believe Nathan is interested in you," said Pete. "Probably it is impossible for him to be interested in you."

Myrna remembered sitting on the lap.

"Nathan hasn't kept his promises," she said. "His promises, his promises."

Pete said he would take a plane: he would get Myrna and the boy away from that.

Pete arrived. Nathan was at work, the elevator man. Pete stood in Myrna's doorway.

"Come in," she said. How the fireman wanted to start: he kissed Myrna's neck. There was his loud laugh.

In the afternoon Myrna packed her things and Lewis'. When the boy came home from school it was all called some vacation. So Myrna put on a dress. They went to Pete's hotel.

That night Myrna called Nathan.

She told him that Pete would help in raising a son. That he, Nathan, went nowhere.

"Will you wait one minute?" said Nathan, but you have seen a disgusted person throw a tennis racket to the ground, a tuba into the closet. Thus Myrna and the life with Nathan.

Myrna and Pete talked to Lewis, each in bright pajamas.

Myrna said, "Pete is better than Nathan."

"Better?" Lewis asked. There was a room with a rabbit asleep plus the room with a staring rabbit. In a control tower a sheep talked to the handsome pilots.

"Like to sleep on it?" asked Pete.

"That's all right," said Lewis. "I'm not tired."

Myrna knew he was trying to understand. What to say? She wondered. I am tired of thinking about it.

"Pete slides down a pole," she said.

The raccoon, thought Lewis. Finally a frog saved the cat, and her clear eyes.

Outside it was already getting brighter. The sky seemed oddly lighted.

"Asleep," smiled Myrna, "this boy seems better. That's what it's for." She sat on Pete's lap.

"What are you thinking about?" he asked. But just then the day began.

117

Royal Blue

(for Pilar Lorengar, soprano: La Contessa Almaviva)

—a regal blue, flowing like a wave around
    her distant whiteness there behind a
marble balustrade
    in the tempered light of chandeliers like
clouds, luminogenic clouds—a light that
    contains us
at her behest, a medium
                  in which
    we move.

Up there among the others behind the
    pillared marble looking out over the sea
(of humanity) she, *como una reina,* waves
    a white arm with slow largesse, accompaniment
of the stiff blue, her gown, in obeisance,
    ripples & swirls about her, the light
doing its bidding & hers.

She is the sea, the sky, the clouds, the very
    light: the merest wave of her wrist
before the blue are whitecaps, precisely.

O loke doun at us, verray mistresse,
    with benignite and gentilesse

—I say it silently,
    looking into her far-off eyes, my hands
in my pockets.

———————————

No, not "look down," not even "look."
    —Connect us
per your eye-beams;   enter,
    if only per the light from your eyes,
the light that contains
    us, the medium in which we move.

RON LOEWINSOHN

Rapunzil

An old woman, her butt spread on the stoop,
Scratched her knees and Jesus Christ
The sidewalk:

"The gentamin usta tamper with me reg'lar,
The asssuckun bastards; reg'lar. Came struttun
Their spigots, riddy ta piss in my pipes
Like I wuza goddamned privy.

"Get me bloat bellied 'n' forsake me 'til
I'd dropped their brats 'n' then they'd
Sashay back, the motherfriggers;
Wantun ta dung more seeds ta life.

"They pinched my tits 'til lumps growed
'N' screwed scars deep inside me;
Then laid me in an o.r. room 'n' chopped
My sex ta slops.

"My diddlun days 'r' done; but you,
You hoteyed babes, purrun bareassed
Where I usta lay, you'd do well ta cool;
Let 'em pocketpool."

FAYE KICKNOSWAY

The American Tourist

Alongside a new road each morning, rising
from the motel bed he prayed all night
he would not awaken in, the aging tourist

reloads his car with his scuffed, bulging family
of luggage, like a state treasure of gold bars
that must be hauled everywhere, and, priceless,

is valueless to him, for it belongs, in fact,
to the office that he, the husband and father, holds
only temporarily, and whose seal he wears like a leaden

honor around his neck. He fingers one of the maps
that cling to his body like benign growths,
spoiling the fit of his clothes

and marking him indelibly for ironic waiters
and women with blue lumpy legs from his home state.
He sets out for the next landmark, always

pretending to have the same conviction: something
will happen: he may arrive at the Jersey shore in time
to witness the largest high school band in the world

sinking in their barge, twenty-five yards off the coast
of Atlantic City, all hands lost, the tide
washing up tubas and white boots for weeks.

Or he might reach New York harbor as an outrigger
arrives full of crazed Africans with a plan
for assaulting the Statue of Liberty,

chanting war-tunes as they toss her
stone skirt up over her face and give her the devil.
Or—a miracle!—the Lincoln Memorial may begin to weep,

shedding a broken necklace of marble teardrops
onto the marble floor, while the rapt tourists
skate over them, hugging themselves for joy.

He drives possessed by the fragile house of his car,
on which the vacationland sun bangs
like an unlatched door; he drives

like a child with an urgent bladder, tortured
by the knowledge that he will be too late, that
the demented beauty will have put her clothes back

on, the crowd dispersed; that the whole continent
will already have slid beneath the waves, and
there will be nothing left to be savored years later

as having been seen—except for
a white spume on the face of the endless waters,
and the patronizing smiles of other tourists

who arrived in time, and tell him what he has missed.
His hands close in panic on the steering wheel.
All will be over before he can get to it.

It is, after all, home, the target receding behind him,
that troubles him most; it
will surely be gone before he can get back to it,

and not even a nickel card to show what it was like.
He recalls with suffocating pathos the familiar goods
there, which he has trusted all his life

to serve his deepest needs—the sensuous black
stem in the corner of his private closet, for example;
though he cannot now remember if it is the grip

or his expensive driver
or the barrel of his twelve gauge.
And he fears it no longer makes any difference.

The first sight is not yet in sight
and already things are beginning to turn out badly:
the sun lies steady in the sky, the hills are peaceful,

the chance of his getting lost grows more and more remote.

JAMES CRENNER

On a rainy night, an ape in Scarsdale, N.Y., returns a library book

for Robert Bly

He pulls his car
under the running, street-lit leaves. 2 A.M.
The dashlight reddens his jaw;
and his eyes, like thunder,
disappear. Or I think that

about apes. Gets out. & slams the door.

Hand & hand, over the olive lawn—
Will his wife, in New Jersey, worry?
About the lateness of the hour?
The black wells of rain-water
lining roads all the way home?
The lawn sighs
beneath his weight. Damp circles start
under his elbows and knees.
At a darkened doorway, he stops:
he cools his head on a stone.

A book
whistles down the chute.
That's all?

Back over the lawn,
the trees hang down, the moon
frankly looks at this. Low moans
circle his sweaty head
& fly away. What if he sang?

Robt., I mean this:

He carried the moon
like a book beneath his left arm.
And before we could speak:

     He drives away.

          JON ANDERSON

First snow

in all the feats of the snow there is not
one speckled egg
everyone uncovers his head
the bedding is washed, the last desperate crow
thrashes in its thickets
on the lines the sheets snap
dreaming of reins . . .
before this the urine was the only passage to the earth
before this all the alleys examined
the pearls of spit
the curbs gave up their last feathers to the vagrants
the shoeless dead
now the beautiful widow steps onto her porch
high under the eaves . . . sends a moan through the pulleys

DENNIS SCHMITZ

Love—three stanzas—2 lines

I lay in her humus breaths
And she was fulfilling her essence
As music, perfume, wine of future loves
Whose birth she was lighting in me

Nakedness exists only an instant
Quickly becomes flesh, becomes thought
Nakedness exists to light up love
To resurrect the present with a touch

The night is a torch of comas
Wondering, I look at lovers
Each inhales the other's visions
And they burn deeply, like a torch of comas

SAINT GERAUD

Camping in the valley

Here is a place for my gun.
I need everything less and less,
have you noticed?
But I feel something, almost

anything is having some effect
on me. I think I believe
what I'm saying.
Are you having a little trouble

keeping up, dear?
Now I am ready to survive,
though I suppose we are in danger
sitting here, arms crossed,

in the valley
with the black pig on the spit,
our little doggy.
I have faith the air will

soon cohere or speak,
tomorrow morning as you are
pulling on your boots,
my love, by the fire.

I can't see what the blue mosses
are doing now, dripping
from the bridge I'd guess.
The toads beneath travel home

through the sprung doors
of the river;
on either side of myself
the water is seldom

so navigable. Yes, it behooves us
to close our eyelids again,
the cold front, the rain,
the sun rising around 5:17,

an important mission in the morning:
what was it? The juniper berries?
The death we thought we left
in the mountains like a child.

JAMES TATE

The bruises, the flowers, the boil, the love

What is it that
I lack there is
nothing

that I've taken
back except these
bruises a blue

vase with a huge
yellow flower & white
clump of flowers on

a single stem next
to orange flowers bent
outward like hands

limp with apology
& dying & imagined
the swelling on my

neck was a boil
thinking of one
time when

a friend drew
the white core out
of his side by

heating a bottle
& fitting the mouth
over the red hump

with a cold
towel at its
base to make

a vacuum
& a pale slug eased
out with clots

of blood & the bruised
skin marked
me with its brand

of flesh horror &
pain recalled
those who had

relieved their
hours extracting from
them & me

in closed rooms
stems of sores found
in talk & that exchange

cut & bottled up
& fresh kept
us safe without

ever showing want
or having what
we'd given taken back.

KEITH ABBOTT

Poem — six lines

What language will be safe
When we lie awake all night
Saying palm words, no fingertip words
This wound searching us for a voice
Will become a fountain with rooms to let
Or a language composed of kisses and leaves

SAINT GERAUD

Monkey business
JONATHAN PENNER

Columbus Day, no school, Susan was going out with her mother and Peaches
Great Bear. Her mother's new boy friend looked like a Negro but wasn't
one; he was an American Indian. What tribe? Peaches had raised his eyebrows and stroked his thick moustache: Delaware. Susan would have preferred Comanche.

Nevertheless she screamed more than once, waiting out the morning.
She had dressed first thing, fancy, and couldn't go out. For a while she read
Mystery of the Secret Stallion but it was no fun any more because she had it
all memorized. She flopped on her bed. She got up and went to the bathroom.

Her mother Hillary, listening downstairs, wondered what Susan was
doing in there. Susan went to the bathroom now more than anyone possibly
could, and Hillary was sure she was doing something. Hillary blamed herself. It was hard being alone, but she felt she should be doing more, saying
something, to help Susan grow up. She worried what Susan might be picking up by example. Since Joe's death, Hillary knew, her own life hadn't
been anything to parade in front of a daughter. That was why Peaches was
especially important; Hillary hoped for something permanent.

"Come have a little brunch," she called, not getting up from the couch.

128

Susan didn't answer. Hillary sighed, toppled over awkwardly onto her shoulder, then quickly straightened so she would stay neat. She was carefully made up and had already been to the hairdresser. Not looking well, she had learned, increased her nervousness. She was scared enough as it was. She knew she had a kind of blindness about men. Had she and Peaches been living in a fool's paradise? She had insulated their affair carefully, showing him to no one. But now she felt so good about him that the time had come to make the rounds. Her friends would call her up next day to say what they thought. They always did.

"Hey," she yelled. "I spoke to you." As she expected, there was no answer. Hillary was afraid to press it. Whatever Susan was doing, the important thing was to avoid a fight. If Susan got into a mood the afternoon would be lost. For a child not yet eleven she could be an amazing bitch. So Hillary just called, "I'm making an omelet," and got up and went to the kitchen.

Susan, naked to the waist in front of the bathroom mirror, listened to Hillary's high heels going back and forth on the linoleum. She knew if her mother called once more she would have to go down. Both faucets were running in the sink, so it would sound like she was washing up. Susan ran a forefinger from armpit to armpit, across the soft band of padding she now had. The softness was pleasing to her, but what she was looking for was roundness. The only thing she was sure of today was that her nipples were bigger. Anyway, they felt bigger. She wet them with cold water because she liked the tingly feeling. Then she had the idea of wetting the soap so if her mother checked it would really seem she had been washing.

She felt like using some of her mother's cosmetics. From the medicine cabinet she took lipstick, rouge, eyebrow pencil, and began applying them with care. As always she became tired and impatient, and the job finished sloppily, but as she surveyed it in the mirror she thought she was improving. She would have to wash everything off before going downstairs. First, for a while, she wanted to enjoy the made-up feeling. She posed for the mirror. After a few minutes she crossed to the bathroom window and stood looking out, her elbows on the sill, her bare chest pressed against the cold glass.

The bathroom window was on the side of the house, and Susan could see a long car just turning the corner, heading down her block. It wasn't Uncle Sam's Caddy, because the Caddy was black and this car was blue as the sky. Then Susan remembered Peaches's car was blue, and she was so excited she raised the window to lean out. What she saw amazed her: the driver of the car was a big woman with what looked like a tiny monkey sitting on her shoulder. And Susan could see the car was going to stop. She shoved the window up as far as it went and leaned way out, her belly on the window sill and her feet thrashing behind her, but the car stopped just out of sight, hidden by the corner of Susan's house. The car door slammed. It sounded like the woman was going into Alan's house.

Susan pulled back in, her body all goose bumps from the cold. She struggled into her top and rushed downstairs, yelling "Mama! There's a woman with a monkey!" "What?" Hillary called. Susan ran into the kitchen and stopped short.

"Your face," said Hillary. "Look at you." Tears came to her eyes. She crossed the kitchen to Susan, who cringed, but Hillary only held her daughter, hugging Susan's gaudy face against her big perfumed breasts. "My poor baby," she wailed. "You look like a tramp. Oh, my darling."

Peaches Great Bear came bounding up the walk. Between the slats of the Venetian blinds Hillary and Susan peeked out at him, both breaking for the door a split second before his crashing knock. In the living room he was huge, towering above them like a gleaming mahogany totem pole. He hugged Hillary, who melted against him. Then he grabbed Susan under the arms and swept her up so her face was on a level with his. When he kissed her his moustache tickled. She laughed nervously; it was a long time since anyone had picked her up like that, and she thought she was much too big. But Peaches held her easily. He seemed almost as strong as her father had been.

Hillary had coffee ready. When Peaches drank he kept both elbows on his knees, bending forward and lowering his lips to the cup, but his dark eyes stayed fixed on Hillary, rolling to the tops of their sockets as he bent his head. "I must say, you girls look charming today," he said. His voice was deep and English sounding.

"You look pretty sharp yourself, Peaches," said Hillary. "Susie, Peaches paid us a compliment. What do we say?"

"Thank you, Peaches," said Susan. "A lady with a monkey came up in a blue car just like yours just now."

"A what? A lady with a what?" Peaches let his jaw drop to show how surprised he was. His mouth was very large, his teeth large and white, the roof of his mouth pink. He stared at Susan without lifting his head, so that his pupils swung dizzily, as though magnetized, from the ceilings of his eye sockets.

Susan laughed. Then, watching him, it came to her how much Peaches himself looked like a monkey, with his brown skin and big hanging jaw and flat nose. She knew that it would be wrong to tell him, so she only said, slyly, "Sometimes people look like monkeys."

Peaches snapped upright, and Susan turned faint at the anger in his

130

face. But it was her mother who grabbed her and shook. "Apologize to Peaches!" Hillary demanded. "This minute. And never say that word again to—to anybody."

"I don't mind," said Peaches, subsiding. "But she'd better learn if she says that to a Negro she'll be in trouble."

Susan apologized. Hillary asked Peaches if he wanted more coffee and he said no. "What's the first stop," he said. "You know, fill me in."

Hillary pointed. "The Stones, right opposite. He's a doctor, kind of a funny-looking little man, but their kid is a real doll. A year older than Susan. The mother is kind of little and fat. They're all very very sweet, but sometimes they act kind of above it all, a few years back they did a terrible thing to his father. Sent him away. I don't know how interesting you'll find them. But really," and she laughed in surprise, "they're our best friends."

"Oh yes?" said Peaches. "I don't think you've mentioned them. You always talk about the Lennons."

"Lannons," said Susan, then clapped her hand over her mouth.

"Right," said Hillary. "They're our best friends too."

"He's in insurance."

"Now. He was an accountant but not making enough to satisfy her. But she's such a genuine person it's hard to blame her for anything. You'll see what a character she is. They have a kid too, he was twelve just the other day. Their past I won't go into with present company. The three kids used to play together quite a lot."

"Okay," said Peaches. He had the habit of drumming his right fingertips along the back of his left hand. Susan was fascinated and he caught her staring; she made a face at him and looked away, feeling very hot. Peaches rose. "All right, now I'm equipped." Hillary got coats from the hall closet, and Peaches held them. Susan saw that when he helped Hillary he squeezed her from behind, putting his arms around her waist in a strong hug. Over her shoulder his long jaw hung slack.

Lorraine Stone's Carolyne served the coffee clumsily. She was very old and stiff and she was a big tub of fat, with breasts flopping down like pillows onto her belly. "We've really just had some," Hillary said. Peaches said "Oh, I don't know. I've got room for another cup."

"Wonderful," said Aunt Lorraine. "Or we'll think you don't like us, right, Carolyne?"

Carolyne chuckled, her flesh swaying. "Tha's right," she said. She set a cup down in front of Peaches and waited while he chose from a plate of macaroons and ladyfingers. Then she waddled back to the kitchen. Susan's eyes followed her every minute. Ever since Susan and Julie and Mona had

131

begun looking at chests they hadn't been able to decide whether a colored woman's breasts were white or black.

"It's so good to see you, Mr. Bear," said Aunt Lorraine. "Hillary is *always* talking about you. Whoops," and she pressed all ten fingertips to her cheeks, "I shouldn't have let that slip out. Now, you own a gas station, am I correct?"

"Great Bear," said Peaches. "Actually, you're almost right, but I own three gas stations. I still haven't gotten used to it. At one time they belonged to my wife's father."

"Yes," said Aunt Lorraine. "They must take a great deal of your time."

"A good deal, yes. But since I've been separated from my wife I've been spending a good deal of time on my novel."

"Hillary mentioned, yes. Mr. Bear, I'd be terribly interested in hearing something about it. I used to write myself in college, nothing very good I suppose but I did try to express my feelings. What type of book are you writing? I still read a lot but some of this business, you know, I just don't know. Mr. Bear, what do you think of Henry Miller?"

"Great Bear," said Peaches.

"Great Bear," said Susan.

"Great Bear, pardon me," said Aunt Lorraine.

"Maybe I'm a maverick of some kind, but I think you were just dead center," said Peaches. "God, we're all human beings. If you can really express your feelings, if you can really be authentic, you've just got to communicate. You've just got to."

"What's authentic?" Susan asked.

"Absolutely," said Aunt Lorraine, nodding fast.

"Who cares about some tired old man's metaphysical philosophy?" Peaches went on, crossing a knee. "But the trick is to express yourself honestly. With the mass media and all we're trained to see things in such artificial terms. And then we're all so damned afraid of offending one another."

"What's metaphysical philosophy?" Susan asked. Her mother said "Later," and Aunt Lorraine said "Oh yes, but Henry Miller—"

"Miller? He has a certain lyricism, but really it's all"—Peaches looked at Susan, drummed his fingertips, then continued—"it's all mental masturbation. But damn it, there are other options. Now my book, or so I hope, will suggest some of these. It will be something new for the novel, a breath of fresh air if you'll pardon the cliché. The biggest problem of course is economics. The publishers are loath to take on anything really new. But my agent's been sending my first chapter around and we've had several very encouraging responses, especially from Apex."

"Well that's very encouraging," said Aunt Lorraine, looking delighted.

132

"It really is very encouraging," said Peaches modestly.

"What's the name of your book? We'll look for it when it comes out."

"Come Pussy."

Carolyne shuffled back in with the coffee pot. Peaches accepted a re-fill, and munched another lady finger. "Tha's right," Carolyne approved. "What an appetite," said Hillary, "Lorrie, isn't he amazing?"

"He's amazing," said Aunt Lorraine. She pressed all ten fingertips to her temples. "I was going to ask him something."

"About my book?"

"That's it. No, your voice. Your diction is so perfect I wondered if you ever give readings. Where did you study, or are you from England?"

"That's a very perceptive question," said Peaches.

The back door slammed and Aunt Lorraine screamed, "Take off your shoes!" A minute later David and Alan padded in. "We got kicked out," Alan said. "Hi, Aunt Hillary. This lady's visiting my mother with a *monkey.*"

"I said that," Susan reminded her mother.

"Aunt Neva wouldn't let us touch it," David complained. "We just wanted to play with it for a minute. It just sits there on your shoulder and it holds its tail in its hand, and it's got clothes on because it's winter out, the lady said. Hi, Aunt Hillary."

"Boys, I'd like you to meet a friend of mine," said Hillary. "This is Peaches Great Bear. He's an Indian. This is Lorraine's boy David. This is Alan Lannon from next door."

The boys mumbled hello, but Peaches jumped up and crossed the carpet to give them powerful handshakes. "It's no fun being replaced by a monkey, is it Al," he said. Alan shook his head. Then, surveying Peaches, he said, "I didn't think you looked like an Indian." And David said suspiciously, "An American Indian?"

Susan was pressing her hands over her mouth to keep from laughing. When Peaches mentioned the monkey it made her think again he looked very much like a monkey himself. Carolyne, too, looked like an old fat monkey. Susan got the boys off in a corner and whispered this to them, but they scowled and shoved her away.

"Easy, men," Peaches said, and it made Susan happy to see they were afraid of him. "We're going out," said David. "We're gonna see her come out."

"Can I come?" said Susan.

"No," said the boys, together.

"Let her," said Aunt Lorraine. "How about it, fellas." But Susan's mother said she couldn't because she was wearing a good dress. The boys laughed and went out, and Susan flopped back in her chair with clenched fists.

"That's all right," said Aunt Lorraine. "You just wait another year or two."

Hillary said, "Susie doesn't care, do you darling. She'd rather play with the girls anyway at this point."

"Yeah," said Susan. "I'm not interested in boys yet."

"But just wait a year or two," said Aunt Lorraine. "You're going to be lovely. I can really see it, now that your face is rounding out. And your figure is going to be just like your mother's."

Susan didn't say anything, but she stared secretly at Aunt Lorraine's mushy-looking chest, and was glad her figure wasn't going to be like *that*.

"I wonder what on earth that monkey business is all about," Aunt Lorraine said. "There must really be a real monkey."

Susan's mother said, "You know what some of their friends are like. It's probably some of those beach club people. When they want to make an impression I guess there just aren't any boundaries."

"I guess," Aunt Lorraine agreed. "Now darn, what was I going to say."

Peaches cleared his throat.

"Now I remember. Your voice." With both hands Aunt Lorraine pulled one thick knee across the other, then tugged down her skirt. "Where did you pick up such magnificent diction?"

"Well as it happens," Peaches said, "though I am Delaware Indian, I do also have Negro ancestry. I was born on a reservation but I grew up in the slums of Baltimore. I didn't always talk like this. For the first twenty years of my life I spoke a standard Southern Negro drawl. Then in my first year of college I decided to be a writer so I quit and headed for New York."

Carolyne shuffled back in. At a nod from Aunt Lorraine she began removing the coffee things. Susan could hear her grunt as she bent over.

"Of course there are all kinds of Negro artists," Peaches said. "I didn't want to produce just racial propaganda. That's purely a personal decision, I don't mean to criticize anyone else. I greatly admired Basil Rathbone. A girl I knew gave me a record of him reading 'A Christmas Carol,' and I played it over until I had it memorized and could say it just like him. Ha-ha-ha! Meddy Chdistmas! Meddy Chdistmas! That's how I learned. But every now and then, particularly if I've had a cocktail, you can hear the old drawl pushing through."

"I truly hadn't noticed," said Aunt Lorraine. "But now that you mention it, I believe I can hear faint traces."

"You must have an excellent ear," Peaches said. "Most people can't hear a thing."

134

"Oh, it's *very* faint," said Aunt Lorraine.

"Hey," said Susan, who was sitting nearest the window. "They're coming out. Look, Mama." Hillary and Peaches and Lorraine came to the picture window, forming a half-circle behind Susan. Even old Carolyne, standing behind them, craned for a look over Lorraine's shoulder.

Backing slowly, black-gloved hands slashing the air, a tall woman in a heavy fur coat was edging down the sidewalk of the house next door. She seemed to be talking to someone remaining out of sight in the doorway. On her far shoulder, almost hidden by her hat, squirmed a tiny monkey. His tail thrashed the air behind her.

"Mama, the monkey!"

"My God," said Hillary.

Lorraine said, "I'm just dying to know what gives."

Peaches said, "That woman is driving my car."

"No," Susan corrected him. "Your car is the other blue one."

"Tha's right," Carolyne said unexpectedly. Everyone stared at her.

The monkey woman was climbing into her car. "I guess it's safe to go over," Hillary said. "I'm just dying of curiosity. Lorraine darling, thank you for the lovely coffee."

"You're welcome my dear," Aunt Lorraine said. "Don't be so absurd. Call me as soon as you can, it's killing me. Susan darling give me a big hug, ye-e-es, be a good girl. It was *so* nice meeting you," she turned to Peaches, "Mr. Bear."

He turned to her formally, took both her hands in his. "Please, Lorraine," he said. "Just call me Peaches."

"I'm afraid the truth is terribly unexciting."

"Well?"

"It's very simple," said Aunt Neva. "She's an old college classmate. I haven't the least idea why she decided to drop in, we were never the least bit close."

"Does she live here in town?" Hillary asked.

"Uh-uh. New York. I doubt I'll ever see her again. I don't think I was any too friendly."

Susan said, "Did she tell you the monkey's name?"

"She did, several times. The Missing Link."

Peaches shook his head. "I can't quite place her, but somewhere I've heard of a woman with a monkey. I just can't put my finger on it. Who is she?"

"Her name?" said Aunt Neva. "Oh no, I doubt you'd know her. Her name is Tillie Thomas."

135

"No," said Peaches, shaking his head. "That doesn't ring any bells, to coin a cliché."

"What's cliché?"

Peaches frowned at Susan. "That's when someone uses a very common expression, like true blue. I don't intend any criticism, but when I was your age I had the habit of using the dictionary."

"So? So do I," said Susan, and she ran to Alan's room where there was a dictionary, to look up a word she was wondering about. She wasn't too sure of the spelling. The closest she could find was *master-builder*.

When she came back Peaches was telling Aunt Neva about his novel. "It deals with problems of identity," he said. "There are certain things I've been trying to work out for myself. It's therapeutic."

"Have you a publisher?" Aunt Neva said.

"Apex."

When he said that it flashed into Susan's mind: Ape X. Peaches's publisher was an ape. She put her hands over her mouth and hid her face in the arm of her chair. But her back heaved with the laughter inside.

Aunt Neva said, "Well. Look what's so amused."

"Maybe I should go on the stage," said Peaches sourly.

"Peaches dear, don't be upset," Hillary said. "She's just giggly because that's the age she's at."

"Look, the house is a mess," said Aunt Neva. "Rachel was too hung over to come in this morning. But why don't we all pretend we don't notice a thing and we'll go on into the kitchen so I don't have to run back and forth. I think the water is still hot from my last visitor."

They went to the kitchen. Hillary said she couldn't hold another drop, but Peaches had a cup of coffee and Aunt Neva had tea. Hillary said she didn't know where Peaches put it all.

Susan got chocolate milk. She sat with one leg tucked under, one elbow on the formica table, and sipped without interest. She didn't feel like laughing any more and was beginning to get bored. The next stop was Mona's house and she wished they would hurry up and get there. Whatever the conversation was didn't interest her at all, so she just looked at Aunt Neva, who had fascinating eyes: very large and rounded, with pupils the color of rich brown earth. The whites were so clear and liquid you felt like you could sip them through a straw. Aunt Neva's face was triangular and thin, her neck thin, her body thin and strong as a boy's. Her clothes always fitted tightly and she was always tucking and pulling at them, so that her small breasts jutted sharply. Susan thought she was very pretty and young-looking, even though it was strange she was so pointy and Uncle Fred was so soft and fat.

136

Susan didn't pay any attention to the conversation for a while. Then she heard they were talking about marriage. She wasn't sure what Peaches had just said about it, but Aunt Neva was saying "Yes. I couldn't agree with you more."

"I don't blame anybody," Peaches said, and Aunt Neva kept nodding her head up and down sharply, saying Yes. Yes. Peaches said "But when she got sick, you know, she really became incapacitated. To be a wife, I mean." He glanced at Susan. Aunt Neva nodded sharply, yes yes. "So," said Peaches, "we both decided the best thing would be a divorce."

"I sympathize completely," said Aunt Neva. "I couldn't agree with you more. My own marriage is a good case in point. We're concerned about Fred's heart, and I guess he's what you'd call partly incapacitated, and it's not easy living with such a person, even though Fred and I do share a great many other things."

Peaches rubbed the back of his neck, sinking his chin on his chest. His eyes rolled up, still looking at Aunt Neva, as he lowered his head. "What a shame for you, a young woman like you. And my God, how sad for him. I imagine he must be a good deal older."

"Somewhat. I shouldn't sound like I'm complaining. We've had some nice times, over the years." Aunt Neva smiled slowly and slid down in her chair. Her corduroy slacks rode up, exposing slim ankles and the beginnings of slim muscular calves. Her foot was going up and down.

"Naturally," said Peaches smoothly. "We had some good years too, Kathy and I, which confounded a lot of people. Kathy is Caucasian, you see."

"I didn't," Aunt Neva said. "You certainly have a lot of courage."

"I wish I could take credit for that," Peaches said. "It's just the way I'm built, Neva, and I've had to take a lot of criticism on that score. Ever since high school I've preferred to date Caucasian girls." He smiled. "I don't know why that is."

"Well," Aunt Neva said, "I don't know who criticized you, but I certainly don't think it's anyone else's business but your own."

"Certainly not," said Hillary, and everyone laughed. She reached over and squeezed Peaches's biceps and let her hand stay there.

"Some people like tall girls and some people like short girls," Peaches said. "Some people like blondes and some like brunettes and some like redheads. Now I like a girl to be certain things. I like her," and he smiled at Hillary, drawing his hand toward his shoulder so that her fingers were pressed in the bend of his arm, "to be big and well-built and intelligent, and I like her to have"—he smiled at Susan—"a beautiful ten-and-a-half year old daughter." He pointed his long jaw at Aunt Neva. "And I like her to be Caucasian, as it happens."

"Perfectly reasonable," said Aunt Neva.

"Perfectly normal," Peaches said. "I know I'm prejudiced, but to me it seems perfectly normal. I guess it was a foregone conclusion I'd have some prejudiced ideas on the subject." Peaches was drumming his right fingertips along the back of his left hand. "You see, Neva, my father was one-half purebred Delaware and one-half Negro, but his face was about the same colors as these shoes I'm wearing. And my mother was a very light mulatto, she had blue eyes, a woman of great beauty."

"She sounds very beautiful," Aunt Neva said softly. Susan could see that Aunt Neva's eyes were wet.

"They had a very beautiful marriage," Peaches said, his voice deep. "But it wasn't easy. The community wouldn't accept them. Thank God that's one problem my wife and I haven't had so much, though with us there've been other things."

"There have been. I can appreciate that," said Aunt Neva, very softly.

Hillary cleared her throat. "I'm sorry to say it," she said. "But I can see you-know-who is just lapping it all up." She stopped and listened—Susan too had thought she heard a funny noise somewhere in the house. "Certain people think about marriage enough as it is," Hillary went on.

"Oh, Hillary," said Aunt Neva. "I don't think a child should be shielded. Marriage is a fact of life. What do you think," she said, turning to Peaches.

"Not shielded," said Peaches thoughtfully. "But not treated as though she were an adult, either."

Aunt Neva said, "Oh, but ever since they were this tall Susie and Alan have been planning—" She stopped. This time they had all heard the puzzling sound. "Planning to get married," she said. She got up and opened the cellar door, listened carefully a moment, then returned to her seat.

"What about that, Susie," said Peaches. "I didn't know you were marrying Alan."

"Uh-uh," said Susan, emphatically.

"Well now here's something new," said Aunt Neva. "Who are you marrying then, you flirt. David?"

"Uh-uh," said Susan again. "I'm marrying a travel agent."

Peaches said, "Oh yes? Hmm," and Aunt Neva was muttering, "How do you know Alan won't be a travel agent."

"Or else a farmer," Susan said. "And we'll live on a farm and I'll have a colt."

Peaches hung his head, his eyes rolling up as he looked at her. "But what about babies," he asked.

"I'd rather have a colt than a baby," Susan said smartly.

138

This time the sound was unmistakable, an eruption of giggles which someone was struggling to control. Boiling mad, Susan jumped up and ran out of the kitchen, the adults following her. She ran through the dining room and living room and into the front hall, and yanked open the door of the coat closet.

There were Alan and David hunched together on the floor, hugging their knees and shrieking with laughter. While everyone was in the kitchen they had sneaked in the front door and into the closet, leaving the closet door open a crack so they could overhear. Now they were partly hidden by the hanging coats and a little wall of galoshes they had built. Susan scattered the galoshes with a single kick and began kicking at the boys' shins. Their laughter turned to yelps of pain. "Cut it out! Hey! Cut it out," David kept yelling, and Alan whined, "Hey, watch where yer *kickin*."

Susan's mother grabbed her from behind, and Aunt Neva dragged the two boys out of the closet. "Are you spying *again*," she yelled at her son, and slapped him softly. Alan wailed and the tears burst from his eyes. "Out!" Aunt Neva yelled. She opened the front door, pushed them both outside, and slammed the door after them.

"Everyone, I'm sorry," said Aunt Neva. She pushed some escaped hair back out of her eyes. "For some reason that kid has gotten to be such a little sneak lately."

Peaches shook his head. "That's too bad. He shouldn't, you know, he shouldn't be made to feel he has to spy."

"Right," said Aunt Neva. She nodded soberly. "We're clearly at fault. I'm afraid I blame Fred very much. Have you noticed how Alan only looks at you out of the corners of his eyes? I hate that, it scares me." And she went on for a few minutes more, telling Peaches how sneaky Alan was.

Then Susan's mother thanked Aunt Neva and said it was time to go. "Someone is getting in a foul mood," she explained. "And we still want to see Pearl Popavitch this afternoon."

As she flung into her coat, Susan was still steaming. She was not a bit surprised to see that when Aunt Neva and Peaches shook hands goodby Aunt Neva suddenly jumped up on her toes and gave him a quick kiss on the cheek. Hillary saw that and smiled. But from where Susan was standing she saw something her mother didn't see. She saw Peaches's long hand slide around Aunt Neva's back to the place exactly between her shoulder blades, where one long finger stretched out and scratched Aunt Neva through her sweater once twice three times.

Mona Popavitch was a bore.

"Well what do *you* wanna do," said Mona reasonably.

The trouble was that Susan didn't know. She admitted it, her mother was right: she was in a truly foul mood. This mood was worse than most, the kind her father used to call one of the All-Time Champions.

For a while she had been happy to see Mona. It had been fun telling Mona about Mrs. Thomas, the monkey woman, and her little monkey. Then she told about the boys and their spying, and Mona told about a boy who had pushed her down that morning skinning both her elbows, which she held up as evidence. Mona was a year older than Susan and had more development, but was embarrassed about it and still wore a T-shirt. It annoyed Susan to see that. When she had as much as Mona, she knew, she would definitely be wearing a bra.

For a while they sat in the living room listening to conversation, but it bored Susan because it was the same talk she had been hearing all day. It was all about Peaches's three gas stations and his childhood in Baltimore and his white wife, and *Come Pussy*, his novel, and his publisher Ape X. When he mentioned Ape X that reminded Susan and she whispered to Mona that Peaches looked just like a monkey. Mona saw it right away. Together they clapped their hands over their mouths and ran from the room, choking. Over her shoulder, Susan saw Peaches glaring after them so angrily she thought he must know what she had whispered. That made her feel a little better. She found she liked making him angry.

But after they had laughed themselves out on Mona's bed Susan began to feel sour again. Mona suggested they go visit a girl friend of hers who had a tree house, but Susan didn't want to go out. Mona had her own TV in her bedroom and they watched a while. Then Susan got bored and shut it off. Mona said she wanted to listen to records. Susan said no.

"Well what do *you* wanna do," said Mona.

Susan didn't know. A few years earlier she and Mona had had wonderful times playing together, and she was always expecting that would happen again when she saw Mona. But they were too big for dolls now and nothing else had turned up. Susan couldn't imagine that the two of them would ever have any fun again.

Eventually they went to the kitchen. Harriet was there, preparing a tray for the living room, and took time out from her work to give them Hawaiian Punch and Oreos. Harriet gave a big smile when she saw Susan. "Hey, Susie," she said. "It's good to see you. You sure have gotten big." Harriet had worked for the Popavitches a long time, and Susan remembered, with a little surprise, that she liked Harriet. Today Susan didn't feel like liking anyone. It was hard at first, seeing Harriet as a monkey, but Susan kept at it until she succeeded. Yet even as a monkey Harriet was so pretty and

140

nice Susan couldn't help liking her. Then she felt bad, so she decided she wouldn't look at Harriet that way anymore, but she found it was too late, she couldn't stop.

When Harriet had finished the tray the girls followed her back to the living room. They curled up on the floor in a little mound of scatter pillows, next to the fireplace.

Susan saw that Mrs. Popavitch was just taking her guitar out of its case. "I know you didn't bargain for this, Susie," she said. "But I've been asked to split a few eardrums." She turned to the others. "I may not sing good, but I do sing loud. Thank you Harriet, I would love a piece, maybe Peaches would like some. Peaches, you are taking a cup of coffee. And something to munch on."

"That's impossible," Hillary said. "Pearl, this man has been stuffing himself all afternoon."

But Peaches laughed. "What Hillary doesn't understand," he explained to Mrs. Popavitch, "is that I always take anything that's free."

As he said it he raised his hands, making claws out of them, and made a funny greedy face, and winked at Susan and Mona. Mona laughed, Susan just stared back at him. But Pearl Popavitch clucked her tongue. "I don't like that," she said. "That's the welfare temperament. I don't like that."

"But Pearl," said Hillary. "You have to like it, don't you? You're a liberal."

Pearl Popavitch's eyes flashed. "Hillary, I cannot get this through your head. I'm not a liberal. I'm a revolutionary. The welfare state tries to placate my revolutionary thrust but I will have none of it, I call for a restructuring of society. Hillary, so do you. We've *talked* about this."

"We have," Hillary said humbly. "I remember now. I'm so apolitical it's terrible."

Peaches accepted a cup of coffee from Harriet, then chose from the tray two small cakes and one tart. "Thank you," he said with dignity. There was too much for him to hold in his hands, and he spread a napkin on his lap for the tart and one of the cakes. The other cake he began to munch. "Don't be so apologetic," he told Hillary, a few crumbs dropping from his lips. "Revolution may not be the answer. Personally, I'm opposed to any use of force."

"I can best answer you with music," said Pearl Popavitch. She raised her guitar to her lap and began to strum vigorously. Then she sang. Her voice was deep, powerful, and quite hoarse, with many wild but confident jumps between the octaves. The words were hard to understand. It took Susan a minute to figure out they were in a foreign language.

She liked to hear Mrs. Popavitch sing, and to watch her. Mona's mother was tall and very heavy. She always reminded Susan of two pears: a big one for the body and a smaller one for the heavy-jowled face. Still, she was very dramatic and attractive looking. The dresses she wore were like no one else's, they were tents, with wide brilliant bands of color, and she wore giant-sized beads and low-hanging earrings almost the size of Susan's fist. Indoors she was always barefoot. Her skin was very white, her eye makeup very dark, and she wore two shades of lipstick. Her black hair hung to her waist in a single braid. As she played and sang she swayed from side to side, and her braid swung. Everyone watched her except Mona, who lay on her back staring at the ceiling, but sang along with her mother in a soft voice.

Pearl Popavitch ended her song with a resounding whack on the guitar's bottom. *"Aguila Roja,"* she said gutturally. "A song of the Spanish Civil War. The point I'm trying to make is just this. Here it is. In certain socio-political situations force is the only, the only, what I'm trying to say is there's no alternative to it."

"I see," said Peaches coldly.

"Of course I interpret that liberally, I'm not calling for race war."

"But that's what you'll get."

Pearl Popavitch gave a little grunt of surprise. "Well will you look at that. I've offended you. I'm sorry, what did I say?"

"You didn't say anything," Peaches said. "It's just that you don't understand the strength of the emotions you're dealing with. You can't, being white."

"Ha," said Pearl Popavitch. She jerked her thumb at Harriet, who had put down her tray and taken a seat. "Ask Harriet how much I understand. Go ahead, ask her." Then in a more conciliatory voice, "There are all kinds of positions, I just don't happen to agree with yours. Personally, I have always believed in a complete restructuring. Harriet is more moderate, aren't you Harriet, we've talked about this. But admit it, both of you, force is sometimes the only way." She rapped on her guitar for emphasis, then hugged it to silence it. "How was Little Rock solved? Intervention of federal troops. Armed men with fixed bayonets. You talk about the emotions, Peaches, but the question is *which* emotions. I believe the emotions for our time are indignation and anger." She rapped on her guitar again. "Harriet, am I right?"

Harriet considered the question, her full lips pursing slightly. Susan, watching her, thought again how pretty Harriet was. Now Susan noticed for the first time that Harriet was wearing lipstick and eye makeup. For some reason it had never occurred to her before that colored women could wear makeup too. Susan felt like running out and making herself up, if she could, to look like Harriet.

"You think about that," Mrs. Popavitch told Harriet. "Here's one we can all sing." She strummed fiercely, threw her head back, and there was a gleam in her eyes.

We shall not, we shall not be moved

Mona was the first to join in. Then Susan and Hillary, who had sung with Pearl Popavitch before, picked it up, and a moment later Harriet began to sing. Only Peaches was silent, though he smiled at Pearl Popavitch and his foot was bobbing up and down. Pearl Popavitch glared at him as she swung into the verse.

> **Black and white together, we shall not be moved**
> **Black and white together, we shall not be moved**
> **Just like a tree that's standin by the waters**
> **We shall not be moved**

Susan became excited as she sang, and she was sorry when the song was done. Mona shouted "Olé!" Peaches was applauding softly. "Excellent," he said. "You really are a talent. It's a beautiful way of self-expression, I wish I could do that, I envy you."

Pearl Popavitch scowled. "The self is nothing," she said. "My music is for the masses."

"But it's therapeutic," Peaches urged.

"Never. My art does not belong to me. I serve society just as the farmer does. Peaches, I'm surprised that you as a Negro artist don't feel this way very strongly about the social import of your work."

Now they were both scowling. "I'm not a Negro artist," Peaches said coldly. "I'm an artist. Period. Not a propagandist." Halfway across the big living room, Susan could hear the drumming of his fingertips up and down the back of his left hand.

"This is getting a little too hostile," Hillary said. "I think you two are just using different words for the same thing."

But Pearl Popavitch shook her head impatiently. "Hillary, this man must be made to see something. What I cannot fathom is how he can fail to identify with his people, at least on an emotional plane."

"Fail!" Peaches almost shouted. "Pearl, my friend, the only failure is your failure to, your failure to, I'll just say some people shouldn't throw stones. We'll leave it at that. I personally try very hard not to be a hypocrite."

"Meaning that I don't?" Pearl Popavitch was leaning forward in her chair as though ready to gore Peaches.

"Meaning," Peaches snapped, "that you sit here in your seventy thousand dollar house while your black servant works in the kitchen."

There was a moment of silence. Then Hillary said thoughtfully, "That's not fair, is it? Peaches, you aren't suggesting Pearl should *fire* Harriet."

"Heck no," said Harriet, and everyone laughed. Harriet laughed loudest, full lips parting on perfect teeth, and Susan stared at Harriet's mouth and eyes until her fingertips itched to go work with some cosmetics. So Susan grabbed Mona around the neck and whispered it, and Mona said okay, in a second.

Peaches seemed calmer. "I'm not saying fire her," he remarked.

"Of course you're not," said Pearl Popavitch, just as mildly. "And I'm not saying be hypocritical. In fact it's I who am calling for the overthrow of the whole hypocritical welfare state."

But now he was frowning again. "That's too easy, don't you see? It's the reaction of a dumb animal to say kill, kill, kill, kill, ki—"

"Who's saying *kill?*" she squawked. "Peaches, you are the damnedest man to argue with, you keep misunderstanding everything I say."

"I do not," said Peaches, shaking his forefinger at her. "I misunderstand nothing, you hear me? It's you who don't understand what you're saying. You don't know what Negroes are feeling, you don't see it. You don't know what violence is."

"That's a vicious goddam slur." She had control of her voice, nearly, but her face snarled at him openly, the great brown eyes slitted, the nostrils spreading and heaving. "Look, you. Don't try and pin any white robes on *me*. I've been on the inside of the Negro movement all my life, didn't Hillary tell you that? Did you know I've been to jail for my beliefs? Did you know last year A. Philip Randolph was invited to this house to undress a small group of progressive women? He sat in that identical chair." Susan and Mona were doubled over. *"What's so funny,"* Pearl Popavitch shouted at them.

Peaches said slowly, smiling, "He *un*dressed them?"

"He *ad*dressed us," she shouted. "You girls get out of here. And I'll tell you something else, my friend. Maybe I understand the Negroes better than you do. You've lost touch. You've sold out. You've gone white."

"Now we're down to it," Peaches bellowed. He rose, pointing at her. "You blame me, don't you. One Negro struggles to raise his standard of living and you can't stand it."

Pearl Popavitch shrugged. "Why no," she said innocently. "I don't

144

blame you a bit, Peaches. It's none of my business, is it? It's your own conscience you have to answer to, not me."

"I blame you," said Harriet.

Everyone turned to her. "You?" Peaches spoke as though he couldn't quite figure out what she had said.

"Yeah," said Harriet. "I can't help thinking this, you sound very anti-Negro to me."

He looked at her gloomily. "All right, now. You just tell me one thing. Where were you raised."

"Here, Harbor City. Born and raised and married."

"I hear you. All right, now. You listen, because I'm telling you something." He became aware then that he was still standing, and returned to his seat. The others all shifted in their chairs. Susan grabbed Mona around the neck again and whispered, Let's go. Mona whispered back Okay, wait until Pearl stops looking. Mona always called her parents by their first names.

"I'm dark," said Peaches, "but my mother was very light. She had blue eyes. I was the darkest of the children, me and one of my brothers. The girls are light. In fact one of my sisters is passing today." He crossed a leg, and where his trouser pulled back he circled the place with both long hands. "They spent hours, those girls, fixing themselves as white as they could."

That was too much for Susan. I'm going, she whispered, and got up, and after a second Mona followed her. They tiptoed out. No one even looked at them.

Mona's mother kept the makeup in her bedroom, and that was where they went. They left the door open a crack so they could hear if someone was coming. "It wasn't that bad a place," came Peaches's voice. "My father had made some money." At the same moment the girls dove for the little bench in front of the dressing table, and reached it at the same time. It was big enough for them both. And the tall oval mirror was big enough, too. Their faces shone back at them, nervous and excited, and looking hopelessly pink.

"—nothing we could do. The other children—" Peaches's voice drifted past them but they weren't listening any more. "Let's," whispered Susan. "The same way Harriet is." "Susie, your mother'll be mad," Mona warned, but she was predicting, not arguing. As for herself, everyone knew Mona's parents never punished her.

"I don't care," Susan said.

"—impossibly ambitious? Oh, but her skin was gold. Her eyes—"

At first they couldn't figure out what to use. There were dozens and dozens of tubes and vials, little jars, squeeze bottles. There were waxes and creams and oils, and perfumes whose scents left Susan reeling and excited. Then she spotted something she was sure of: the eyebrow pencil. With bold strokes she drew it across her cheeks. It came out a fuzzy black, but too jagged and irregular. Susan's face looked now like a hunk of meat just removed from the grill.

"Ah." Mona pounced on something. "Eye liner," she breathed. It came with a tiny brush, which she daubed in the eye liner and drew across her forehead. "Susie, look," she marvelled, and they stared into the mirror with delight and awe. The brush stroke was very narrow, only a slash above Mona's eyes, but its color was a perfect dead black. It was far blacker than Harriet, blacker than Peaches, and more perfect, less like makeup than a deep slit, all the way through to the dark insides of the skull.

"Hurry up," said Susan impatiently.

"—those children, those black children, me crying, and she screaming not to touch them, don't play with them—"

"Don't play with them, don't play with them," Susan mocked, catching the tail end of his phrase.

Mona worked as fast as she could, but the tiny brush slowed her. At last she threw it down in exasperation and gouged her little finger directly into the eye liner. It went on then in great smears. Susan could hold back no longer, and her finger stabbed into the makeup again and again, as quickly as Mona's finger came away. The daubs were crumbly and uneven until Susan hit on the trick of using spit to wet the stuff down, dilute it, spread it. That made the makeup go a long way, but even so they used all of it, and there was barely enough. When they were finished it was all gone. They looked in the mirror. Then they looked at each other.

"—dark, the darkest. But he was our father. We looked at him, then, one day—"

Susan giggled. "You look like a monkey."

"No," said Mona. "*You* look like a monkey."

"—features, black skin, curly wool on top—"

They stared together into the mirror, and two monkeys stared back. Mrs. Thomas's little monkey was cute, Peaches was big and funny, Harriet was pretty. But these two monkeys were the ugliest Susan had seen all day. She was disappointed and disgusted.

"Lipstick," she demanded.

"—because the children there were mainly white. My mother wanted—"

The lipstick was no help, an irrelevant red smear across their mouths. Now they looked like monkeys dressed up as clowns. Mona thought it was

146

terribly funny. Susan did too, partly, but she also wanted to cry. She had hoped they would be beautiful, maybe even pretty enough to return to the living room and show off for everyone. But they looked like monkeys. She knew everyone would just laugh at them, which she couldn't bear.

Unless it was clear that was what they meant.

"They only ate chitterlins—"

If it was clear—

"—turnips and ham-hocks and—"

"Get a belt," said Susan. "A big one."

"What for," said Mona.

"*Get* it."

"—those black little children. Don't play with them."

Mona's father was fat, and his belts were long. She rummaged in the closet and came back to Susan with a rich brown one, scaled like a snake, its buckle gold. Susan took it and ran the end through the buckle. That made a loop. She put the loop over her neck. She dropped down on all fours.

"—and rats. Roaches, spiders—"

She put the end of the belt in Mona's hand.

"—bedbugs, lice—"

Mona understood now. Her hand flew to her mouth and her eyes glistened. She nodded, very fast.

"Let's go," Susan whispered. It was hard moving her face because the makeup had dried like paint.

"The girls spent hours, fixing themselves—"

Susan slid her hand around the bottom of the bedroom door and pulled it open. The hallway seemed filled with sound. An ashtray clattered, Pearl Popavitch cleared her throat noisily, there was traffic in the street. Susan could hear a soft uneven drumming: the sound of Peaches's beating fingertips.

"He was dark, dark as someone's shoes," Peaches was saying a little hoarsely. "She was a woman of great beauty. He loved her a great deal. She was tall, her skin was colored like gold."

The rug in the hallway was luxurious and thick. The monkey crawled through it slowly, her keeper following close behind. Once the monkey stopped to give a practice scratch under her armpit. The keeper barely smothered a snorting giggle.

"—not to play with the ugly little black ones. And so we didn't. Then we'd come home, my brother and I, and of course there were mirrors. And of course there were our own faces, as black as—blacker than—no. Wait, bear with me. What I—"

More and more slowly, the monkey crawled toward the corner where the hall met the living room. Then someone's head was visible in profile. The monkey inched. The head swung around, drew back and shrieked. A final dash and monkey and keeper were in the middle of the living room floor.

There was a sharp tug at the belt, snapping Susan's head up until she was rocked back on her heels and flipped over onto her back. Then Mona remembered to let go. The floor under Susan's head shook as Mona ran from the room, laughing. Susan's neck hurt terribly and she could not get her breath.

Surrounding her on every side, towering suddenly upward from the dim edges of her field of vision, the vast faces of the four adults were soaring above her. Susan's brain snapped them, froze them. For that moment they had the thick paralyzed grace of portraits of gods, floating immensely high on a white ceiling.

Far above her right hand tilted the handsome face of her mother. The eyes were squeezed half shut as though startled or sunstruck. The mouth grimaced, jaws straining together, teeth visible to the gums between skinned-back lips whose insides shone pink and wet. Inches away, opposite, hung the pale fleshy pear which was the face of Pearl Popavitch. The jaw was still ponderous and insensible but the great brown eyes were gone muddy with confusion. The chain of black braided hair plunged plumb-straight toward Susan's belly. Somewhere over Susan's forehead a nest of fingers half hid the face of Harriet, warped with crying. And below, over Susan's knees, was Peaches's face.

It was not tilting like the others but flat and horizontal, like the floor pressing up against Susan's back. His neck was bowed, his temples shone at her, and for the first time she saw the top of his head. She realized with astonishment that Peaches was old: at the crown of his head the thick woolly hair was beginning to go gray. His mouth gaped, the big teeth gleaming. Like a paralytic's, his great swelling jaw crushed twisting into his breast-bone. His pupils were swung toward her, leaving empty seas of white, clinging to the upper margins of their sockets like exhausted swimmers. Below his face, huge as he reached for her, were the bright undersides of his hands. The fingers were spread, stiffened. The webbing where they were set into the hand was stretched taut. The creases on his palms were a maze.

Explorers of movement: American dance in the 1960's JACK ANDERSON

At present, American ballet and modern dance display more signs of creative life than any of our country's other performing arts, with the possible exception of the cinema. Drama may be in the doldrums. Opera may be moribund. Dance is flourishing. Between January 1 and May 31, 1967, there were at least 425 dance performances in New York City alone. This is an amazing sum. Still more amazing is the high percentage of excellence among these performances.

Certainly, problems exist. Despite the activity, many dancers are out of work and out of money. Dance is still considered "improper" in some locales and a prejudice against male dancers lingers on. Nevertheless, the fact remains that in less than half a century the United States has grown from a country which had almost no serious theatrical dance at all to a country which, along with England and Russia, is one of the three most important nations of the dance world and the one in which dance activities are the most varied.

While sheer diversity is the most remarkable feature of the current scene, general trends are discernible. First of all, the old rivalry between ballet and modern dance seems to be ending. Each form has proven itself artistically valid. Neither shows any sign of displacing the other. A great many dancers are now proficient in both. Not long ago, some modern dancers liked to predict that ballet, being of aristocratic origin, could not survive in democratic America, while some ballet dancers scoffed at modern dance as a fad which would wither away. None of this has come to pass.

Yet a revolution of sorts has taken place, a revolution of form and content. The pioneers of twentieth-century American dance, in both its balletic and modern manifestations, usually created dances which were narratives akin to plays or expositions of ideas akin to essays. When they choreographed, they sought movement which would express specific aspects of plot, character, or theme. Interesting examples of such dances are still being made. Yet many choreographers are now concerned with movement, not as a method of narration, but as something of interest and value in itself. Dance, in a sense, has become nonrepresentational. While choreographers are still very much concerned with the meanings a movement may possess, they discard dramatic structure and look upon meaning as something revealed through hints, suggestions, and connotations, rather than through statement.

Some of the newest choreographers consider themselves to be explorers of movement. They seek to expand the present boundaries of dance, to incorporate into it movements or theatrical elements not generally considered to be part of dance, and even to tear down the walls separating one art from another.

I

The most important single choreographer in American ballet is George Balanchine, born in Russia in 1904, and the most important ballet company is the New York City Ballet, the company of which he and Lincoln Kirstein are co-directors. Balanchine has been choreographing steadily since the 1920s. His output is Mozartian in both quantity and quality. Like the music of his friend, Igor Stravinsky, the choreography of Balanchine has never really gone out of favor. Instead, Balanchine has created works which constitute a continuing standard of excellence, no matter what artistic vogue may rule. Balanchine's range is enormous. There are impressive narrative ballets from *The Prodigal Son* of 1929 to *Don Quixote* in 1965. There are comedies, dramas, fantasies, melodramas, mood pieces, exotica, and cultivated erotica, as well as pieces which are mere ephemera.

Most important of all are Balanchine's plotless or, as they are sometimes called, abstract ballets. Balanchine was not the first choreographer to create ballets without plots. But before Balanchine no choreographer had

150

devoted himself so thoroughly to the development of this form. By freeing ballet from the burden of plot, Balanchine influenced the whole course of the art. His plotless compositions are a product of the belief, shared by certain ballet and modern dancers alike, that the most important thing in dance is movement itself. Without the drama of motion, the drama of plot, the glitter of scenery, and the rhythms of music count for little. Movement is interesting purely as movement. Dancing need not be bound to any other art. Balanchine, however, has permitted a gentle bondage. He says that his abstractions are inspired by the music he chooses to choreograph; in almost every ballet he carefully matches musical phrases with dance phrases. In his weakest ballets he does no more than this, his choreography becoming a human chart of the structure of a particular score with a formula expression of each type of symphonic movement: thus allegros will feature ensembles moving in geometric patterns, adagios will be duets for the ballerina and her cavalier, finales will find the entire cast arranged in parallel lines and spinning in unison. But in Balanchine's best ballets his choreography simultaneously reflects and transcends the music, taking on its own personality. These ballets may all be plotless, but each is unmistakably individual. There is *Serenade,* with its muted heartbreak; *The Four Temperaments,* whose movements look like animated cabalistic symbols; *Agon,* which might be termed a truly godlike Olympian games; *Ivesiana,* which suggests the terror and sadness of American cities—the list could be lengthened by a score of titles.

In the New York City Ballet Balanchine has an ensemble capable of carrying out his every wish. Yet it is now being regarded with a curious love-hate attitude by many balletomanes. Quirks of policy have begun to warp the company's development. Balanchine tends to have seasonal favorites among dancers, with the result that a new protégée will be featured night after night, while more experienced soloists will be ignored in casting the ballets. The company, with its huge repertoire, occasionally looks overworked and under-rehearsed. In the 1950s the *corps de ballet* was sometimes criticized for an almost mechanical exactitude; some of that precision is needed today. In the old days, when the company danced at City Center, its productions were criticized for being too drab. Now that it is housed in the affluence of Lincoln Center, it is attempting a grand manner, frequently with disastrous results. No major company of the Western world possesses such garish costumes, such ostentatiously ugly scenery. Nevertheless, for all its blemishes, the New York City Ballet remains our leading company, if for no other reason than because it is the company for which Balanchine has created many of his finest works.

II

Ballet's most distinguished dramatic choreographer is British-born Antony Tudor, who has lived in this country since 1940, when he was invited to participate in the first season of American Ballet Theatre. Tudor's reputation rests upon a mere handful of ballets in which he sensitively employs the vocabulary of classic dance to reveal nuances of character development. Among the themes on which he has created ballets are an upper-class marriage of convenience (*Lilac Garden*), sexual repression in a small town (*Pillar of Fire*), the forces which drive a man to crime (*Undertow*), and a communal ritual of mourning (*Dark Elegies*). Whatever his theme, one always feels that Tudor passionately believes ballet to be an adult art worthy of appealing to the adult intelligence.

In the 1940s it was thought that Tudor's dramatic compositions pointed the way toward ballet's future. But ballet has not developed that way. Although choreographers continue to attempt it, the dramatic ballet appears to be declining. Since man seems to possess a natural love of mimicry, it is doubtful whether the dramatic ballet will ever totally disappear. However, no dramatic choreographer has yet surpassed or even equalled Tudor's works in this style. Tudor himself, for reasons unknown and probably unknowable, withdrew into a personal isolation. Never prolific at any time, between 1945 and 1963 he choreographed few ballets, none of them a great success. Since then, fortunately, he has choreographed an anti-war ballet, *Echoing of Trumpets,* and a mystical allegory, *Shadowplay,* both solid, worthy accomplishments.

III

America's leading native-born ballet choreographers are Jerome Robbins and Agnes de Mille. For all their eminence, their careers are oddly unsatisfactory. Both choreographers have devoted too much of their talents to an unworthy cause.

That cause is the Broadway musical. From the late '30s to the late '50s, apologists for the commercial theatre announced that a new era was dawning in musical theatre. Musical comedy, they said, was growing up. The simpering chorine and baggy-pantsed comedian had been banished forever. The new musical would be a fusion of drama, music, and dance, a homegrown version of the Wagnerian *Gesamtkunstwerk*. In retrospect, such supposedly "advanced" shows as *Oklahoma!* and *Carousel* seem merely sentimental. *West Side Story's* greatest virtues were its girls in tight skirts and boys in tight jeans, not its sociological over-simplifications. Broadway

152

took itself too seriously and de Mille and Robbins took Broadway at its word.

Only two of de Mille's small number of ballets have proven durable: *Fall River Legend,* an obvious, yet theatrically effective, melodrama about Lizzie Borden; and *Rodeo,* an amiable bit of Americana. When de Mille first choreographed Americana, it was at a time when skeptics had to be shown that American themes were viable subject matter for ballet. De Mille showed them; that time has passed. Her works now seem smug in their insistent folksiness.

Robbins has fared much better. His first ballet, *Fancy Free,* an anecdote about sailors on shore leave choreographed in 1944, is still charming. His most recent ballet, a version of Stravinsky's *Les Noces* produced by American Ballet Theatre in 1965, is unquestionably his finest. Between 1944 and 1965 Robbins choreographed some amusing comedies, some probing psychological studies, and several ballets successfully fusing classic dance with American jazz. It is not a bad choreographic record. Yet Robbins is now forty-nine years old, and by now someone so gifted ought to have created more ballets than he has. Robbins has spent too much time away from the ballet.

IV

American Ballet Theatre, the company directed by Lucia Chase and Oliver Smith which has produced many works of Robbins, de Mille, and Tudor, has had a good share of troubles in its twenty-seven year history. At present, it is in a commendable condition, with the most diversified repertoire of any company in the world. It is best known for its staging of contemporary works, the newest being *Harbinger,* premiered in 1967. This abstract ballet is the almost frighteningly self-assured debut effort of a young choreographer named Eliot Feld. In addition to encouraging contemporary choreography, American Ballet Theatre has always maintained some of the classics in its repertoire.

In 1967 it presented the complete four-act *Swan Lake,* staged by David Blair of England's Royal Ballet. This production, in which Blair preserved the Petipa and Ivanov choreography of 1895, is the first choreographically authentic revival of the work in its entirety by a professional American company. Its overwhelming success suggests that American audiences are now ready to take the classics seriously on their own terms. While casual balletgoers have always considered *Swan Lake, Nutcracker, Giselle,* and the rest to be "pretty," the dance intelligentsia has been bothered by them. Many

153

of the early modern dancers castigated the ballet classics for alleged triviality. To those of the previous generation who had to propagandize the idea that dance was a serious art relevant to contemporary life, ballet's tiptoeing ladies in fluffy tarlatan tended to be embarrassments. But continued acquaintance with the gyrations of these ladies — particularly in the elaborate classical productions brought here by the Royal Ballet of England and the Bolshoi and Kirov companies of Russia—has revealed that the classics can be taken quite seriously and that they are, in their own fashion, relevant.

Their choreography, judged solely as movement, is beautiful. This, in itself, makes them candidates for revival. Still, if they glorified brutality or foolishness, we would probably leave them unrevived. But the classics not only contain beautiful movement, they depict beautiful behavior. In *Giselle* a cad is morally purged and redeemed by love. The hero of *Swan Lake,* after having been led astray, sacrifices himself, not for sect or party, but for a vision of the ideal. *Sleeping Beauty* is a glorification of right conduct: a king behaves badly by slighting a witch; the witch is likewise reprehensible for seeking revenge; but the Prince and the Lilac Fairy triumph by means of kindliness and courage. In the fantasies of classical ballet, as in the great fairy-tales, the way in which beauty is indissolubly linked with truth and goodness may bring tears of joy to one's eyes. All this, of course, is an expression of Romantic idealism. And Romanticism is once again influential. Romantic piano music is back in favor, as are the operas of Donizetti and Bellini. Allen Ginsberg recommends Shelley to college students. Romanticism is present in the aspirations of the peace and civil rights movements. Romantic extravagance is evident in the eccentricity of Mod fashions and, more disconcertingly perhaps, in the use of LSD to attain what was once called an experience of the Sublime. The success of *Swan Lake* is no isolated phenomenon.

V

One other New York ballet company is worthy of mention, the City Center Joffrey Ballet. Starting out a decade ago, under the direction of Robert Joffrey, as a gallant, but impoverished, touring ensemble, it has become a constituent member of the New York City Center of Music and Drama and, since the New York City Ballet's move to Lincoln Center, the City Center's only resident ballet. Its assets include talented dancers and a splendid revival of Kurt Jooss' 1932 satire on war and diplomacy, *The Green Table,* one of the classics of Expressionist dance and a ballet still eloquent in its rage and compassion. More problematical are the works of the company's young choreographer, Gerald Arpino. They tend to be either collections of vir-

154

tuoso tricks designed to wow the groundlings or intense, somewhat sexy, narratives which seem rich in hidden meanings on first viewing, but prove to be merely vague. Arpino's ballets have too much surface sheen, too little solid substance.

Probably the most heartening recent development in American dance is the establishment of ballet companies outside New York. While, to a limited extent, there has always been local dance activity, particularly in Chicago and San Francisco, the past decade has witnessed astonishing growth. Several professional companies (including those in Philadelphia and Washington, D.C.) and scores of non-professional companies have been founded. The non-professional companies, often referred to as regional ballets, constitute a dance equivalent of America's community playhouses. Some are amateurishly inept. Others are very competent. The Boston Ballet has successfully graduated from non-professional to professional status. The Atlanta Civic Ballet is presently in the process of turning professional. If no major choreographer has yet appeared in regional ballet, there are, nevertheless, able choreographers associated with regional companies who are doing a praiseworthy job of helping dance grow at the grass-roots level.

VI

To my own taste, I often find ballet more satisfying than modern dance. This is not because I believe ballet is necessarily the superior art, but because ballet, being older than modern dance, has accumulated a larger body of choreographic masterpieces. On the other hand, several factors cause me to find the work of young modern dance choreographers often more interesting that that of most young ballet choreographers. A young ballet choreographer's works are usually seen in repertoire alongside those of his elders and betters, and any discrepancy in quality between them is immediately apparent. A modern dancer with choreographic aspirations will probably found a company all his own. In the works of some of these choreographers there is a sense of adventure which lends special excitement to a modern dance concert. While many novice ballet choreographers seem satisfied to offer pleasant rearrangements of traditional steps, the modern dancer, particularly the experimentalist, creates out of a conscious desire to push outward and ahead in his art.

Among extant modern styles, the dramatically motivated dance is waning in vitality. Because this genre dominated modern dance from the 1920s to the 1950s, its decline has occasioned angry debate, its defenders accusing the new dancers of betraying the essential spirit of the modern dance movement.

155

In the past, modern dance works tended to be either narratives or dances which developed, often in a form analogous to that of a musical suite, separate aspects of an easily definable general idea. Choreographers of this sort of dance include Martha Graham, José Limón, and the late Doris Humphrey. Limón's taut re-telling of *Othello, The Moor's Pavane,* is a deservedly popular dramatic dance. Graham's *Primitive Mysteries,* concerning a cult of the Virgin Mary, is a superb example of the dance suite, each of its sections examining some discrete aspect of the cult's adorations. In its beauty of movement and its balance of restraint and ecstasy, *Primitive Mysteries,* choreographed in 1931, may well be the finest work ever created by an American choreographer. However, other once-celebrated works have begun to look over-simplified and even false to the truths of experience as we now feel them. Since the expression of dramatic and emotional truth was among the goals of the older dancers, this last charge is particularly serious.

Doris Humphrey, who died in 1958, remains important for devising a carefully conceived method of dance pedagogy. Her choreography, however, has lost much of its old appeal. *Lament for Ignacio Sanchez Mejías,* based upon Lorca, now seems to make its points with shrill and monotonous insistence. Worse still is *Passacaglia,* in which Humphrey uses Bach music as the basis for an heroic communal celebration. Historians often cite *Passacaglia* as among the achievements of 1930's modern dance. Its historical significance is indisputable. But historical significance is no guarantee of continuing vitality—how many drama groups have produced *Gorboduc* or *The Spanish Tragedy* lately? Revivals of *Passacaglia* make the choreography look rough-hewn and banal.

Regarding this, the historian might say that Doris Humphrey's works look different today because they are performed by different kinds of dancers than those for whom they were created. Many of the early modern dancers were earthier, even heftier, than their counterparts today, who are apt to be willowy as ballerinas. Moreover, dances usually tend to look better when performed by their original casts than when they are performed by subsequent casts. Since dance is the one art in which the creator must compose his work directly upon the person of his interpreter instead of upon some intermediary substance, such as musical staff-paper, the bodily configuration of that interpreter will almost always influence the creative process. Nevertheless, any good theatrical work not improvisatory in nature ought to be repeatable with some degree of effectiveness. Doris Humphrey's works have not aged gracefully.

Of all the modern dance pioneers, Martha Graham is unquestionably the finest. A discussion of her accomplishments can be found in any dance history. Here, however, I would like to take a deliberately cantankerous view and point out elements of Graham's work which some choreographers are now rejecting.

Since the 1940s, Graham's dramatic dances have usually concerned characters from literature or mythology. It is for these dances that Graham is most renowned. And it is precisely this sort of literary or mythological dance which newer choreographers reject, although audience members addicted to interpreting art in terms of archetypes and Jungian psychology continue to find Graham's myths fascinating. The danced myth inevitably refers one back to the story's literary expression in tragedy or epic poetry. Thus dance unintentionally becomes, not an independent art, but a mute subdivision of literature. Defenders of the use of myth claim that myths supply us with a common store of meaning, which the individual artist can then modify as he chooses. But this assumption is being challenged throughout the arts. Regarding poetry, Robert Bly has flatly declared, "Since Zeus, or Troy, or Aeneas have no emotional meaning for us at all, these words act as a sort of open sluice to drain all the sincerity and emotion out of a poem in which they appear. Consequently, the usual effect of a classical reference is to kill the poem instantly." Many choreographers share this viewpoint. Indeed, if one insists upon having readymade, widely recognizable figures, one might better turn to comic strip characters, movie stars, and the iconography of pop art than to the Greek gods.

Along with her myths, Graham's special type of symbolism has come under attack. In *Cave of the Heart,* the Graham version of *Medea,* the enraged heroine pulls a red string from the bosom of her dress. This string really symbolizes a serpent which really symbolizes diabolical cunning. Later, Medea locks herself inside a spiny sculptural construction which symbolizes her isolation from humanity. The symbols form a kind of code and interpreting them becomes an intellectual guessing game. Just as comparable guessing games are disappearing from our literature, so are they disappearing from our dance. Martha Graham is the intellectual contemporary of the New Critics. The shift in taste which has diminished the influence of some of the literary works these critics praised (now branded as "academic") has also diminished the influence of the allusive dance of Graham. George Jackson, a young dance critic, has written that some people now try to regard Graham's compositions solely as studies in nonobjective movement, completely ignoring their mythological content. But this must be as difficult and as

157

frustrating as trying to regard a certain Whistler painting as an "Arrangement in Black and Gray," and not as a portrait of a dignified matron.

VIII

Choreographers who reject the older modern dance frequently verbalize their objections in terms of two artistic problems. Choreographers interested in movement alone, and not in movement as a conveyor of ideas, find symbol, plot, and theme unnecessary encumbrances. But the old modern dance is also rejected by choreographers intensely concerned with the power of dance to express in some meaningful, but non-literal, fashion, levels of reality and perception. For these choreographers, the old modern dance is too simple and complacent. Reality is more complex, more ambiguous, more dismaying and wondrous than anything depicted in our dances. Consider such an ordinary occurrence as this: on a hot day I walk down a street, watching pedestrians and autos, eating an ice-cream cone, glancing at the headlines at a news-stand, and remembering an unhappy love affair. Experiences akin to the simultaneity of mental and physical events which we experience every moment of the day—unless deadened by habit—are what many choreographers hope to create in their dances.

One aspect of Martha Graham's work—her narrative structure—hints at a way of attaining such a desired complex of experience. The typical Graham narrative dance begins at a crucial point in the life of its protagonist, then proceeds both forward and backward in time, the protagonist recalling his past as he meets his destiny. This kind of narrative, based upon man's ability to do many things and mentally be in many places at the same time, is rich in unexplored possibilities—unexplored because Graham has used the form for little else than myths.

In the 1950s when the first radically different modern dancers began to attract attention, audiences, accustomed to dramatically motivated works, were often baffled by what they saw. Then and now, hostile observers have accused the new dances of "dehumanization." But once this seemingly dire objection is analyzed, it usually turns out to mean nothing more than that the accuser is uneasy because the new dance does not tell a story. When this objection was raised against his abstract ballets, Balanchine observed that two dancers dancing constitute "a story in themselves."

The newer choreographers attempt to orient audiences in various ways. One important and articulate choreographer, Erick Hawkins, finds it beneficial to discuss his dances in terms of F.S.C. Northrop's theory of the two functions of art: art in its first function being art concerned only with the

158

shape, form, and texture of its materials; art in its second function being art concerned with some meaning beyond its materials. Hawkins believes that once the first function of art is made clear to the general audience, it can be led to appreciate nonobjective choreography. Merce Cunningham frequently includes among his program notes the statement: "Dancing has a continuity of its own that need not be dependent upon either the rise and fall of sound (music) or the pitch and cry of words (literary ideas). Its force of feeling lies in the physical image, fleeting or static. It can and does evoke all sorts of individual responses in the single spectator. . . ."

IX

Among the choreographers who have sought alternatives to the older modern dance forms, the most influential has been Merce Cunningham. Through his choreography and his collaboration with such painters as Robert Rauschenberg and such composers as John Cage, Cunningham has significantly expanded our vision of what modern dance can be.

Much—possibly too much—has been said about Cunningham's use of chance methods to compose some, but not all, of his dances. Elementary examples of such chance methods are the establishment of the sequence of events in a dance by tossing coins or drawing from a hat slips of paper with names of movements written on them. The importance of such methods lies, not in their oddity, but in the fact that they indicate Cunningham's refusal to be intimidated by aesthetic pre-conceptions and his recognition of the diversity, even the contrariety, of experience: in this universe anything can seemingly follow anything else, and yet we also feel that everything is, somehow, interconnected—although the least convincing kind of connection is the simplistic cause-and-effect pattern glibly offered as "psychological motivation" by so much fiction, drama, and dramatic dance.

One reason why Cunningham's dances are so theatrically rich is that he lets all their elements—choreography, decor, music—peacefully co-exist. Balanchine's abstract ballets freed dance from dependence upon literary ideas. But there usually still remains an obvious phrase-by-phrase equivalence of movement and music. In Cunningham's works music and dance are neither subservient nor hostile to each other, they are parallel. The comparison of Cunningham with ballet is not farfetched. When the Cunningham company visited England, alert critics were startled to note that Cunningham's choreography, with its clean, precise phrasing, was not entirely unrelated to that of Marius Petipa, the choreographer of *Swan Lake* and *Sleeping Beauty*. There is an innate elegance about Cunningham's choreography which is classical in the best sense of that word. Curiously enough, this same elegance can also initially confuse people who, having heard that Cunningham is "experimental," attend his concerts expecting to see freakish contortions.

Although lacking precise subjects or specific messages, Cunningham's dances range widely in atmosphere. *Suite for Five* is utter tranquility. Watching the dancers in *Summerspace* becomes like watching the whorls of color which can be seen when one closes one's eyes after staring into sunlight. In *Winterbranch* the hobbling dancers seem inhabitants of some wasteland of despair. The percussive, relentless choreography of *Place* evokes anxiety, ulcers, and bitten fingernails. *Variations V* seems very urban. At the back of the stage are screens on which films of landscapes, architecture, and abstract patterns are projected. As the dancers perform, their movements—by means of special electronic equipment—activate sound-producing devices whose noises become part of John Cage's musical score. The conglomeration of sounds, dancers, and moving pictures suggests a choreographed metropolis, a place where something is always happening somewhere and lots of things are happening everywhere. Any city dweller who has observed the blocks of buildings and the constant flow of people and events around them has had experiences related to *Variations V*. Each work by Cunningham must be savored on a moment-by-moment basis. Cunningham shares with many contemporary artists a desire to redeem the present moment. In literature, his work might be compared with the verbal mosaics of John Ashbery or with Charles Olson's dictum that in poetry one perception must immediately lead to a further perception. By freeing us from our customary sloth, inertia, and inattention, Cunningham's choreography effects a cleansing of our sensibilities.

X

Two aspects of *Variations V*, choreographed in 1965, point to areas now being explored by several choreographers: the use of movements not usually considered to be "dance movements," and the use of "mixed media." In *Variations V,* in addition to turning, leaping, balancing, and performing other stylized movements we customarily label "dance movements," the cast does perfectly ordinary things: one dancer rides a bicycle, another fusses with a potted plant. Choreographers are not only expanding our ideas of what constitutes acceptable content in dance, they are questioning old assumptions as to what is and what is not acceptable dance movement. Today, in a sense, anything goes—provided the choreographer can make it effective. A dance may combine bits of traditional ballet and modern dance movement with gymnastics, movements used in physical labor, or everyday utilitarian

160

movements. Some dances contain no conventional dance movement whatsoever. Unsympathetic observers call such pieces "anti-dance" and fear they herald a lowering of performing standards. These fears may be exaggerated. For if a choreographer is free to demand of a dancer anything from scratching his head to turning multiple pirouettes, then the ideal performer is someone bodily equipped to do everything—which may necessitate, not less, but more and more varied kinds of dance training, as well as more varied kinds of dancers, than are customary.

Concurrent with an interest in mixed kinds of movement is an interest in mixed media, in creating theatre pieces in which elements of separate art forms are reordered into a new hybrid. *Variations V* hints at such hybridization through its use of dance, films, and electronic sounds. It is not surprising that artists should be interested in mixing media; thanks to technology, our daily life is full of mixed media situations: we may read books while listening to recordings; we may talk on the telephone while watching television; we may travel in an airplane which allows us the alternatives of peering out the window at the scenery or watching movies (quite possibly, movies about other scenery someplace else). Artistic precedents for mixed media include the collage and assemblage tradition, plus that more recently developed theatrical assemblage known as the happening. The first happenings were the products of painters and sculptors. But as the artists ventured into theatre, dancers also experimented with similar works.

Unfortunately, "happening" has popularly acquired connotations which make it synonymous with "free-for-all" or "hurly-burly." Department stores no longer have sales, they have happenings. Some dancers would prefer to replace the term with one less sensationalistic (dance critic Jill Johnston suggests "theatre of action"). Whatever term is used, it describes a type of theatre piece, frequently involving dancers, which is visual and kinetic, rather than verbal, and which lacks the drama's logical progression of exposition-development-resolution. These pieces attempt an intersection of artistic experience which their creators believe more fully expresses multi-leveled reality than conventional dramatic form. Artists concerned with such works often treat the theatre's proscenium and auditorium, not as pedestals or frames for action, but as a total environment, with the result that the boundaries between stage and audience, even between life and art, may become blurred. By implication, every place is a potential theatre: theatre pieces have been staged in such locales as parking lots, railroad stations, and street corners. That being so, everything is capable of being transformed—or salvaged or saved—by art. At this point, if one wishes to make the connection, aesthetics can meet a radical libertarian tradition, which John Cage acknowledged when he remarked, "Though I don't actively engage in

161

politics I do as an artist have some awareness of art's political content, and it doesn't include policemen."

XI

An important choreographer investigating theatre of action is Ann Halprin of San Francisco, one of the few avant-garde American dancers who has developed primarily outside New York. Halprin once summed up her approach to theatre by quoting the Sanskrit proverb, "Wherever your attention alights, at this point experience." She views dance as an on-going process of creation for the performers and of discovery for the audience. She choreographs, not by teaching movements by rote, but by devising, often in collaboration with artists and musicians, sets of situations, games, or problems which the dancers must live through and improvise upon. These situations may require a direct response to shapes or sounds, or to personal relationships in the manner of certain types of exercises used in training actors. Halprin edits the products of these exploratory sessions until she achieves a satisfactory theatrical form. One result of her approach, with its emphasis upon responding to immediate situations, is that her group's performances are notable for their intensity and for the rapport which exists among company members.

Halprin's concern for the here-and-now prompts her to regard each theatre in which she performs as a unique environment demanding either new works or modifications of old. Her *Parades and Changes* is structured to make use of whatever stage equipment a particular theatre may possess. When asked to choreograph for a low-ceilinged theatre shaped approximately like a shoebox, she created *The Five-Legged Stool,* which emphasized horizontality in its movements and stage pictures. Invited to present a work at the Teatro Fenice in Venice, she stressed the auditorium's height by hanging a cargo net from the proscenium arch, on which the dancers climbed and swung. Critics occasionally wonder whether Halprin's pieces should be described as dance or theatre. Because they involve bodily reactions to environmental stimuli, Halprin believes the term dance remains applicable.

XII

Two other choreographers, Paul Taylor and Alwin Nikolais, are often listed among the principal developers of non-dramatic modern dance. They are undeniably rebels against older forms. Yet, in my opinion, each has acquired annoying choreographic mannerisms.

Taylor's early concerts shocked people. In one "dance" he did nothing but stand stock-still. In another, he crawled across the stage to the accom-

162

paniment of time signals ("At the tone, the time will be 5:07 . . ." etc.); ironically, he called the piece *Epic.* In the light of Taylor's subsequent development, these pieces do not seem to be signs of radical innovation (after one has danced a motionless dance, where else can one go in that particular direction?), they seem like jokes. Taylor, a genial performer, has become a genial choreographer of genial comedies and lyric dances. They are always meticulously choreographed. But their geniality eventually becomes tiresome and I long for works with higher choreographic blood pressure. Taylor's newest creation is *Orbs,* a meditation upon birth, death, and rebirth, set to Beethoven quartets. In it Taylor successfully sustains long phrases of movement—no mean accomplishment. Nevertheless, the work's theology is uncomfortably close to "positive thinking."

Alwin Nikolais aspires to be a complete man of the theatre. He choreographs, composes electronic music, and designs elaborate decor and lighting. Each Nikolais production contains some new marvel of stagecraft. Witty and erudite, Nikolais has stated that he wishes to push beyond the traditional boundaries of the theatre and transcend the usual limitations of the performer. He shares these ideas with many contemporary dance experimentalists. Nikolais' most common practice is to mask his dancers and tie hoops, poles, capes, or sculptural forms to them which extend and distort the natural line of the body. This, says Nikolais, makes the dancer super-human, even super-heroic. But there is a wide gap between Nikolais' theories and the way his productions actually look. His choreography for his fantastically garbed dancers tends to be technically clever, yet repetitive and conventional. To borrow a phrase from Ferlinghetti, Nikolais' productions are Coney Islands of the mind. He does what he does well enough. But since he has publicly set higher goals for himself, well enough is, finally, not enough.

XIII

Many of New York's most promising young choreographers have participated in the dance concerts at the Judson Memorial Church, a Baptist church on Washington Square South in the heart of Greenwich Village. The church has a tradition of encouraging artistic expression and liberal social action, a tradition admirably upheld by the present ministers, the Reverend Howard Moody and the Reverend Al Carmines. Dance found a home at Judson in 1962 when its pastors offered the use of its facilities to a workshop group of dancers, composers, and painters. Although there no longer exists a workshop at Judson (dancers outgrow choreographers' workshops just as poets outgrow creative writing workshops), the church remains a center for dance experimentation. Dancers there continue to be interested in collaborating

163

with representatives of the other arts. Among the artists and composers who have worked with the Judson Dance Theatre are Alex Hay, Robert Morris, Robert Rauschenberg, John Herbert McDowell, Robert Dunn, Philip Corner, and LaMonte Young.

While some antagonistic viewers regard all Judson dance activities with equal disapproval, the Judson dancers differ markedly. Perhaps all they share is a willingness to work together. One group of Judson choreographers seems preoccupied with problems of movement invention (whether it involve new movement, adaptations of traditional dance movement, or nondance movement), compositional techniques (including improvisation, chance, and the use of objects or sculptures to stimulate movement), and movement qualities (e.g., feet walking on wood and feet walking through sand may both be walking, but they are kinesthetically different; swinging an arm while empty-handed and swinging an arm while clutching a brick are both swings of the arm, but they are kinesthetically different). Choreographers who have displayed strong interest in such matters include Deborah Hay, Lucinda Childs, Judith Dunn, and Yvonne Rainer. Dunn, a former soloist with the Cunningham company, is a formidable technician of striking stage presence. She choreographs movement which is complex and surprising, yet beautifully ordered and as clear as springwater.

Rainer first attracted attention with dances which were violent outbursts. She has since pared down her style, possibly as a result of her interest in minimalist painting and sculpture. What is now most unusual about Rainer is not her assertiveness, but her disdain of spectacle and showmanship. Rainer's new dances seem to take place in unvarying white light. Although fleetly gymnastic, they are virtually devoid of accent, emphasis, gradations, and dynamics. These dances do not call attention to themselves, they do not disclose any secrets. If some are rarefied almost to invisibility, others—once an effort has been made to concentrate upon them—seem emanations from a state of unshatterable equilibrium.

XIV

A totally different sort of dance at Judson might be termed neo-Romantic. It exemplifies all the traits of the Romantic temperament from a longing for beauty and nobility to a fascination with the picturesque and bizarre. Wafting nymphs, beach-boy Adonises, yearning lovers, sad clowns, hooligans, soap bubbles, and sequins may all be part of certain Judson dances. Naiveté is combined with worldliness. Much of the movement is semi-balletic. The music may be by Berlioz, Massenet, Liszt, or Satie. Popular with young au-

164

diences, this neo-Romanticism is the modern dance world's parallel to the ballet's renewed interest in the classics. Among the Judson Romantic choreographers are Remy Charlip, Aileen Passloff, Deborah Lee, and James Waring.

Because he has created many deliberately comic works and because there is an element of preciosity about much of his choreography, some people assume that everything by Waring is parody or camp. Waring choreographs a ballet to Mahler adagios—people wonder why it is not funnier. He choreographs some *Mazurkas for Pavlova*—it is interpreted as a spoof. He choreographs a danced version of *The Phantom of the Opera*—the critics cry "camp!" On the contrary, as far as I can tell, Waring is not kidding; he really likes Mahler, mazurkas, and Gothic novels. We may not share his likes, but that is no reason for scoffing at Waring for making his choreographic Valentines. Among the most unusual are literal, almost gesture by gesture, duplications of 1930's movie musical scenes, staged with more affection than contempt. And why not? Why should cowboys and pioneers be sanctioned as legitimate subjects for balletic Americana, while old movies are considered fit for hoots of laughter? For many of us when young, movies were wonderful adventures; for many of us, they still are, although we may not admit it. James Waring says so choreographically. In addition to his nostalgic excursions, Waring choreographs lyrical plotless dances, one of the best of them being *Northern Lights,* a dance of wispy, shifting patterns, appropriately dedicated to Odilon Redon.

XV

Meredith Monk and Kenneth King, two young dancers only recently out of college, have staged, at Judson and elsewhere, mixed media experiments involving dance, stage props, *musique concrète,* and films. These pieces suggest that they have assimilated the discoveries of their choreographic predecessors in a very personal way. King and Monk combine an interest in purely structural problems with a desire to elicit specific emotional responses from the audience. Yet they make their emotional appeals in ways quite unlike those of the old dramatically motivated dance. King's *Cup/Saucer/Two Dancers/Radio* is a composition utilizing indeterminacy, permitting the actions to be performed in any of several possible orders; but it is also a malicious satire on suburbia. *Camouflage* is a study in verticality in which King emphasizes his own height and thinness; it is also an antimilitarist piece in which King dances in toe shoes—that most traditionally feminine of footwear—to suggest battle fatigue and military drill.

Monk's *Duet With Cat's Scream and Locomotive* consist of variations upon straight and curved lines, as expressed in movements and in such props as stilts, curved woodblocks, and cut-outs of lips and feet. But *Duet* is also a meditation upon loneliness. *16mm Earrings* is an ingenious study involving surfaces. A live dancer moves, films are shown of this same dancer, the dancer masks her face and films of that face are projected upon the mask. Another film shows a doll being consumed by fire, but the doll is replaced by a real girl being consumed by illusions of flames. Monk is here concerned both with surfaces of objects and with the way passion affects the surfaces of the human body.

XVI

Dance is the most ephemeral of arts. Its capacity for change is one reason why dance history can seem so melancholy—so many dances are so easily lost. The history of dance is assembled out of speculation and gossip. Yet this very changeability is also one reason for dance's artistic vitality. Because it cannot be tied down, it is always on the move. It moves so quickly that it is dangerous to predict where it will move next, although one can hazard some guesses.

Ballet will surely continue to develop in both classical and contemporary styles. Further examples of the classical repertoire will probably be staged in reasonably authentic versions. Conceivably, at some future date a standard repertoire of classical works may crowd out attempts at innovation in the larger ballet companies, just as in the opera house standard repertoire now takes precedence over modern operas. But if this should happen (and it will not happen soon), one hopes that there will be young iconoclasts bold enough to establish their own ballet companies. Ironically, what is now America's most creative company, the New York City Ballet, may become, with Balanchine's retirement, a dance museum specializing in Balanchiniana. American Ballet Theatre will presumably maintain its present eclectic policy.

It is harder to speculate about modern dance, since modern dance lacks organizations comparable in stability to the big ballet companies. Should Graham or any of the other older choreographers retire, an entire repertoire, brilliant and tedious works alike, may vanish completely. This would be calamitous. But at present there appears to be no way to avoid it, although several suggestions have been made. One is to notate repertoires. Unfortunately, no universally accepted system of dance notation exists. Choreography survives largely in the memory of dancers. When memory fails, choreography dies. The perfection of a simple and accurate system of notation would completely revolutionize the dance world.

Another suggestion for preserving older works involves the establishment of a modern dance repertory company corresponding in policy to such drama companies as the Comédie Française. While many people say they favor such a company, no one has yet managed to get one going. It is also conceivable that some of the modern dance repertoire could be performed by ballet companies. Our dancers are versatile enough. But remnants of the old and, by now, meaningless rivalry between ballet and modern dance have hindered action in this direction, although several ballet companies have commissioned new works by such modern dance choreographers as Merce Cunningham, Anna Sokolow, Glen Tetley, and John Butler.

The newer modern dancers will probably go on developing movement invention, theatre of action, and other possibilities of non-dramatic dance. Neo-Romanticism will be around as long as there are choreographers of neo-Romantic sensibility, but one wonders whether it will continue to be popular once *art nouveau* posters, beads, and peacock feathers are no longer in vogue and should its youthful audience discover the more sumptuous splendors of classical ballet. Current interest in such dancers as Ann Halprin and in such dramatic experiments as those of the Open Theatre, the Living Theatre, and Jerzy Grotowski's Polish Theatre Laboratory may eventually even engender some entirely new form of mixed-media theatre, neither drama nor dance as we have traditionally defined them. Still another fruitful area of collaboration has opened up between artist and technologist. A much-touted series of experimental collaborations of dancers, musicians, and painters with scientists and technologists was held in the autumn of 1966. Most of the experiments were, in themselves, fiascos. Nevertheless, they managed to provoke salutary interest in a new aspect of the performing arts.

Presumably, American dance groups will continue to tour the world, just as other countries will send their own companies to the United States. Some observers grumble that such visiting groups as the Bolshoi or the Royal Ballet have gained an inordinate amount of publicity in the press and status in high society. While there is a measure of truth to these allegations, international touring has done far more good than harm.

England's Royal Ballet has acquainted us with the work of Sir Frederick Ashton, one of the half-dozen or so most important living choreographers, and with such "modern classics" as Bronislava Nijinska's original 1923 choreography for Stravinsky's *Les Noces.* The Royal Ballet was also the first company to show us how magnificent the late nineteenth-century classics can be if they are respectfully presented in their entirety. The Royal Danish Ballet revealed to us a charming nineteenth-century style which survived in Copenhagen long after it had disappeared elsewhere. The Soviet companies, despite their occasionally overwhelming flamboyance, have reminded us that dancing is, after all, a physical act and that there is nothing necessarily reprehensible in virtuosity (although some of the uses to which the Russians put their virtuosity may be legitimately questioned).

American modern dancers touring abroad have introduced audiences to what is, for many Europeans and Asians, an almost totally unknown— and tremendously exciting—art form. Our ballet companies have demonstrated that Americans are proficient in the international language of the classic dance. Repertoires of European companies are now filled with almost blatant imitations of American choreographers. Since it has made international touring part of its regular schedule, the Royal Ballet has lost much of that prissy quality which used to annoy critics and balletomanes. Whatever Moscow officials may claim, Soviet ballet has not been immune to the influence of the dance it has encountered in Western Europe and the United States. On its most recent American tour, the Bolshoi displayed a marked increase in the sophistication of its decor, choice of music, and subject matter.

Truly, American dance seems destined to live happily, if not ever after, at least for a long time to come. This optimism is predicated on the assumptions that the world will be spared from a holocaust and that America will be spared from political hysteria or repression. The condition of the world in 1967 makes these assumptions seem distressingly shaky. The abrupt cancellation, for political reasons, of a tour of Russian dancers this past summer has cast some doubt upon whether impresario Sol Hurok will be able to import the Bolshoi Ballet, as promised, for a fourth American tour in 1968. But should these dancers return, it is a sign—a feeble one to be sure, yet a real one—that the world's intellectual frontiers remain at least partially open. And so I look forward to the Bolshoi's return—just as I look forward to the day when some enterprising impresario will bring to America the celebrated dancers, mimes, and acrobats of the Peking Opera.

Suite to appleness

I

If you love me drink this discolored wine,
tanning at the edge with the sourness of flowers—
their heads, soldiers', floating as flowers,
heads, necks, owned by gravity now as war
owned them and made them move to law;
and the water is heavier than war, the heads
bobbing freely there with each new wave lap.

. . .

And if your arm offends you, cut it off.
Then the leg by walking, tear out the eye,
the trunk; body be eyeless, armless, bodiless.
And if your brain offends you . . .
If Christ offends you, tear him out,
or if the earth offends you, skin her
back in rolls, nailed to dry
on barnside, an animal skin in sunlight;
or the earth that girl's head,
throwing herself from the asylum roof,
head and earth whirling earthwards.

. . .

Or if we reoccur with death our humus, heat,
as growths or even mushrooms; on my belly
I sight for them at dead-leaf line—
no better way—thinking there that I hear
the incredible itch of things to grow,
Spring, soon to be billion-jetted.

. . .

Earth in the boy's hand, the girl's head,
standing against the granary; earth a green
apple he picked to throw at starlings,
plucked from among green underleaves,
silver leaf bellies burred with fine white hairs;
the apple hurled, hurtling greenly with wet solidity,
earth spinning in upon herself,
shedding her brains and whales and oceans,
her mountains strewn and crushed.

II

In the quonset shed unloading the fertilizer,
each bag weighing eighty pounds,
muscles ache, lungs choke with heat and nitrogen;
then climbing the ladder of the watertank
to see in the orchard the brightness of apples,
sinking clothed into the icy water, feet thunking
iron bottom, a circle of hot yellow light above.
. . .

The old tree, a Macintosh:
68 bushel last year,
with 73 bushel the year before that,
sitting up within it on a smooth branch,
avoiding the hoe, invisible to the ground,
buoyed up by apples; brain still shocked,
warped, shaved into curls of paper,
a wasps globe of grey paper—
lamina of oil and clouds—
now drawing in greenness, the apples
swelling to heaviness on a hot August afternoon;
to sing, singing, voice cracks at second sing,
paper throat, brain unmoist for singing.
. . .

Cranking the pump to loud life,
the wheel three turns to the left,
six-hundred feet of pipe laying in the field;
the ground beneath begins shaking, bumping
with the force of coming water, sprinklers whirl,
the ground darkening with spray of flung water.
. . .

After harvest of cabbage the cabbage roots,
an acre of them and the discarded outer leaves,
scaly pale green roots against black soil,
to be forked into piles with the tomato vines;
a warm week later throwing them onto the wagon,
inside the piles the vines and leaves have rotted,
losing shape, into a thick green slime and jelly.

III

Or in the orchard that night
in July: the apple trees too thick
with branches, unpruned, abandoned,
to bear good fruit—the limbs
moving slightly in still air with my drunkenness;
a cloud passed over the moon
sweeping the orchard with a shadow—
the shadow moving thickly across the darkening field,
a moving lustrous dark, toward a darker wood-lot.
. . .

Then the night exploded with crows—
an owl or raccoon disturbed a nest—
I saw them far off above the trees,
small pieces of black in the moonlight
in shrill fury circling with caw caw caw,
skin prickling with its rawness
brain swirling with their circling
in recoil moving backward, crushing
the fallen apples with my feet,
the field moving then as the folds
of a body with their caw caw caw.
Young crows opened by owl's beak,
raccoon's claws and teeth;
night opened, brain broken as with a hammer
by weight of blackness and crows,
crushed apples and drunkenness.
. . .

Or Christ bless torn Christ, crows,
the lives of their young
torn from the darkness,
apples and the dead webbed branches
choking the fruit;
night and earth herself
a drunken hammer, the girl's head,
all things bruised or crushed
as an apple.

JIM HARRISON

Treetops

My father moves through the South hunting duck.
It is warm, he has appeared
like a ship, surfacing, where he floats, face up,
through the ducklands. Over the tops
of trees duck will come, and he strains
not to miss seeing the first of each flock,
although it will be impossible to shoot one
from such an angle, face up like that
in a floating coffin where the lid obstructs
half a whole view, if he has a gun.
Afterlives are full of such hardships.

One meets, for example, in one's sinlessness,
high water and our faithlessness,
so the dead wonder if they are imagined
but they are not quite.

How could they know we know
when the earth shifts deceptively
to set forth ancestors to such pursuits?
My father will be asking, Is this fitting?
And I think so—I, who, with the others,
coming on the afterlife after the fact
in a dream, in a probable volume, in a
probable volume of dreams, think so.

MARVIN BELL

Via Sinistra

Hard to avoid
other worlds . . .
To find you now

I must go into the streets,
the terminals,
a world

of agreements.
Ledges and cornices
fitted to vault us.

'. . . and it is so much
useless talk.'
Can we form

a pact?—
some wedge to drive
beneath the feet

of the hobbyists,
the loveless.

C. G. HANZLICEK

Milkweed

I

Today we are walking
between the split shells.

Some we hit—
with fists or sticks

or with our flat hands,
to beat, not

really these sick pods
packed with silk,

but ourselves,
or others who we suspect

are taking their ease
underground, or saddled

in the grass.
Beat them for compassion!

Mad, scarred
until their lives' ends

they will remember
(hopelessly) love.

II

Bitch, today I
rummaged in a picture book,
horny for myself.

One word got through: Excuse.
A few of the rest
crawled away blind, & hid.

So when I gave up
& jacked off
(not without delicacy

or thoughts of you), those
incomprehensible remainders
like ticks & beetles

walked under the bed.
Then came, whispering
to lunch: I mean

meanings
in the sweet, pale milk.
Marry me, we

can abuse each other
skillfully. We
can beat our kids

black & starry with love
until, like white
hairs or

parachutes, their tiny
silken cries
fill up the night.

JON ANDERSON

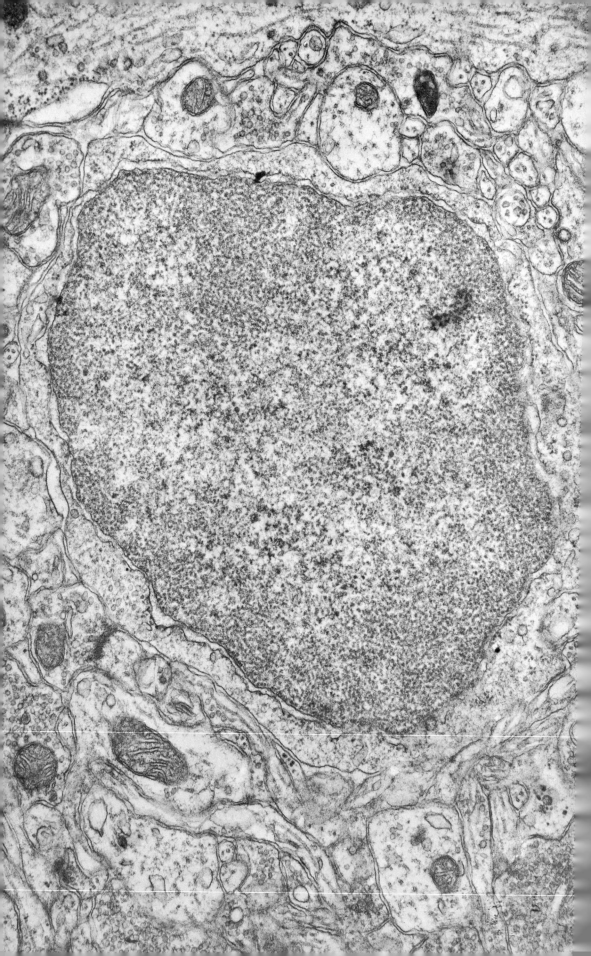

Photomicrograph of a brain cell

"The gaps between them . . . can be
jumped by the electrical
currents of nerve impulses
when chemical conditions
are proper."

       And so for weeks
I've searched for the image; at
some point each day, looked at this
photo, then returned to the
window, waiting—

       This web of
live black threads, liquid, magnified
three thousand times;

       Those branches
at the window, arthritic
and old—

       It came to me on
the bus: there *is* no metaphor
here, no sharp electric jump
over this synapse, no wind
in these branches.

ANDREA PFEIFFENBERGER

Estuary

Hear when, persona tide,
eolian wet,
redounding
in venery of likenesses

enacting puerperal song,
magenta soft,
urging quiet
in loud estrual regions

beyond thin epic sheets,
visceral liturgy
in elan of orbit
ails an hour's dominion.

R. J. WILSON

Tike's days

JONATHAN STRONG

It is raining. I have my own room. There is no windowshade. The trees outside are shaking. My radiator steams. The cold weather is coming. I am sitting in my chair with my bare feet on the desk. Papers are all over the desk. I am wearing jeans and a sweatshirt. My other clothes are in a pile on the closet floor. The sheets on the bed have not been changed. McDog is asleep under the bed.

I have a good victrola. The speaker on the bookshelf is aimed down at me. The one on the floor is tilted up. My records are all over the floor. I could spend my days like this. I am listening to *Siegfried*. I can imagine the boy and the dragon as if dragons existed. In modern productions they use lighting effects for the dragon, but I would prefer a regular dragon that I could see. In this rain I can imagine him poking his head through my window and singing to me in English instead of German and calling me by my name, which is Timon Larkin, Tike for short. I am twenty-one. I have not finished college, though I started it. If I do finish I do not know what I will do then.

I stop *Siegfried* at the end of Act Two. McDog has crawled from under the bed and gone to his favorite place in the fireplace. He barks when there is thunder. I feel like going outside. I throw McDog a cracker, a thing I do when I leave him alone, and without putting on my shoes I leave the room.

No one is in the hall. I do not know anyone in this building. I have lived here three weeks. I imagine the other tenants would like to smash my victrola and strangle my dog for all the noise I make, but I have heard nothing from them. When I step into the hall I always think what a grand waste of space it is. There was a lot of ceremony in old buildings. I would rather live here than in the concrete buildings across the street. There is no mail for me. It is the first time I have been down today. I open the front door.

The wind which puffs at me is still a warm wind, probably the year's last. The rain is colder. My feet on the wet steps are very cold. The lights in the windows and the lights of cars make the street warmer. It will be very cold and dark when I come home from work tonight.

I am walking slowly on the sidewalk. I do not know anyone here. I will not be walking barefoot outside again until Spring. My feet are numb. I want to take off my sweatshirt. I do take it off. My skin is immediately wet. My jeans are wet and heavy. The wind makes me warm, but the rain makes me shiver. My mind feels very clear. I think of going back to the room and wrapping up in blankets and listening to Act Three. I turn around.

It is a quiet neighborhood. There is no one to notice me walking in the rain without a shirt. Most people in this town would look twice if they saw me, but most people would not see me in the first place. The trees shake and drip. The street is entirely shaded by trees. It is a lovely place. I stand on the steps of my building and look back at the street. My hair is tangled and wet in my face.

I am climbing the first flight. The door at the top opens. It is too late to put on my sweatshirt. She has seen me. The door closes. I hear two girls talking behind it. Their last names are on the door, Wood and Ehrhardt. I do not know their first names. They work during the day. I climb the second flight.

My room is warm. My teeth are chattering. I am turning red from the warmth and the embarrassment. McDog looks at me from the fireplace, wags his tail, and stretches. He steps down from the hearth and comes to my feet. I pull off my wet jeans. I am naked. I dry myself with a dirty towel. I try to untangle my hair and comb it out. It is long and light brown. I turn on the victrola. There are four sides of *Siegfried* to listen to.

I pull a blanket from the bed and wrap it around me. My body is brown with a white stripe around the middle where my swimsuit was. I spent the summer on the beaches before I came here. I am about to put the needle on side seven, but I hear a whisper in hall. There is a knock on my door. McDog barks and wags his tail. He runs to the door sniffing and barking. It is the first knock he has heard in our new room. I wrap the blanket tighter, but I am excited. I am naked under the blanket. McDog stops barking when I give him a cracker. I open the door a crack and say, "Who is it?"

"Hi, Tike," is the reply. "We finally got a glimpse of you." She is smiling and friendly. The other one is silent and stands behind in a shadow. I open the door a little.

"You must be Wood and Ehrhardt," I say smiling. "How did you know my name?"

"We see your letters," she says. "It was all we knew about you until this evening."

"And now you know I run around in the rain and answer the door in a blanket."

"You've made yourself very intriguing," she says. I cannot see her face clearly. There are no lights in the hall on my floor.

"Is your name really Tike?" she asks.

"Timon."

"But everyone calls you Tike."

"Yes."

"You're in school here."

"No. I work at the library in the evenings reshelving books."

"That doesn't sound exactly fascinating," she says. "We decided you must be a music student."

"No. I don't know anything about music. I like to listen to it, that's all. I know I play it too loud."

"Not if you like Wagner," she says. McDog has finished his cracker and pokes his head between my bare feet.

"Do you?" I ask.

"Not at all," she says. "Don't worry about it. We're either at work or asleep when you play the damn thing. It doesn't bother us. So that's the dog. I knew it was a Scottie by its yip. We were taking bets whether it was black or white."

"Did you win?"

"No," she says. "Sophy did. She said it was black."

"He's so cute," I hear Sophy say quietly. She means the dog. If the other one had said it I would have been sure she meant me. She seems the sort who lets you know what she wants. I do not know whether to open the door and ask them in or ask them to come back later. My face must be very red. I am very excited under the blanket. I think she wants me. I want to see her face.

"Let me take a bet which of you is Wood and which is Ehrhardt," I say.

"All right."

178

"Well, I would say, since you don't like Wagner, you must be Wood, because Ehrhardt sounds German and Germans like Wagner. How's that?"

"Absolutely wrong. It's Sophy Wood and Valeska Ehrhardt, and I am German, though I detest Wagner. Call me Val for short."

"But you don't have an accent," I say.

"No, I don't. I have a good ear," says Val.

"Would you both like to come in?"

"You're not exactly dressed for company, are you, Tike? But I don't mind," she says.

"Oh, Val," says Sophy quietly. "I'd better check the dinner. It's almost ready."

"Maybe he'll join us," says Val.

"There isn't enough, I'm afraid," says Sophy. "How about tomorrow instead?"

"You'll come eat with us tomorrow, Tike?" says Val.

"Yes, thanks." Sophy goes downstairs. I have not seen her at all.

Val says, "Can I come in?"

"Certainly."

"Your room is a mess," she says. She closes the door after her. She is beautiful. Her hair is blond and long. Her face is delicate. I wrap the blanket tighter around me. She looks around the room noticing the titles of my books, the records I have, and the empty cracker boxes. "Whatever do you eat!" she says. I watch her closely. She is wearing a light dress with flowers on it. It is very short. It twirls as she walks around the room. It is exciting to see a girl with very feminine clothes. Heavy, square clothes do not excite me. A girl should be pretty and light. The skirt should float across her thighs and puff out and sink with the wind. She picks up an open jar of peanut butter and shakes her head at me. She puts it down and smiles. McDog has stopped wagging and sniffing and is back in the fireplace watching the girl closely. "Is it a boy?" she asks.

"The dog?"

"Yes, of course. I know what you are," she says.

"Yes, it's a boy."

"You are nineteen," Val says.

"No, I'm twenty-one."

"I was sure you were nineteen. I'm twenty-three. And I teach school."

"High school?"

"Yes. Boys." She smiles and giggles. "German is a very popular subject this year."

"I don't understand why you don't like Wagner."

"Let's not talk about smart things, Tike, please," says Val. "When I

179

saw you coming up the stairs this evening I was very happy."

I sit on my chair and pull my legs under me. I hold the blanket tight. "Why?" I ask.

"Because it was nice to see. You don't find it sexy at all, do you. You were just thinking how nice the rain was." She sits on the bed. She crosses her legs. I watch her knees. "I am jumping to the conclusion I am hoping is true," she says.

She does not say anything more. I do not say anything. I look at the record albums on the floor: Mahler, Wagner, Richard Strauss. I think of *Der Rosenkavalier,* the mood it has of gentle and tender expectation.

"Your dog is rather goofy," says Val.

"I know."

"You have had him a long time."

"Three years. Since he was born."

"He has gone everywhere with you."

"Yes. I got him the first year at college. When I quit, he came home with me. When I left home, he came along. We spent the summer on the beaches."

"You're shivering, Tike," she says.

"I shouldn't go out in the rain. I'll get sick."

"We'll take care of you," she says. Her calves are rubbing together. She is wearing slippers. They fall off at the heel. Her legs are very long and tan. "You're going to work tonight," she says.

"Yes."

"Whatever will you wear?"

"I'll drag something out of the pile."

"That stinking pile on the closet floor?" She laughs and leans back on her elbows. She has round breasts, and the material of her dress is thin. I feel more relaxed. I let my legs hang down to the floor outside the blanket.

"Your legs aren't very hairy, are they," she says.

"I guess not."

"I was sure you were nineteen."

"I'm not. I'm twenty-one."

"I'm glad," she says. "Where are you from, Tike?"

"Kansas City. Didn't you see the postmarks?"

She laughs. "We forgot the postmarks," she says. "Why did you come to Chicago?"

"I like it more than Kansas City."

"Kansas City, Kansas, or Kansas City, Missouri?"

"Guess, Val."

"Missouri, of course," she says.

180

"Bad guess. I'm from Kansas." She has stopped smiling. She looks at me with her light blue eyes. She is very warm. She puts her finger in the jar of peanut butter and scoops out a mouthful.

"I would live on peanut butter if I lived alone, Tike. It's Sophy who plans the meals. I would die if someone didn't take care of me." She looks away. She looks out the window. It is still raining.

I reach my arm out of the blanket and bend over to pick up *Der Rosenkavalier*. The blanket slips off my shoulder. I leave it where it has slipped. "Do you like this?" I ask.

"Now there you have something," she says. "I love it. Hofmannsthal was a poet after all. And Strauss really has more of Mozart than of Wagner. You must play me some of it sometime, the presentation of the rose scene. Das ist ja bezaubernd schön! But stop it, Valeska, we weren't going to talk about smart things."

She stands up and walks toward my chair. She puts her hand on my shoulder. We look at each other. Her hand feels my bare shoulder. My hand is on her left knee. It is on her thigh. Her lips shiver. She forms two quiet words with them. "Sanft," she says. "Zart." She turns away. Her skirt twirls. I imagine all of her. She is at the door. She is gone.

Poem — thirteen lines

I pull the beard of my birth, it mumbles,
dodders off. Whiskers sprout on my grave,
which grows old without me. Only this poem has
a memory of me. For a while. While I'm writing it.
The white columns of Greece stroll by not even nodding.
Remember me? I flew too near my life and caught fire.
I am your somersault son. Soon as I lie down,
my eyes burn down through my brain, out the back of my head,
through the bed, floor, house, earth, the blind universe. . . .
Flesh inlaid with hypnotics flows by.
I cower beneath my resurrections. Angels
in formaldehyde, remember me!
Remember this effigy burning the real.

SAINT GERAUD

181

Patch in the Dutch boy's britches

SYLVIA WILKINSON

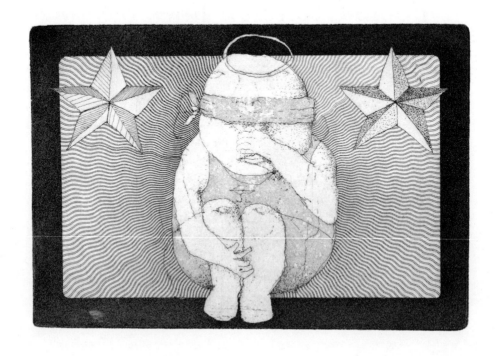

The day my roommate left school, she was sniffing and crying. It seems like she was always sniffing, even when she didn't have tears in her eyes, and for a while I got the whole room to myself. I couldn't talk to her or help her because everytime I would ask her what she was afraid of, she would get mad or say something dumb like "things, mean scary things." She told me she saw things coming up out of graves when the lights were turned off in the room. I don't think she had ever seen a real grave. I didn't tell her I'd seen a lot of graves, and that what was really scary was that people *didn't* come out of graves. Once they were there, you never saw them again, and you just had to try to remember them, what they did when they were alive, going places with you, things that weren't important then; they only became important when they were dead. Dead people are in little bits in your mind and the longer time goes on, the more you forget their voices or their faces. Sometimes I think if I don't try real hard to remember people right now that they will disappear forever. Even away from Miss Liz for just a few months, though I know she is alive, this happens to my memory of her unless I paint her. I don't see how anyone could be afraid of what's in graves, dead and rotten things. The people never really come back, even in thoughts and paintings, good or bad people, not really. I have this thought at night some-times, that what would really be better, better than any of the faces and voices that I try to remember and to paint, would be a rabbit or a puppy like I had once. They died too, but with animals you get another one and get used to it and love it just as much; it's different than with people. Cecie would say I was too old to talk like that, if I told her what I wanted, but I bet Miss Liz would have something in a box for me by the time I woke up the next morning.

Before we left the farm Miss Liz handed me a package wrapped in newspaper, and all the way back Aunt Cecie was waiting for me to open it, so she could see what it was, but I didn't have to open it because I knew what it was. Miss Liz had made me a big piece of soap like I asked for, to do a carving with, and until we got ready to leave I thought she had forgotten.

I get my wood carving tools and a nail file and put them on the floor of my closet. My flashlight is already in there, where I read at night, and now all I need is a towel to put under the door crack. I stick my pillow under the covers and cut off the lights, just in case Cecie looks in the door. After I get in the closet and close the door, I stuff the towel in the crack and then flick on my flashlight. I had better wad up the newspaper and put it out of the way so there won't be any noise.

The soap is almost completely smooth and white. There are only a few dark spots that show in here, though there may be more in the light outside. Miss Liz said she never could make a perfect piece of soap. I usually worry a lot about the first cut I make into something like this; it's so different from clay where you can stick it back on if you slip. But I already see the little white slivers start to fall on the floor, small, like cut fingernails as I carve at first, but larger soon as I get more nerve. I am going to work only on one side, so if I mess up I can always turn the soap around. Pretty soon I have the little round shape that I wanted. It is the shape of my little bird and though I haven't carved hands for it to sit in yet, there seem to be hands under it. Rough ugly hands though, as rough as the real little bird's feathers were. But I am going to make him smooth like a grown bird, only the size of a little baby, make him like he could tuck and fold all his feathers down smooth just like Mrs. Stile's white chickens. When I smooth the soap, making little grooves for feathers, it gets warm and sticky in my hands.

My hands stop moving as I hear my door crack open. Cecie is looking in my room to see if I'm in my bed. I feel my heart start going fast, because I don't know if I really made it look like I was in the bed. If she looks and sees it is only my pillow, then I'll have to tell her I'm in here and why. I watch the door to the closet. Oh, how awful if the light is showing under the door. But I can't cut off the flashlight because if she should hear the clicking sound and open the closet door, I would have no place to go. I do not move and make no noise, yet I cannot hear any noise on the outside. Cecie would think it was foolish to be in here and not to wait until tomorrow to do it. Then the door to my room shuts, and I wait a moment until I hear her footsteps in the hall and the door to her room opening.

I look back at the soap, and it doesn't seem so white now. My flashlight is getting weak, that's why. It fades almost out, and glows and fades again. I shake the batteries in the case and the light seems to get a little brighter. As I look at my own hands in the light, I try to make the hands under the bird match them, but my own hands are covered with the dark ridges of my veins, and they get darker and tighter as I work on the soap. I would like to carve my little bird in the soap and keep him to sit on my dresser beside my statue of Miss Liz. If I can carve him good, then I'll always be able to remember him even after he grows up and Miss Liz has to turn him loose.

It is quiet outside now. I look at the hands in the soap under the little bird a long time; I look at them until I see they are like an old man's hands, like Dummy's hands drawing a tear on his face, making a moustache, hiding his eyes and peeping through his fingers, with the bright yellow fingernails. It's Dummy who wants to hold the little bird, so soft and little, and he is afraid to close his hands around it to feel it, afraid he might hurt it. He is afraid someone will take it away from him. I start to carve Dummy's face in the soap that is above the bird. I will make it look the same as his face, only it will be in the white soap. And I will look at his face in white and know where the dark speckles are and will know the color of the shag of his hair. Soon I have the face. It is his face but with his eyes hollow and white, like a Greek statue, staring at me like eyes but just as white as the rest of his face. I put the soap in the corner of the closet and look at it for a long time with the light of the flashlight moving over the surface. In the hands is the little bird, the little bird is still there below the face of Dummy, and Dummy's old hands are holding the bird up. But I have done something all wrong, something is the matter, there was not enough soap for that. I have ruined the soap. I have carved it too soon and ruined it. The little bird is smooth and the face is jagged like flint rock and they do not go together and the hands should not be there. I have ruined the soap and will not get another piece like it for a long time. I should have waited. I shouldn't have carved it when I was tired. I remember Dummy, that isn't what is wrong. I can see him, eyes like blue flowers when Miss Liz said "died," hair yellow like broom straw only dull yellow, persimmon stains, blood, and Dummy playing dead in the field—all colors and the soap is white. I wanted him to see how pretty the bird was, to let him hold it. His blue eyes aren't there and he is afraid, afraid to hold the bird in Miss Liz's soap.

It was Cecie's fault, coming to my door. I don't want to see it in the morning when there is light; Cecie ought to leave me alone. I put my head down on the floor of the closet for I am getting very sleepy, and pull my furry bedroom slippers under my face. I cut out the flashlight and for a moment the white soap glows in the dark. Miss Liz would use it to wash with. She used all of Papa's little animals to wash with. If she were here now, she would. She wouldn't believe me if I said it was ruined because she cared nothing about the little animals Papa made; to her it would still be soap and just as good as ever because it could be used to wash with. And I could never tell her I carved Dummy's face; if I told her that, she would be glad I ruined it.

Suddenly my closet door pops and starts to move open. I jump to my feet and a coat hanger crashes to the floor behind me. But there is no one opening the door; I am alone in the room. I hear footsteps in the hall and I run to my bed and get under the covers. The footsteps go by my door when I slide between the cold slick sheets of a fresh-made bed, and I hear Cecie shut the window at the end of the hall.

On the edge of my bureau across the room, I see my statue that I made a long time ago, the one of Miss Liz carved in wood. The wood was dark and smooth and I could see the grain run through it and feel it with my fingers. I remember the knife, how I was afraid to touch it with my knife the first time, and I waited and tried three times before I could make myself cut it. And tonight I ruined my white soap. So stupid to do it in my closet the first day I had the soap. I ruined it trying to carve Dummy, trying to carve that dirty Dummy. Dummy of all different colors, in a white piece of soap. And the little bird—making my bird all smooth with feathers instead of the rough and prickly little thing I left with Miss Liz—my bird was ugly, not smooth and white. Miss Liz, she made the soap for me, and I tried to carve Dummy in it. I tried to carve Dummy's face as it would be if he was holding a warm little bird, and Miss Liz helped me ruin it. She would take it and wash with it until the big piece of white soap was nothing but foam and bubbles. She would be so angry with me if she knew I had carved him, and let him hold the little bird, like he held the chicken. She would have beat him with that wooden spoon.

Across the room I see the square of light, the window shade over the street lamp and moonlight outside, and as the sheets begin to get warm with me, I can slide my feet down further. I hear the tadpoles still smacking slowly at the top of the water, and before I close my eyes, I look at the window. It is almost a warm feeling, the square of light like the sun, breaking through the clouds after a rain, or is it the first patch of blue on a gray day, and Papa says:

"Yonder it is! Yonder's the patch in the Dutch boy's britches!"

And I hear the wind outside hitting the tree, thumping the branches on my window, sucking them away and thumping again, and the wind will slowly break the gray sky away until it will all be blue, as blue as the patch in the Dutch boy's britches, and the wind will blow the water in and crash the waves and spread white foam along the sand.

I saw Papa last night. And it wasn't just a dream, I am sure that part of it was real. Before, when I remembered Papa alive, I saw mainly his clothes, the denim of his overalls, wet when he was holding Maylean, or I saw his hands nailing up the sign on the crib, or his feet stomping the copperhead. This time I saw a face, a real face on Papa that was more than just a moustache the color of straw. In fact I saw two faces—I will explain it.

When I have seen him before, it always seemed that someone was laughing at him, always Miss Liz was laughing; and Papa's face was way up above me where I couldn't see it. Once when Miss Liz moved the bed and didn't tell Papa, he went in the room in the dark and jumped in it like he always did, and it wasn't there. They'd poke fun at him about it, and I thought he might get mad because he had knocked his breath out bad and had broken his false teeth, but he just laughed instead. I guess Papa never really got mad and said anything cross to anyone. At least I didn't think I remembered him being mad, that is until last night in the dream. I remember his face that time. It was when we were at the ocean, so I know it really happened, Papa was already an old man and had never seen the ocean. Miss Liz and I hadn't seen it either but I remember way back then having to beg her to lock up the house and leave, to please let us all go just for one afternoon, when Aunt Cecie and Uncle June said they would drive us down one Sunday.

When we got there I walked out with Papa, up over the high banks of sand. I had never seen the ground glare so brightly, and the sand was hot as it rose around my feet. That was when Papa said to me, "That's a poor-looking dirt to have all them oats a growing in it. Look at them seeds on them, Ramie. Twice as big as a rye pod."

The sea oats scratched and thumped against his pants when he walked across the sand, like they were trying to beat his thin legs from under him. Papa was walking so fast I couldn't keep up. Finally he stopped and lifted me up on his shoulders when I got a spur in my toe, up where I could see his face in the white glare of the sun, as shiny as my cake of soap with his eyes behind his white lashes. The sky got bluer as the wind blew the clouds further into the land, and Papa's eyes behind the white lashes were like the blue sky behind the clouds, the patch in the Dutch boy's britches. Soon I was up where I could see over the hills of sand, and when I was looking at the blue water and the blue sky out in front of me, Papa stopped walking and said,

"I declare. I declare, Ramie, there ain't no end to be seen. There is water clean to the sky with no other side there a'tall." He said that over and over, "no other side there a'tall."

I don't know if he stopped talking then or if I just couldn't hear him for the sound of the water coming in. He walked down to the edge with me still on his shoulders and he got closer and closer to the water until the waves were breaking and hitting his shoes and getting his pants legs wet. He wobbled in the water like a skinny tree in the wind, and I held to the top of his head for fear I would fall. I guess it would have been Papa who would have fallen, not me, but I felt like someone had tossed me into the air and if he forgot to snatch me back, I would be sucked away in the wind.

Then I heard them hollering, Aunt Cecie and Uncle June and most of all, Miss Liz, and I turned to see them dark against the white sand, swirling and looking almost like tops where the heat rose around them. Papa went walking back until soon only a thin little shoot of water reached out and sucked at his wet shoes, and I moved with him, still on his shoulders.

"Just look at you," Miss Liz said, "soaking wet and with your shoes on to boot. Acting like you ain't got good sense." Papa set me down then.

As I felt the ground under my feet again, I saw that his Sunday pants were dark and wet and his shoes all stuck up with sand.

"Look at that, Lizzie," he said from above me. "Look at that water just sucking in and out and bubbling whitelike. Why it looks like it could just reach out and grab you."

"I see it and I ain't going near it. You taking that child out there! Why it could just snatch her away from you in a minute!"

Papa acted like he didn't even hear her. "And look at them little birds just running in and out and a pecking up grubs like they could outrun the devil! Water right over their heads, just a smashing down, meaning to get them . . . and zip . . . they ain't there no more!"

As we watched the little birds run in and out with the waves, Papa laughed and said to me, "You see them, Ramie? I declare I ain't even seen one of them get wet; just teasing that water to beat the band."

He stooped and picked up a tiny little pair of shells that was opened like a lavender butterfly. He said, "Ramie, do you reckon that there is two of every one of these on the ground, that here somewhere every one of these little covers has got another side, but only the Lord above knows for sure where it is?"

And he spoke more of the shell in his hand; he closed the butterfly up into a little empty case and said how pretty it was just to be a dead thing . . . that is when it happened, when he was speaking of the shell and how many of them must have died for that many shells to be on the beach.

"We are going home. I'm not a mind to stay another minute. We have seen it and we are going home," Miss Liz said and turned her back. I saw the shell Papa was holding fall from his hand in little pieces and hit the ground beside me. I looked upward at his face. It was bowed down, and in the sun Papa who always looked golden and shiny like ripe grain had turned dark. He did not move when Miss Liz started across the sand with Cecie and June. He just stood with his face in that shadow, until this strange feeling had drained away from his hands and face, and he could follow them back across the sand.

I think that what I saw in Papa's face, though I never saw it again, had to be put away somewhere inside of him and kept with him until he was dead, because he never had any way to put it outside. And what he said, the words I could not understand then, but could feel go cold inside me when I heard them: "There is some things you can't whip, Lizzie. There is some things in this world that won't stand for you to whip them and they will wait, Lizzie. They will wait and take you in time."

When I was walking with Papa back to the car, I saw in my mind then, when I was a little girl, Miss Liz beating on a lion, which was the biggest

188

animal I could think of; Miss Liz with a stick beating on a lion and it was growing bigger each time she hit it, but she wouldn't stop beating. Her face drew up tight and the three pins in her hair came loose and it all fell down, gray and stringy and wet looking. Her hair got wilder and wilder until I could barely see her eyes shining through it, getting wilder each time she hit the lion. Soon the lion was so big her stick was just a twig and she seemed as tiny as my wood statue of her. Then the lion smiled and ate her. I started crying on Papa's lap when the lion ate her, and though they thought I was crying because we left the ocean so soon, I never told them different.

But the funny thing is, this part of my dream last night was different, different from what really happened that day at the beach. In the dream I didn't think of the lion, in the dream we never went to the car. The water came a long way up the shore, sucking at our feet and pulling the sand from under us, making us wobble a little each time. I turned and saw one of the little birds running from the water. But it fell, it fell and rolled over and over as the foam pulled it into the ocean. And I saw it rolling and rolling and getting larger, until I saw it wasn't really a bird after all. It was a person. Just before I woke up, I saw the face of the person rolling in the white foam, the face of Miss Liz as she was pulled out into the water, and I turned to look beside me on the sand and Miss Liz was gone.

Memo from the cave

O love, you airtight bird,
My mouse-brown
Alibis hang upside-down
Above the pegboard
With its dangled pots
I don't have chickens for;
My lies are crawling on the floor
Like families but their larvae will not

Leave this nest. I've let
Despair bed
Down in your stead
And wet
Our quilted cover
So the rot-
scent of its pussy-foot-
ing fingers lingers, when it's over.

LOUISE GLUCK

189

Poem in 5 parts

I

We live in mirrors but don't look in them.
Or else they are kaleidoscopes of
Denial, maybe boredom, terror
I don't know
This is imagination at its worst
A meager sift of snow
While telephone rings really
Urgent bells occupy the livingroom.

The time came for us a moving out ceremony.

II

The mood is there
A kind of fierce animal
Tight fur, implacable
Snide eyes, knowing
Its own power.

Clocks waited around us, our hands
On the arm of phones, knob
Of doors.

III

To see yourself is to make faces,
To be able to open to other's making faces,
the games you hate or fear grow real.

Let us be.

IV

Then it was summer
And the heat makes us sweat.
We move our time outdoors.
In offices they plot vacations.

Kyrie eleison
Hello willows
Go easy on those I love.

V

For him the car waited
Impatiently in the driveway.

He kissed me, but he was leaving so I leaped
Away and danced across the grass in the dark
And he came
After me, we ran
Away and together my laughter rang
All round me, jumped
Out of my belly
It was a water balloon
and burst, making rainbows
Like a lawn sprinkler
Out of moonlight.

KAREN HANSON

The creature on page thirteen

The creature spread on page thirteen
Is nothing to me. She wears black lace briefs, holds
An intellectual magazine,
And is self-consciously puffing an Old Gold.
A wrinkled pair of white boots and dense streams
Of tangled black hair cover her extremes.

On pages fourteen and fifteen
She is raised from the revolving stool to lie
On the bar where she is better seen.
Like a salesman showing gadgets I might buy.
In eight pictures she drops a dozen eggs,
Rearranges her nest and spreads her legs.

On sixteen they tell us her name
Is Cleopatra. Personally, I believe
It. Her prop here is a coke held firm
Between her teeth. We're told how she likes to live,
What she likes to read and eat. This creature,
On each page, gives you a different picture.

The photograph on page eighteen
(Suggested gifts for men this year) represents
The alternates—collector's items
Composed in just that way, presents
Irresistible, bound to please—for sure.
I write for the name of my nearest store.

WALTER HALL

The mixture

I am a mixture of feelings without beginning
or ending,
a pinch of this,
    a pinch of that.

I'm a horse with an army in my belly
and a rowboat.

Open your fist, you garbage collector,
I know that smile you are hiding
isn't really a smile
. . . it's a shoehorn.

It's a shoehorn that jumps the puddle
and lands in the lake.
     I am that lake
that is leaking all over your rug.

Simplicity is my motto.
For simplicity is the most complicated way I know
of expressing
    complications.

I go down to the corner *groceria*
to buy a can of soup.

(Chicken vegetable.)

But the *groceria* is closed.

Up, up. Up over the airmail stamp
and into the shoptalk
and into the neon
and into the cream.

Violins become newsprint
and noses
turn to roses.

. . . I can't decide which I would rather be,
an orchestra or a streetlight.

   JOHN PERREAULT

A royal visit T. VOSS

At sundown the gates of the city of H. . . were always closed and locked, and the key was brought to the governor by a sentinel. The governor, who had a reputation for politeness, always thanked the sentinel and placed the key in a leather sack which hung from a leather band around his wrist, as had been the custom with the monks who used to inhabit H. . . before they renounced their celibacy and thereby their right to be monks. The locking of the gates was always accompanied by the howling of the sentinel-dogs, who knew that they were about to be released from their kennel to roam the ramparts of H. . . all night and frighten off the panthers, which frequently forced their way into the city. The sentinels could control the number of panthers which broke into the city on any given night by increasing or decreasing the number of sentinel-dogs which they released from the kennel. The panthers lived in large numbers on the slopes surrounding H. . . . When they forced their way into the city it was generally the sick who fell victim to them, for the sick were always placed in the streets until they recovered or until they died.

A domestic conflict of some importance existed between the sentinels and the artists with respect to the sick. It was the duty of the sentinels to kill the panthers with their automatic pistols. Since it was the sick who attracted the panthers in the first place, the probabilities of a sentinel's killing a panther on any given night were increased if the particular sick person which the panther was attacking was dead or had died during the night before the panther attacked him. The sentinels had noticed that a sick person tended to struggle, albeit feebly, with an attacking panther even if previously he had been too weak to so much as nod his head or wink his eye. A panther seemed to be more alert to his environment if a sick person resisted, and often a panther which was attacking a struggling sick person would turn on the sentinel who was approaching with his automatic pistol for the kill—and the sentinel himself would become the victim of the panther despite his weapon and shrieking for help. On the other hand, a panther which was attacking a dead sick person seemed to lose contact with its environment: so up to the ears in pleasure did it find itself that its sense of taste dominated all the others and it never heard or smelled an approaching sentinel.

The artists disagreed with the sentinels with respect to the absolute value of dead sick persons. Whereas the sentinels would have left the dead sick to mortify in the streets even if they had died during the day, the artists argued that, first of all, the dead sick made inferior subjects for their paintings because, as had been demonstrated time and time again in practical experience, no one in the metropolis forty miles away had ever purchased a painting of a dead sick person, as such a painting was not only esthetically unpleasing but also such a painting never depicted any form of suffering or anguish on the face of the subject but, on the contrary, only peacefully relaxed features; and, secondly, the artists claimed that the stench of a mortifying sick person, caused by the combination of a torrid climate and myriad unclassified microorganisms, not only precluded any serious concentration and made one's brush quiver at every breath but also limited the proximity at which a given artist could paint a given sick person; for an artist had been known to sit in a sick person's lap for more than an hour if it meant catching in detail every line of suffering in the sick person's face.

Having heard these arguments of the artists the most clever of the sentinels evolved another argument for their side: that if too few panthers were killed, this meant that too few panther pelts could be supplied to the caravans, which always arrived in the morning, thus limiting the number of camels that the cameleers would allow to be shorn of their hair by the children of the artists as compensation for the panther pelts, thus limiting the number of camel's hair brushes which could be produced by the wives of the artists, thus limiting the number of paintings which the artists could produce, thus limiting the income of the whole city, which was dependent on the barterers and their skill in haggling when they traded the paintings of the artists, later sold in the metropolis by the cameleers, for the essentials which the caravans brought with them, such as food, fuel, and even water, of which H . . . had no independent supply.

196

Since the artists had run out of arguments, they issued a manifesto which enumerated their esthetic principles and also affirmed their loyalty to H . . ., only occasionally taking short ironic jabs and thrusts at the sentinels, never calling them by name, however, but rather using such clauses as, "Those who would have us allow the sick to rot in the streets. . ." or, "Those who are inconsiderate enough of sensitive natures to think that. . . ."

This manifesto was signed by all the artists, except those who were sick, and presented to the governor.

The governor not only had a reputation for being polite but also for being wise. Clearly this was a case in which a compromise would have to be effected. And although this was the first he had heard of the conflict, for he usually spent all of his waking, as well as all of his sleeping, hours in his office-mansion signing documents, for which purpose he employed three secretaries working around the clock to assist him (muffled typing could be heard at all hours emanating from his outer offices), he took swift action and presented the manifesto to the Diet, permitting one representative from each side to speak for fifteen minutes in order to describe and otherwise justify the cause which he represented; and he further allowed a fifteen minute period of debate between the artist-representative and the sentinel-representative in which they directly came to terms with each other; so, as it turned out, the Diet was not needed at all, and the artist and the sentinel arrived at a compromise which served their mutual interests, such that a maximum of ten sick persons who died during the day could legally be left in the streets until dawn the next day if, and only if, the sentinels took care to pile the ten dead persons in a certain designated area, one on top of another, in as compact a body as possible, until sunset at which time they could be separated and redistributed. The sentinels readily agreed to these conditions because the panthers never forced their way into H . . . in the day time and also because they sympathized with the artists' sensibilities more than they admitted.

In the morning a sentinel would always go to the governor's mansion and fetch the key to the gates, and when these were unlocked the day officially began. Outside a caravan always awaited the unlocking of the gates, and if the cameleers thought the sentinel was especially late a great commotion would be heard inside the gates, which intensified the longer the sentinel delayed. When the gates were finally opened after a long delay, the cameleers would tumble through, sometimes five abreast, even though the gates were wide enough for only three camels abreast, and in this way a rather weak or diminutive camel was occasionally squeezed or trampled to death amidst a swirling cloud of thick dust. The cameleers knew that these deaths were their own fault but they always blamed the sentinel and thereby would avoid, as compensation for the camel, paying part of the heavy tax which

197

was arbitrarily levied upon their goods, since no system of taxation had ever been codified by the Diet.

Immediately the barterers would begin trading panther pelts with the cameleers, sometimes before they had even dismounted, and the children of the artists stood ready with their scissors to shear the camels' hair, which was necessary if the artists were to have brushes. An expert artist could produce three paintings per day, and the barterers always collected as many goods as possible from the cameleers for the paintings of the sick, since they too were experts. The paintings were titled according to the particular disease, if known, which the sick person had contracted. Thus, paintings were called such things as, "Coup de Soleil," "Morbus Gallicus," "Proud Flesh," "Gutta Serena," and the like, and always signed, not with the name of the artist, but with a large H.... In this way the city of H... had won its fame.

The sentinels and the cameleers talked with each other a great deal during the day, for the sentinels were always curious about the various intrigues and goings-on in the metropolis from which the caravans came. It happened that one day during one of these conversations one of the cameleers chanced to tell one of the sentinels in passing that the Prince of the metropolis had decided to pay a personal visit to all the cities in the area and that, of course, H... would be foremost on the Prince's list not only because H... was so famous but also because the governor of H... was the son of the Prince's closest adviser without whose counsel and guidance the Prince would long ago have lost power.

This news the sentinel found extremely exciting because the last royal visit had occurred so long ago that only his grandfather remembered it, and even though he had been a small boy at the time, still he vividly recalled all the pomp and ceremony which had attended the last royal visitor. As fast as his legs would carry him the sentinel ran to the governor's mansion and, after transmitting his news to the secretary on the first shift, he was admitted to the governor's inner office where the governor was sedulously signing documents and attaching the Great Seal of the City of H... beside his signature. In the most formal manner that the sentinel could affect he related what he had just learned in conversation with the cameleers, who all knew of the Prince's imminent visit and the honor and fame such a visit would bring to H.... The governor leaned back in his swivel chair as he had seen his father do many times, drummed the top of his head with his finger tips, signed another document, and then politely thanked the sentinel for his information and his quickness of thought, after which the sentinel was excused.

After attaching the Great Seal of the City of H... to the document

198

he had just signed, the governor made his way to the hall in which the Diet was always in session. Striding to the podium he rapped his gavel for silence and then said: "I have just been informed by messenger of a great honor which will soon be bestowed upon our humble city: a visit from the Prince!" At this announcement there were many cheers and much applause in the hall. "It seems to me," the governor continued when the cheering had died down, "that the Prince should be received with all the pomp and ceremony which is his due, considering his importance and position. But also—and I think you will all agree with me in this—would it not be a good thing if the city were made as presentable as possible in honor of the Prince?" The Diet agreed with the governor's suggestion, and so a Purgation Committee was appointed. The Purgation Committee would meet all day and all night and in the morning it would make recommendations which would be summarily passed upon by the Diet, for no one knew what moment the Prince might choose to make his visit.

As he walked back to his mansion it struck the governor that it would be a good idea if a representative of H . . . journeyed to the metropolis to ascertain when the Prince planned to visit H . . . . In this way everyone would know how much time he had to complete whatever project he was engaged in in preparation for the Prince. As it was, however, no one in the city of H . . ., including the governor, knew exactly where the metropolis was located, and this for three reasons: first, no one, in the past, had ever needed to know where the metropolis was located; the governor could attest to the fact that it did exist somewhere forty miles away, since he had lived there as a child, and this was enough for the citizens of H . . . because they trusted the governor implicitly in such matters and because they assumed that the caravans came from the metropolis, for where else could they come from? Secondly, for as far back as anyone could remember, no citizen of H . . . had ventured outside the city gates; for, according to the religion of H . . ., as long as one was inside the city one was under the protection and in the sanctuary of the Great Sentinel; but if one went outside the city gates, one ran the risk of being devoured by the Great Panther. This was demonstrated every night, *mutatis mutandis,* by the fact that the panthers were themselves protected by the Great Panther outside the city—none had ever been killed outside the city—but once inside the city they forfeited their protection and were on their own, usually to be killed by a sentinel wielding an automatic pistol. Thirdly, none of the cameleers would permit anyone from H . . . to travel with him to the metropolis because if he did so, he ran the risk of being mistaken by the Great Panther for a citizen of H . . . and being devoured indiscriminately along with his traveling companion.

199

Here, indeed, was a dilemma. But the governor had already made his decision: he called for the sentinel who had originally imparted the information about the Prince's visit to him and told the sentinel that he would have to follow the caravan, at a great distance, of course, but keeping it within view, until it arrived at the metropolis, at which time he would make inquiries about the arrival of the Prince and after which he would return with a caravan departing the metropolis on its way to H. . . . The sentinel, although he believed in his heart of hearts that this was an insane course of action and undoubtedly would result in his death in the jaws of the Great Panther, nevertheless acquiesced because he decided it would be better to die for H. . . gloriously, firing his automatic pistol at the Great Panther, than to be ignominiously executed by his fellow sentinels for refusing to comply with an executive order. And so at sundown, just before the gates were closed and locked, the governor stood on the ramparts of H. . . watching the caravan snake its way from the city and watching the sentinel follow at a great distance; and all the citizens of H. . . and the governor were very relieved when the Great Panther did not come pounding down the slopes to devour the lone sentinel shrieking in his tracks, even though, as far as the governor could remember from his childhood, the metropolis lay in a direction opposite to that taken by the caravan.

The next morning the Purgation Committee was ready to present its recommendations, and they were these: that the sentinels clean and polish their weapons every day until they shone like new and that they polish their boots until they could see their faces reflected in them; that the artists wash their feet every day and that they wear smocks so that their shirts would not become stained with paint, and that they button their shirts all the way to the top; that the children should all get haircuts and clean the rust from their scissors every night by soaking them in paint thinner; that the wives of the artists should stay indoors whenever possible; and that all the sick should be removed from the public streets and placed in a special building until after the Prince had come and gone. Each of these recommendations was passed into law, to be in effect that very day.

When the artists and the sentinels heard that the sick were to be removed from the streets and placed in a special building until after the Prince had come and gone they could not believe their ears. Some of them wandered about the streets as if they had been struck on the back of the head with a blunt object; some of them pulled out their hair and stamped their feet until they were surrounded by swirling clouds of thick dust; some of them fainted dead away; but most of them marched to the hall in which the Diet met to protest. But their protests fell on deaf ears. For example, one of the artists who protested that he would have nothing to paint because

200

the building to which the sick had been removed—the only one large enough and available at the time—had no windows and therefore no natural light, was told to paint something else, like his wife or his child or his house or the sentinels or another artist or, for that matter, himself. When one of the sentinels protested that there would be no more panthers to kill because the sick, who attracted them, were no longer out in the open, he was told to lie in the street himself, as if he were sick, and wait for a panther to come. "There is no alternative," was what the Diet said to the artists and the sentinels.

So the artists began to paint each other painting each other, even though they were no longer as inspired as they had been when painting the sick. And the sentinels lay down in the streets at sunset, but the panthers came in smaller and smaller numbers when they discovered how quickly they were killed and how desperately a decoy sentinel fought for his life if he was caught napping and awoke to find himself smothered by a snarling panther with bared fangs and flashing eyes. And, furthermore, the artists began to run short of brushes because the cameleers would no longer allow the children to shear their camels without compensation, and the wives of the artists had nothing to do; and the cameleers kept returning the paintings that the artists had made because no one in the metropolis wanted to buy a painting of a healthy artist, and the barterers had nothing to do; and the people went hungry because the cameleers began to inspect the paintings and would no longer trade goods for them and even threatened not to come to H..., and the sentinels had nothing to do.

And then one day at dawn when the sentinel opened the gates of H... there was no caravan waiting outside, and he became delirious and ran up and down the streets of H... shouting at the top of his lungs that there was no caravan outside and everyone was going to starve to death—he himself had not eaten for a whole week—and finally he became so deranged that he ran through the gates and out into the desert where he was instantly devoured by the Great Panther in full view of all the citizens of H... except for the governor, who was in his office signing documents.

Fractions
ANDREW FIELD

for Michele

"Not bein' an author, I'm a gr-reat critic."
—Finley Peter Dunne

"You will not understand my thoughts
until you grasp the fact that neither you
nor I . . . no one in the world is empowered to arrange human life as he
wishes and to repay thereby those who
in our opinion have acted badly. That
we are not empowered in this way is
evident from the way in which we wish
to do one thing, but something quite
different occurs. The one thing to which
we do have a calling and that does lie
within our power is to live out our lives
well."   —Leo Tolstoy

"Rotten," the Baron said.

"Tory, come read that story to me!"

Tory turned from the window and, tightening her bathrobe, strode to
the bed with a vague and sleepy, somehow ambiguous smile. Then, undoing
the just-tied robe, she flipped its back up over the bedboard where it spread
out evenly like a flowered cape in flight; it still covered and warmed her
arms and breasts.

"Here." She took the coffee from Dirk, and her face relaxing at the first
taste of its bitterness (Tory's favorite fruit was the lemon, and she habitually
sucked them by the half, much to Dirk's discomfiture) she placed the cup
and saucer on the night table from which she took the thin manuscript in its
styrene folder.

203

She sat silently scanning and flipping the pages of the little short story, and it seemed that by just a glance at the pages, a sentence here, a word there, she had taken its full and adequate measure like one of those inscrutable judges at a dog show who judges a full line of show animals without breaking stride.

"*Room on the River.* Hmmmmm. It appears that our Dicky hasn't yet finished with his State Department jaunt to Eastern Europe, Dirk. This little gem is set in Moscow, and I'll bet it has even more Slavic thung than that one about the Bulgarian poetess, remember?"

It had begun most promisingly, and both could see that they would have an interesting evening.

"Hey, Tory, why don't you give the guy a chance? You haven't even read the thing yet. And besides your husband *is* writing a book on Upjohn, and *The Bulgarian Poetess did* win an O. Henry Award."

"Yeh, and I'll betcha he won the Bulgarian poetess. . ."

"OK, shut up and read—I don't stand a chance if you get yourself this wound up before you even start."

Tory shifted slightly in her place, hunched her knees up, and pulled the covers in around her legs. Then she took another long sip of coffee, and began.

"Oh good, Dirk, I see that it's got an *epigraph!* writers who use epigraphs are so . . . so literary, don't you think? Only one this time though. Tolstoy. Remember the time he had three, Stevens, Barth, and Pascal?" She laughed with abandon and shook her beautiful red hair to the side to look at Dirk quizzically. He leaned over and kissed her long and intently. "Later, later, I haven't even begun yet."

"Lots of young writers use them. Why should you hold that against Upjohn? The epigraph can be very important, and some of Upjohn's are quite interesting, too."

"And almost every last one of them comes straight from Bartlett's. This one, too, I'll wager."

"Well, let's have it."

" 'One must always remember about love that it is a concept which one must either accept or reject. And if one recognizes the grace and necessity of love, then one must accept love in all its forms . . .' Dot, dot, dot: note that especially now. That means that it's been yanked out of context from somewhere, and Tolstoy's love is most certainly of quite a different hue than your Mr. Upjohn's. It really is somewhat banal."

"What, Tolstoy or Upjohn?"

Tory laughed again and brushed his cheek. "Love, of course, birdie.

This excerpt forms chapter three of Andrew Field's forthcoming novel, *Fractions.*

The Tolstoy probably is as well, but we have only a fraction of it, so we can't very well judge it."

"Why not, you've already judged the story."

"Well I might. We've been through all that. It's admirable enough to earn one's living by the pen, but there's a price to be paid, and in his case it's these little four and five page stories, poignant episodes with elaborate poetic filigree. A guy meets a divorcée at a party. A husband sees a friend kissing his wife through a kitchen window. I have nothing against our age, but I really do think that they told that sort of thing better in the nineteenth century. Doesn't Guy de Maupassant have a story that begins, 'Love had fallen over him like a net'?"

"Yes, but I think that the man meets the woman in the sentence before."

"Too bad. Nothing's more important than the opening sentence. I remember a de Maupassant story with perfect opening and closing lines from college. It began 'Great tragedies don't bother me much,' and ended 'No doubt you will find all this ridiculous.' What was in between wasn't quite as good though." She drew a sudden breath. "Oh dear, we can't very well talk about *that* in connection with this gem. It's got a Samuel Morse opening, and the closing sentence is simply silly beyond belief."

"Which means that what's in between might be pretty good, right? Please do get on with it, Tory." She took another breath, of deep resignation.

"In Moscow it is no simple matter for a young couple to arrange a night together. Especially if one of them is an African."

"The riverboat *Gogol* left its Moscow pier at seven sharp, twenty minutes late. Its smudge-green hulk squatted over the water. The lower deck, partially enclosed by glass panels, threatened fitfully to touch the water's surface. The *Gogol*, née *Stalin* (still discernible on the port side), moved with surprising speed and a perceptible roll. Some years ago the boat had run aground near Voronezh, damaging her keel, and, perhaps because of the boat's namesake (it was changed only in 1956), it was improperly repaired. But the boat's captain, Ivan Korneichuk, gradually grew fond of her eccentric course and would declare, after a second vodka, that the *Gogol's* roll made the ship easier to navigate. How, he never said.

"Everything about the *Gogol* was pleasing to Lyuba. It was not her first boat, and it was certainly not even the best boat she had been on, but it was her first private room. Cabin 40. Two metal spring chairs—they have chairs like that at Sochi, she recalled—and a roughly made-up iron bed bolted to the deck, with a faded tomato throw-on. The wooden walls were painted green, a kissing cousin, doubtless, of the color which formed the boat's outer attire. Before the walls had been a pitch-like mahogany color which here and there had successfully resisted both the scraper and the brush. A speckled, micaceous mirror was perched high in one corner almost where, in another century, an icon might have hung. Lyuba at that moment was looking down absently at her freshly polished flats, which, if one squinted hard, reflected the semblance of two half-faces, and her auburn hair, her warm brown brows, and the sharply drawn isoceles triangle of her nose were framed in the mirror in what was, in fact, an icon. The bed on which Lyuba was sitting . . ." Tory paused and reached out for her coffee. "Just a minute, birdie," she said into her cup as she drained the dregs. "The bed on which Lyuba was sitting occupied the entire wall opposite the cabin door; the spring chairs faced one another from the other walls. Lyuba, trying now to find her smile in her shoes, thought of how a couple might sit in the two chairs talking aimlessly, while the bed, duenna-temptress, waited beneath its tomato cover."

Dirk had rolled over onto his left side and scrunched the pillow up under his head. He reached out and stabbed at the button that turned off the thin beam of light on his side of the bed. The blinds of the other bedroom window were tilted at a forty-five degree angle, and they reflected light from outside, mainly, judging by the undulation, the beer sign. Tory read on, and Dirk let his eyes run along each slat as she read as though he were following the text.

"The door opened, and Olorun appeared with four tortes on one plate and two glasses of coffee with lemon slices, perched precariously against each other, on another. He raised one foot to cross the slightly elevated portal as the *Gogol* reached the apogee of its starboard roll and began to descend while his leg was coming down. There was a moment, less really, of crystal decision. The worth of the tortes was a ruble four kopecks, while the coffee . . . the glasses flew out in a low trajectory, retaining all the while their contents, and burst with a delicately explosive tinkling sound at the base of the wall under the bed, slightly to the side of Lyuba. A tide of coffee edged forward, and, with a new roll of the boat, fell back again and then emptied into the space along the edge of the floor, dripping down onto the wall of the cabin on the deck below where a Rostov kolkhoz official and his Moscow companion failed to notice its hesitant, branching descent. Beneath the bed the glasses were now a jagged, translucent mountain range in a fragrant mist of coffee behind which a lemon moon rose precariously. In the foreground, plate of tortes still in hand, sprawled Olorun, polar bear fashion, his wide grin revealing a set of squarish, perfectly even teeth."

Tory put aside the manuscript and reached for her empty cup which she handed to Dirk. "I didn't know they served coffee with lemon in Russia. Where did we get it from?"

"That Serbian couple, the friends of Bob, who were going to Canada to do something with a mining company, remember? It was about two years

206

ago." Dirk swung his legs over the side of the bed and headed towards the kitchen with the little thermos pitcher. "I seem to recall that they said the custom was brought to Yugoslavia by the Turks, and it probably went to Russia from there. I read an interesting article last week that traced playing card names on a squiggly path across Europe in the fifteenth century, and then used that to make certain speculative corrections in accepted trade routes. I wonder if. . ." But Tory was no longer listening to Dirk in the kitchen. She was plunging ahead in *Room on the River,* and she finished the story just as Dirk returned with the filled thermos and two new cups on a small teak tray. Holding the tray with his left hand, Dirk crouched down and with his right hand carefully removed the two empty cups and saucers and placed them on the floor beside the bed. As he did so his left hand holding the tray with the pitcher and two full cups rose above his head, and his exaggerated version of the classic waiter's way of carrying a tray, on five fingertips, caused his cargo suddenly to slip precipitously to one side.

"DIRK!!!" But it was too late. One cup hit the edge of the tray, and the downward angle and force of the collision were just barely enough to tip the fulcrum and send one cup and its contents spilling onto Dirk's side of the bed. Some peppery hot splatterings hit Tory's exposed buttock and sent her vaulting from the bed cursing unreservedly. Dirk quickly set down the tray with its unspilled cup and pitcher on the night table and began to strip the bed with its sprawling stain, like some sort of shameful body emission, still steaming vigorously. Without a word Tory went off to the toilet leaving Dirk to do the work. When she came back in a few minutes the bed had a new pad and crisply fresh sheets on it. Petulantly Tory tried to give Dirk the story to read himself, but he at last coaxed her into resuming.

"I'm really sorry that I'm so hopelessly clumsy, darling, but you will admit that it was a nice instance of life imitating art."

"I admit nothing, and I haven't the slightest interest in such arch ideas. . . Now where was I? Imagined conversation. Complexion. No, here it is—the African is spread out on the deck."

"His abundant head of hair formed a semi-circle which had been trimmed with the attention given usually only to a beard or moustache. Along the hairline of his forehead, there was a slight protruding rounded edge which produced the rather startling effect of a sculptured hat. Lyuba, when she first met Olorun at a Friendship Dance at Lumumba, had had an overwhelming urge to touch it, to see if it followed the contour of his head. His complexion was a fine umber which for all its paleness bespoke pure Yoruba blood. His most remarkable feature, however, was his magnificent nose. Its gently sculptured surface rolled and dipped, it seemed, across his entire face, striving in vain to outdistance his boundless grin. As he laughed his nostrils flexed rhythmically and sensually.

"Lyuba also laughed, quietly and quickly, echoing the glass, and still sitting on the bed, she extended a hand to the stretched-out Olorun who took it gingerly in his giant hand and rose without using it for support. Then he gracefully raised the hand to his lips, kissed it lightly, and turned and sat down in one of the spring chairs. It lowered with a wrenching screech to within a hand's reach of the deck. Lyuba got up and sat in the chair opposite him.

" 'And what will you do to amuse me next, my friend?' she asked, laughing affectedly.

" 'Let me tell,' he said, and the Russian vowels tumbled out strangely, melodically over his foreign lips, 'let me tell you about how we live in the trees all year long in Nigeria, and how we swing from limb to limb, wife to wife. The bananas are free, and so are we.' Now Olorun leaned forward laughing, and his enchanted nostrils entered upon a fresh choreography. It was their private conversation, for she had once asked him questions very much like that.

" 'Why look at all those English suits in your closet, and that typewriter, and that radio. You weren't telling me the truth downstairs at all!'

" 'You see, it's not so bad in the trees, and when you come to visit us, you'll live in a tree, too.'

"She leaned forward and touched his knees. 'I love you, Olorun.'

" 'You love my curly hair,' he teased.

" 'Yes, I do.'

" 'You see, and my chocolate skin.'

" 'But most of all, I love the way you spill the coffee.' "

"Judas Priest!" Dirk cut in rather loudly, and Tory looked at him and wrinkled her forehead slightly. "This must be Upjohn's weakest story of all time, Tory. It's rotten. I know that *Atheneum* hasn't yet turned back one of these little doodles, but don't you think Jenny Lincoln ought to speak to him about this thing?"

"I rather *like* his story, if you don't mind." (Now it was Dirk's turn to be surprised.) "Wait a minute, birdie, and see if you don't warm up to it."

"I thought you said that you hadn't read it."

"I hadn't, but I was reading ahead while you were in the kitchen. Just wait a minute." She started in again, but by now her voice, through having read ahead and her decision that she did like the story, was smooth and rich, and her breathing was almost professionally controlled.

" 'But most of all, I love the way you spill the coffee.'

" 'You are funny, little Lyuba. Tonight you will love me in other ways,

208

too, but, you see, you must let me get fresh coffee to go with your tortes.'

"She made a movement of her lips, but Olorun was already up and on his way out of the cabin. All Africans were like that, so much more polite than Russian boys.

"Alone, she crossed her arms, and, with a steady pull, she slid her heavyknit tan sweater up. She paused with arms outstretched to press her face against the wool and, with her head thrown back, slowly breathed in her own sweat as though she were draining a cup. She tossed the sweater at a chair and deftly undid the buttons of her skirt and blouse. With her hands extracting the clips from her hair, her tongue—a Slavic trick—clicked off her thoughts, a private abacus.

"Olorun strolled along the deck. Couples lined the rail. In Russia commerce runs East and West; rivers flow North and South. Another African, with a girl not as pretty as his, walked towards him, and Olorun nodded recognition to the dark stranger. Over the heads of the couples the lights of country dachas clustered together in spots. The river quiet was filled by a melancholy singer whose voice seemed always about to break but never did."

"There's some sort of Russian line here. *Zabeaty nyeshneeye lobzaneeyah.* Or something to that effect anyway. We'll have to check on that, because Upjohn sure as hell doesn't know Russian. I think something like that should be done in a very careful transcription with stress marks or italics. These must be the English words to that song."

" *'See how the wind scatters the leaves in Autumn splendor.'* " Tory began to improvise a pseudo-Slavic doleful melody, but Dirk reached out and gently put his fingers on her lips, and she cut short her burlesque. " *'How old memories of past love lose their meaning, are swept away by the flow of time.'*

"From time to time another passenger would join in for a few bars and then, again, fall to listening. Olorun allowed his thoughts to sway with the boat and then to arc out beyond the dark shore with the melody. It was far from the Kaduna.

"He turned into the hatch and went below deck to get the coffee. There was, as he expected, a long line at the snack bar. The air was a mixture of heat and breath and, from the toilets, urine. The glass was fogged. As he looked about him Olorun counted one, two, three. . . four, five. . . six. . . seven heads of unevenly dyed auburn hair. Behind the counter an old woman, wearing a soiled linen kerchief tied around her head and a flat blue smock, tugged away at the handles of an Italian espresso machine. Her concentration, regular movements, and the bursts of steam which issued from the apparatus might have led one to think that the old woman somehow played a vital role in the navigation of the *Gogol.* Of the people coming into the snack bar, perhaps two-thirds went to the end of the ill-defined line. The other African whom Olorun had passed came up to him and gave him the money for two coffees and two tortes. He went away and joined his girlfriend without saying anything else to him. Olorun smiled and took the money. The line, like all Russian lines, shifted imperceptibly towards the counter.

"In the cabin Lyuba had already eaten one torte and was standing in her bra and pants regarding herself in the speckled mirror. She hitched in her stomach a bit, and, her arms making wings behind her back, she unhooked the brassiere, a new bright blue satin one. She bent down to her pocketbook at the foot of one of the chairs and pulled out a small vial of *Red Star* perfume which she spread lightly and quickly over her breasts and then, throwing her loosened hair forward, more liberally at the base of her neck and behind her ears. A fragrant wave spread outwards from her, and soon it had enveloped all the diverse smells of the cabin which had mingled together freely and independently a few moments before.

"Lyuba hurried, for soon Olorun would be returning with the coffee. She put the *Red Star* back in her pocketbook and drew out a tightly rolled up rayon bundle. It was a hideously purplish nightgown, also new. She spread it out and shook it several times to remove the wrinkles, stirring up a fresh ebullience of perfume. She quickly slipped the nightgown over her head, smoothed it down, and adjusted the strap on one shoulder.

"Tense with excitement now. . ."

"Hold the phone, Comrade. Comrade Yarborough wants to go to the john before the sex starts."

"OK, but pour me another cup of coffee before you go, will you? And I'd like a fresh slice of lemon."

"I'll have to go the kitchen for that. Let me have your cup, *ma lectrice*." Dirk kissed her as he took it, and Tory's warmth and the anticipation of the as yet unread sexual scene aroused him to the point of considering momentarily the possibility of making love to her again. But only momentarily, for he did have to go to the john, and he did want to hear the rest of the story. After he had brought her the lemon, Tory got out of bed and went to the kitchen to turn off the light that Dirk had left on. As she came back to bed, she could hear Dirk urinating loudly. She winced and turned her head away. He always left the door ajar and pissed directly into the water rather than onto the side of the bowl.

"Now then. On with the show. I wonder which one this will be, lyrical or electric." He smiled to himself and began reading the blind slats again.

"Tense with excitement now, she pulled back the tomato throw-on and the top cover of the bed. Lyuba recoiled abruptly and stared down in disbelief. The sheets were unspeakably soiled. A mural of brownish, almost

210

excremental stains lay before her, and in her mind she saw the scores of previous travelers in Cabin 40. They stretched down the river, hovering above it, a fetid human fog. 'Her cabin.' A small fist clenched tightly in her chest. She saw the night before her. Sadness smothered the excitement within her, and she felt again the cabin's unpleasant dampness.

"Outside the cabin Olorun stood for a moment carefully balancing the coffee glasses in one hand while he reached for the door handle with the other. Inside the cabin the stains on the sheet grew darker before her eyes, swirling in sinister configurations. Lyuba shivered, but then her eyebrows lifted her face into a smile. As the door began to open, she shivered and, making the sign of the hammer and sickle over her chest, dived into the bed." Tory stopped reading, and there was a protracted silence.

"And that's *all?*" Dirk, who had been half listening to Tory and half letting his mind wander into college and a certain boat trip he had once taken around Manhattan with a young lady about whom he often wondered and whose eye had stopped midway through one of the uppermost of the illumined slats, sat bolt upright in bed and started at Tory in disbelief.

Tory, who had put down the story and was finishing her (which, good reader?) cup of coffee, looked at her husband with mild amusement. "Why what ever more did you *want,* birdie?" Sides had been taken, and the play was about to begin.

"In the first place, it's so out of character for Upjohn. His characters always screw, sometimes in the very first paragraph, but certainly before the end of the story." Tory started to speak, but Dirk cut her off with a gesture of his hand. "No, don't interrupt, I'm on quite firm ground here. Of eighty-nine short stories there is screwing in all but nine, and in many of those cases there are extenuating circumstances such as the age or physical condition of the characters. Remember that story where, after the bad car crash on a lonely country road, the guy falls onto and eventually screws the girl he was driving home from the party even though she had evidently been partially paralyzed? But even beyond that, I've calculated that in eighty-three percent of the chapters of his nine novels, someone either screws or gets screwed."

"That's very much one and the same thing, don't you think? I mean it's not something one ordinarily does by oneself. Unless you mean to use the concept in both its figurative and actual senses. You know, someone gets screwed and so doesn't get screwed."

"To which I suppose I ought to say, screw you."

"But you just did, dear, you just did. Don't you remember?" Gay little fireflies danced in her eyes. "It is a most interesting impersonal expression though. It's clearly pejorative, and so it must have intimations of, if not rape, at least strong reluctance and be implicitly directed at a feminine object. But

I've often heard men say it to other men or in reference to other men. Odd. Very odd. Almost as odd as 'make love'."

"Most of the cultures and languages I know anything about use various ingenious references to one's mother in such situations. I think we're the only ones who somehow contrive to make the act itself, divorced from any circumstances or particular people, an ill omen. The Portuguese, I know, simply say: Your Mother, as though any further elaboration on that declaration was quite superfluous. And subtle refinements may be added by changing the case." He pulled open his night table drawer, got out a pad and pencil, and scribbled a hurried note to himself. "I think there may be a damn interesting piece in that. I wonder if we couldn't get someone like Pidgeon or Prescott to write about it. I also wonder if you aren't trying to get off the hook."

"Nonsense. The actual screwing would just spoil the whole thing. This way everything is perfectly prefigured, and no further action is necessary or desirable. It's the essential, reduced fraction as it stands."

Dirk had been preparing to defend the story, but its abrupt, unexpected ending and Tory's unusual opinion (or was it merely a strategem?) had forced him into a position he neither wanted nor was fully prepared to defend. All the same, he was willing to accept the challenge, and, after treading water for just a moment ("Well that, I'd say, depends upon how one chooses to look at the thing"), he quickly marshaled a basic plan of attack and had, for starters, two promising diversionary skirmishes in mind.

"In the first place, the story as it stands isn't really a story at all—it's a preamble to a story in which some coffee is spilt and some more is gotten. The actors have just made their entrance and not even reached center stage yet, when—zap!—down comes the curtain. The one who really gets screwed is the reader. I'll wager this is just the first few pages of an abandoned work. To pay for a trip or a new hi-fi or something."

Tory extended her arms out in front of her and crossed her slender fingers carefully to make a trellis, through which, as she brought her hands closer to her face, she neatly framed the curious lithograph, an orange and yellow circle of tangled limbs, neckties, and brassieres around a perfectly blank center, that was hanging on the wall opposite their bed. Carefully she turned her fingers so that the garland was eclipsed, and she could see only the large grayish central portion of the picture which in normal light was bright white.

While her attention is so fixed, looking through that blank to something we cannot see, we may profitably seize the moment to project Victoria Yarborough's visage onto that unused portion of art paper as the artist might

212

have drawn her had he been present in the bedroom then. The line and taper of her nose, the fall and perfect rise of her chin, the thin restraint of her lips, all of this produced the effect of almost classical tapered New England beauty as sketched by Ingres in the nineteenth century. But as is frequently the case with redheads, her sumptuous hair, now copper, now orange, which was casually twirled together into two interlocking buns (at that moment, however, her hair had half fallen, and this added an element of wildness to her refined beauty), dominated her face, and its pale beauty was almost an afterthought or appendage that was required, but not really credited in any way except in its impudent absence at odd moments and turns of the head. Shadows seemed to be more important on her translucent face than the features which gave rise to them. Most important of all were the free form shadows which began at the highest point of her cheeks and formed two perfectly similar pendulate shapes, as though the shadows really were a permanent feature of her face, in no way dependent on light. The shadows said dolor, or perhaps it was just the natural weariness of not quite natural, long held beauty. Dolor concolorous with tomorrow's yesterday. . . .

Her bra size was 34B. One of her feet—but I forgot which, and it doesn't really matter anyway—was slightly larger than the other. She weighted 118 pounds, stood 5′8″ in her bare feet, had a delicate little garden of pimples in the least accessible part of her back, and with her hair down and head tossing there was something positively equine about her. 5,923 miles away, in the city of Kalinin, a girl, whose shadows and certain features were remarkably like those of Victoria Yarborough, tossed her hair out, and it was also red, but the heavy and deep reddish auburn of a badly made and then fashionable hair coloring. She began to brush it vigorously with a cloudy plastic brush, and individual strands on the uppermost surface of her hair were given static life and curled and danced like snakes in the electric field. *Her* shadows were real and deep, not at all ornaments. But she, too, was beautiful. She brushed and brushed and thought of the pointless but sweet affair, lasting only three days, hardly an "affair" at all, that she had had with the visiting foreign poet several months before. All she had was a dull, dotted picture from *Nedelya* that made him look like one of those idiotic cosmonauts, that and a poem scrawled in pencil in a language which, save for two words (one of them misspelled), she could not read:

> **Tongue without sonance, sun without sky,**
> **Worn but unknown syllables to try.**
> **Still free, unhaunted by slow shadows,**
> **It runs from lower bounds,**
> **Falls up, over, out of sounds.**

Slipping through a turn of red it goes
Sliding down a narrow smile,
Hiding again in the silence of certainty.
And yet I spelled you properly by guile,
And all your letters were neatly drawn by me:
Cheek and nose before hair except after eye and heart.
What a strange, soft, silent mirror that I hold!
No, let it stay unsaid, unspoilt. Nothing need be told.
And you, Любовь **must die, for still you are put part** мая

She had acquired a little English grammar with the intention making herself able to read the poem, but the first sentence, and especially the fifth line with its profusion of prepositions, had been quite confusing, and she decided finally that it would be the more beautiful for remaining mysterious and unread. Various things she had heard and read about him subsequently, as well as the velvety French in which he had conversed with her (actually, it was far from perfect), were enough to support this supposition. The poem was an unpublished one, but, except for its last line which had been altered very slightly, the poem had been written about another young lady several years before.

Tory undid her finger trellis, and, bending her fingers outward till they cracked (at which Dirk made a low whispering noise of muted displeasure), she let a smile and a yawn struggle on her face.

"Oh, birdie, *must* you throw my own discarded arguments back at me? I hope that he gets a very nice hi-fi or trip or whatever he wants, but that really has nothing at all to do with the quality of the story. It's a beautiful story because it's a perfectly chosen moment that supplies its own pre- and post-narrative course, and absolutely nothing else need be given."

"Nothing? And what, if I may ask, does your sure sense tell you this Olorun character is going to do with the fresh coffee when he comes into the cabin? Set it down and leap into the bunk with Lyuba? Make her get out of bed and drink it with him first?"

"There's no problem. *You* know. They'll make love first and have the coffee and tortes afterwards. Even we've done that."

"Ah, but we've got a thermos pitcher."

"And lukewarm coffee can be very good sometimes."

"I've got a little list. . ."

". . . which never will be missed."

"As I was saying, I've got a little list of probable errors and sure ho-kinesses. How has he spelled 'kolkhoz'?"

"K-o-l-k-h-o-s."

"Wrong. It should be with a 'z.' "

214

"And that, dear adversary, is quite irrelevant. Upjohn's failure to spell properly, in his own much less other languages, is a constant. His best things and his biggest mistakes share that, and if you follow that line far enough your book will be stillborn."

"Don't try to pass under the question, Tory. If you can find enough tiny faults, the main structure itself soon begins to acquire a jerrybuilt. . ."

"For want of a shoe."

"Pre-cisely. The most disconcerting item by far is the inept way in which he handles maritime terminology. Beds. Doors. That's very lame. I can't speak for the African's name, but the way his complexion is described he sure as hell ain't Yoruba. And I don't think the Kaduna runs through Yoruba country. This story's creeping with things like that. Another thing—his thrusts towards pointless symbolism really puzzle me: the boat's name, the years, the espresso machine, the boat's roll. I wonder if large operative boats really do that."

Tory scratched her chest nonchalantly. "Maybe they don't, but one of your favorite Upjohn stories, *Four Sides of One Story,* has a boat with a 'goodly roll' just like this one, and I don't recall that you took exception to that. Remember the 'quivering Daiquiris' and the 'thrashing water' in the swimming pool?"

The tide of battle had shifted.

"Well yes, but that was an ocean-going craft, whereas this is a river boat."

The gentle and patient smirk of triumph broke through and lit up Victoria's face. "Ah, but the point, the point, I do believe that you've missed the point of the whole story, dear husband." She paused, and Dirk said nothing. *"Room on the River* isn't about screwing, Russian river boats, African students in the Soviet Union, or the amatory habits of young Russian girls.

"Room on the River is really about balance and the unnoticed but essential equilibrium at the heart of all Upjohn's best works—*The Catcher in the Rye, The Centaur, Fathers, Grace and Combat, Seymour, New Axis, Rabbit, Run*—oh lots of them."

Dirk still said nothing, but he got up from the bed and strode into the darkened living room where there was a box of English cigarettes kept (neither of them smoked as a rule) largely for company. He took one, lit it, and inhaled deeply. Then he went back to the bedroom. Tory stuck out her lower lip in a childish pout which gave it unreal fullness. "Aren't you going to offer your wife one, too?" Dirk turned on his heel and went obediently back for another.

Tory took her cigarette, which Dirk had lit for her in the living room, and blew a sharp stream of smoke through her nostrils. The high intensity bedlamp, very near her right nostril, gave a rather demonic air to her at that moment.

"Where do you see that in *Rabbit, Run?*"

"The first scene's as good as any—the poise and perfect balance of that swish shot when Rabbit comes into the kids' basketball game. And do you remember a certain sentence in the last paragraph of the novel?"

"You mean the 'Runs. Ah—runs.'?"

"No, just a little before that. 'This illusion trips him.' *Rabbit, Run* is about balance and harmony and its failure. Remember how Eccles suddenly realizes that the thing that makes Harry unsteady is what is at the root of all the problems?' But it's even clearer in some of his other things. Just keep track of how various characters cross and fold their legs in *The Catcher*. Phoebe sits Yogi style, and Upjohn makes a big thing of that. Holden's favorite place is the museum, because that's where things are stable and fixed, but then he almost faints, falls down when he goes there. He plays on this theme in dozens of ways. The skating, for instance. I think I know it by heart — 'You could put a skate key in my hand fifty years from now, in pitch dark, and I'd still know what it is.' "

"And that gets picked up in the semi-autobiographical *Fathers* where his father meets his mother while skating, then skates with him, and finally the young father skates with *his* daughters."

Tory affected a shrug of Gallic resignation. "Pre-cisely, as someone, I think, so wisely said. Rabbit runs, and Buddy is 'the Fastest Boy Runner in the World.' In *A Perfect Day for Bananafish* Seymour is horrified by his feet in the elevator."

Tory blew cinematic puffs of smoke at the tangled wreath across the room. "Now listen carefully, birdie. This is important. We're accustomed to only the Viennese variety of feet, but the Greeks knew that the soul is located there, and Mary Magdalen pays obeisance to Christ's feet. You have to pay the strictest attention to how Upjohn's characters stand, sit, cross their legs, and that's how you find out who, or how, they are. It's clearest of all in *Grace and Combat* when Grace and Rev. Combat try to pull the Bible out of each other's hands—they can become lovers because Grace draws Combat off balance and to the ground, whereas before, when he tries to draw her to him, she pushes him off and he slips into the rain-filled ditch. Now the thing that is so impressive to me about *Room on the River* is the way in which the motions of balance have been made to stand on a par with the characters themselves. I don't think Olorun and Lyuba are intended to be as important as the little allegory of fall, redemption, and ironic self-immersion. This

216

story could even be a signal that Upjohn is finally wending his way back, via Moscow, from that Far Eastern crap that louses up so many of his stories like *Franny and Zooey*."

Dirk was now all attention and had put out of his mind all the minor stylistic faults in the little story that he had been preparing to throw at Tory. Tory took a last deep drag on her cigarette, and very slowly she released the smoke directly over her head. It streamed upwards, and then it curled over like a whirling, blurred Doric column, its head gathering in size until it had attained the dimensions of a dark cloud tree. With her right hand she turned her lamp directly on the smoke, and it seemed to Tory as though the sun was at last shining through the now tranquil aftermath of some awesome, mysterious, and microcosmic conflagration or explosion. Dirk looked up at it and saw pages, curling, swirling white themes, a whole new chapter!

For want of words, he slipped out of bed, slipped on his bathrobe, and began to collect the coffee cups. As the bedroom door was closest to his side of the bed he first fetched Tory's cup, replete with lemon peel scraped bare as though by some avid rodent and, resting against it, a soggy, decayed, blackened log. Back at his own night table, Dirk removed the cup from Tory's saucer and set it down, and then he took his own cup from its saucer and in the same way got the third saucer on the floor by the edge of the bed. With these in his left hand, he carefully stacked the three cups—the little tower resembled some outrageous miniature Finnish apartment house with conical balconies—took the pitcher in his still free right hand and headed towards the kitchen.

At the doorway he stopped in mid-stride. The tower continued to wobble. In mid-stride, at the doorway, he stopped.

"Hey now, let's wait a little minute. Can't one play that game with any and all writers? Take Bellow, for instance." (Oops, a bad choice that. A long painful silence, Tory looking at Dirk with bright curiosity. Turn away, Dirk. Look toward the kitchen. There, that's better.) "Augie March's fashionably pointed shoes."

"The shoes, I believe, were his brother's, dear."

"Well, there's Gersbach's artificial leg."

"He's a brother-in-law. What about Herzog himself?"

"Herzog. Herzog. Let me think. No, I guess it's mostly elbows there. But what about elbows in Upjohn? I mean, that's literature by laundry list. Given a pencil and a pad of paper anyone can play, but surely you don't think that Upjohn himself sits down and thinks, 'Now how am I going to cross this character's legs?' And I'm sure that if you took the time you could do the same thing with Bellow, Salinger, Ellison, any of them."

"You tried with Bellow, birdie."

"Look, *I* just spilled a cup of coffee. The same way the African did. Are we Upjohn characters?"

"First, not the same way. Second, you're being arch and Borgesian, and it doesn't suit you. Go to the kitchen before you drop them a second time. The defeated clears the battlefield. That just happens to be one of the not frequent enough charming and perfect gestures in Upjohn's writing, but it will lose all that charm the minute you put it into print. Besides, you can't explain those things in words. I shouldn't have told you." She laughed loudly for her own benefit and threw herself backwards onto the mattress with the force of her own hilarity, evidently laughing at some other, private joke.

Dirk shook his head and went on into the kitchen. He edged up to the old oaken oval Vermont kitchen table and, still in darkness, set both the pitcher and the saucers and cups down at once. The tower of cups slowly leaned over, and the top one fell out of the stack and bounced sonorously (tlonng) on the table. He groped about with one hand in the air, and, failing to find it, set to flailing with both arms in slow motion. Then—he had been a small but vital six inches off the mark—his one arm finally brushed the light-cord sending it fleeing off to the other side in an upward arc where the other hand waited to leap out and apprehend it. The large kitchen was filled with fluorescent light which Dirk did not much like and which, moreover, re-minded him of *Atheneum's* editorial offices.

In previous centuries the kitchen was the center of American life, and in some rural and distant suburban parts it still is. What a shame that a country size kitchen such as very few apartments have should have been so wasted. But whether it was the fluorescent light or the ghoulish yellow ap-pliances, too much for the poor table to offset, Tory and Dirk Yarborough spent very little time there together.

He transferred the dishes to the large double steel sink and turned the hot water on at nearly full force. It hushed loudly over the dishes, and wisps of steam began to rise from the sink like ghostly aerial apple peels. Dirk held the first saucer by its edge under the hot stream, and the water opened into a fan. Just at that moment strange, inexplicable noises, like a stuffed clubchair careering down a steep staircase in lurches, could be heard above the noise of the sink. Dirk turned his head and was about to call out to Tory, but his hand moved under the faucet and he jumped back with the pain of the hot water on his thumb and index finger. The saucer fell from his fingertips and broke into three pie-shaped fractions.

With his singed hand in his mouth Dirk trotted into the bedroom where Tory, impeded by the low ceiling, was bouncing from her back into the air in a half sitting position and back again. Groans and occasional rending

218

noises issued from the bed. Tory was laughing too hard to be able to stop. Her gown, which she still had on but untied, tried in vain to enclose her but repeatedly lost her again. Dirk, who had by now completely forgotten his hand, looked at her in utter disbelief.

"Have you gone out of your *mind?!*" he finally called, almost shouted out, but he got no answer, and he suddenly recalled Tory's accounts of how she had gone through four beds while growing up. She went up in the air, and the edges of her robe started to settle in on her sides, but then, ah, she was drawn back down again, down, deep, slowly, and then, her legs cocked as stays, she pushed off again with her back and went up, up, almost, almost to the ceiling. Her laughter filled the bedroom, and it drew Dirk in. Upjohn, feet, balance, his book, all were put aside, and throwing off his own robe Dirk jumped onto the foot of the bed and began to wrestle cubbishly with Tory who changed her game without a moment's hesitation and, still gasping from laughter, began to wrestle Dirk with great earnestness. She grasped the hair on his chest, and, using the distraction furnished by his own yowl, deftly slipped her legs around his waist and applied a surprisingly effective scissors grip.

Both had begun to recover their composure somewhat now though, and their bodies straining against each other, their nakedness, and the joy of the moment led them both—a rare occurrence—to want to take their pleasure a second time that night. The artillery was raised high. The troops were infused with new energy and enthusiasm. Tory released her hold and spread her legs wide, Dirk fell upon her, and thus it came to pass that, with a cataclysmic sound of disintegration, Victoria Yarborough broke her fifth bed, the first since she was thirteen.

A garden of forked paths: *literary directions in review*

WILLIAM A. HENKIN, JR.

And whan his writing was al doon he stod
As everich man most in the eigh of God.
Chaucer—"The Scrivener's Tale"

If, as Borges believes, literature creates its own precursors, then the six books under consideration here, all by writers under 30 years of age, are as important as any literature being produced in the United States today. Besides the books' individual literary merits, each author is concerned, consciously or not, with determining those predecessors who will implicitly define the necessary evolution of new literary forms. Naturally, as the books do not create predecessors with equal success, neither are they equally concerned with their predecessor's creation.

For what literature is attempting to do in this age, as in every age, is to create workable definitions of the known and unknown in contemporary terms. This means searching out new forms and new structures for new ways of perceiving, as content only changes those guises. Contemporary terms, like contemporary men, have evolved, not sprung full-blown onto the scene.

The most striking book of this heterogeneous assortment is 18-year-old Mink Ergo's first volume of poetry.[1] Twentieth-century Rimbaldian in style, Miss Ergo's poems appear, at first, to be a highly studied form of mock-surrealism, replete with vagaries of spelling and grammatical construction.

But this form—physical as well as verbal—works with its own imagery to provide a kind of mental cushion which, rather than diminishing the total effect, increases our capacity to receive it.

In "A Fathom Unknown" the persona fights a losing battle with a rapist. Through their mutual participation in the act she comes, however unwillingly, to a terrible love for her attacker. The poem concludes:

> **Woolen whirl of stars set/ tell**
> **top my fafe . . .**
>   **Pluck! Hair**
> **by hair!**
> **Drop my threads! O my**
>   **bald**
> **head bald**
>   **head.   tear**
> **my small mouth open, cheeks**
> **split.**
>   **O**
>   **stab**
> **your waterfall kiss.**

Other poems succeed less well, frequently because Miss Ergo attempts to force painful content into wrong forms. She is capable of such dull feminisms as even masculine geniuses occasionally fall to, as in "On the Beauty of Love":

> **Daily I curse the beauty of love**
> **that eats my mental heart mad.**
> **like too close suns.**

This particular poem makes a comeback about mid-way:

> **Nothing, in this gorgeous fire**
> **remains soft long;**
> **but shrivels, recedes,**
> **implodes to death . . .**

1. Mink Ergo, *The Origin of the Species and other poems* (Middlesex, 1966), $5.00.

221

but is essentially insubstantial, and falls away to what is the soppiest ending in the book:

Current

on current off
this switch causes crazy things:

enter my vault
        eat me whole
egg out.

Yet she *can* turn such feminisms to simple, eloquent lyric, as in an earlier, somewhat narcissistic poem, "Semiaquatic weasel like animal with valuable fur: therefore":

Daily I curse the beauty of love
that eats my mental heart mad.
like too close suns. [*sic*]

This, by contrast, is a tenderness she is not afraid to face, perhaps because, dealing with herself rather than a Romantic abstraction, she must be honest.

There are, of course, moments of a different sort, when emotional outbursts appear to overcome art:

You! who (@ sch)
           c r a w l e d pro
ZAYic'ly
      out from the
      water to build

THIS!!!???!!!
Come Off
      it—

Poetry **yourselves!!**

But these are precisely the poems which revel most in their passion; and in our heyday of evolving styles, assertion of violent modes through objects of their own kind must be perceived in total context: they help to determine our *Übersicht*.

It is worth noting that no poem in the volume fits the book's title. While books of poetry have been published this way in the past, nonetheless, this particular title does lead the reader to a certain expectation which it does not, at first glance, fulfill.

Here we face the problem of creating precursors: Darwin is, after all, implied. If the title is an attempt to define the book, as titles usually are, then the implicit definition of this book ought to be an artistic evolution toward the highest forms of life. But does this refer to the artist, or her art?

222

The poems do work that way. Beginning with the elemental they progress to the figured, until the book becomes an argument in favor of the *least possible*; it asks for an art *of life* so perfect that art as we know it must become impossible. If the Hegelian arrangement seems paradoxical, Miss Ergo is prepared: she explains carefully in the book's final selection, "Title Poem":

> **As Oscar:**
> **In'my wildest love;**
> **Build there such dreams as worlds**
> **Wish they might be made of—**
> **Ha! Make men, mine,**
> **Til words cry out for them!**

"In" is the verb; and if one example of Miss Ergo's "wildest love" is her art, then we know from this how to read her.

If there is a contemporary counterpart to these poems, it lies in the best "psychedelic rock" music—the late Beatles, the Jefferson Airplane, or the Grateful Dead. Yet measured against even these approximate peers Miss Ergo's work is unique: it attempts more, probes deeper. If she fails, sometimes, to be anything but trite and adolescent in her realization of feeling, or her description of it, the area of conscious self retains control from underground. Like the *Ur-Faust,* this chthonic book perfects a neurotics of art.

In the essay form, however, Miss Ergo is not as facile. The subtleties, or tricks, of style she appeared to have mastered so well in *The Origin of the Species* get the upper hand in *Understanding Medea,*[2] and dominate most of the essays to the points of blather and incomprehensibility.

It is superb to perceive, as she does in her essay on Sophocles, that the Greek tragic statement is individual, highly conscious insistence upon affirmation in an impossibly negative situation; and that this statement is *therefore* universal at the .05 level; but it is difficult to hold in intellectual awe the author who tells you to

Split the aye f any nay @ sez YOU—Tis I knows aye cant! & struggles—AYE, STRUGGLES!—to say so loud a yea despite it sounds fr a' the whirl t' no (see/hear/ smell/taste/touch/into-it). . . .

This vision, which may still be correct, is hardly that of the detached and objective critic; nor is it liable, in this manner of presentation, to be convincing to any but the most tolerant reader.

2. Mink Ergo, *Understanding Medea* (Middlesex, 1967), $6.00, paper.

Although hers is the approach of a poet-intellectual who is under the delusion that her *vision* is meaningful to the tangible world, nonetheless the insights are genuine, and some other essays triumph less badly. In "Prometheus's Bind", the best essay in the book, Miss Ergo discusses the old question of human law in conflict with universal law. She is perfectly aware of the impossibility of reconciling the two:

To say we must love all denies ourselves. T' say we cant potentially denies everything round us. Acknowledge that we love & hate! The' forking paths're th' only solution— yet—only by perceiving truly; Tis monstrous (ipso facto) t' confuse 'em, love & hate.

She is equally aware of the necessity of eternally attempting the reconciliation:

Craft, say Prometheus, 's weaker thn need. & Y? Cause sch cosmos @ we have we make: we ball out o' th' chaos round us, thinking we do it for We Want/but ah! Brite Want, Y d' We Want if not tht we KNOW We Need??? Mirror this. . . . Th' Fates'r Man's Angelic: keep Him from being sheer beast. Both Man & th Fates develop apace cause if Man's th measure o' a' things & a' things measure Fate, th Fates'r th measure o' Man. βρεκεκεκὲξ κοὰξ κοάξ.

We are reminded of Prometheus telling the Oceanids that not even Zeus can escape that which is fated.

And, of course, in her own way Miss Ergo is attempting to speak of more than Greek tragedy. She is telling us about all art and us through herself as a human medium: and part of what we must understand if these essays are to have any but the most banal kind of scholarly massage is that they are their own medium: that there is a statement in Greek tragedy for us, only the form is different and we must find it or—to exactly the extent that it is relevant to us—perish. Such is the real purport of *Understanding Medea.*

There is something painful about this book. It is an urgent statement of tragedy, and throughout it Miss Ergo's own tragic images make it more a casebook on Mink Ergo, and by extension on her culture, than on the Greeks. For instance, the book is dedicated, "To C. (P.) and too/ To B. (F.)." The people behind the initials, we must assume, belong to Miss Ergo's personal world; but by setting off the two letters she leaves the ordinary reader with exactly the kind of adolescent précis of her book that we should expect from a terribly clever 18-year-old verbalist. To thoroughly understand the real gist of *Medea,* as representative of Greek tragedy, we must "C" our own world and "B" within it. Failure to do so is the impending tragedy of our age. "There are," Miss Ergo says in her introduction,

certain forms & statements wch Men've bothered t' make only out of thr own grate-ness: b'cause Men Didn't Make em atall they were always there: Men merely dis-

covered them. The best 'f th' clas-sicle tragedians ni less ni mo thn th best artists of any age invented only th proper Form fr their time in wch t' set sch nekked observble truths in order tht people w/ spiritual cataracts mite've some chance t' walk uprite rather thn stumble. Til u no what's about u/ y'r in constant danger 'f th' whirl.

Paxton Haskel III is in constant danger of at least the literary world: he does not know what is around him. His intellectual cataract is an *idée fixe* which, like a pair of psychedelic sunglasses, is amusing and strange to look through, but not illuminating.

Except for the last essay, this foolish book[3] ought, certainly, to be avoided. Professor Haskell has set out to find the influence of Melville on contemporary American fiction; he has been dauntless in his search. The 364 small-print body pages—there is also an introduction, as spurious as the rest—contain 74 affirmative essays, some with illustrations, discovering the Melville touch in such authors as B. Traven, Saul Bellow, Kurt Vonnegut, Jr., and Alex Austin. Sometimes, as in the Vonnegut piece, Haskell is convincing, but sketchy and trivial. We need not be told in very great detail, for instance, that *Cat's Cradle,* which begins, "Call me Jonah" derives in some way from *Moby-Dick*. We might like to know more about the relationship, but this time Haskell is content to state his position, and feels no need to follow it with a case. On the other hand, the facts of a New York setting and a resolution toward individual human *angst* in Austin's *The Blue Guitar* do not constitute an extended *Bartleby*.

In the most amusing essay, Haskell finds Bob Dylan's *Tarantula* to be a "direct dialectical throwback" to *Moby-Dick*. Ordinarily, the position would be difficult to dispute, since Dylan's book has not yet been published. (It was scheduled for 1966, but was recalled by the author.) But the logic of Haskell's discussion, which depends on Jack Arnold's film, *Tarantula* (Universal Studios, 1955), is so rife with absurdities that disputation is irrelevant.

According to Haskell, Dylan's conceptual Tarantula derives from the "scientific experiments in the film, which produce an immense, deadly example of *Lycosa tarentula*." The spider, artificially exaggerated to some six or eight feet in diameter, escapes its cage during a laboratory scuffle and roams the countryside wreaking tarantism and destruction until it is overcome. Says Haskell:

The Dylan Tarantula constitutes a totality of that universal allegorical experience discovered singularly in the sixties. Surely, as in Dylan's lyrics and poems, the primary level is the essential one; but we must not be misled by its prominence to ignore the

3. Paxton Haskell III, *The Omnipresence of Herman Melville* (University Press, 1967), $7.50.

real, underlying themes. Within the allegory this Tarantula of modern life is the wildly enlarged killer of Arnold's film. Finally sought only to be destroyed, it is yet a victim, not only of its own urges, but also of those definitions forced upon it by its creators, the man-gods of science.

Likewise, the Great White Whale is perceived as Melville's universal allegory of a century ago, only recently comprehended. It, too, is seen as "a victim of its own properties, in part, but more, a victim of Ahab's—and Melville's—intellectual impositions."

If we allow the tautologies to stand, as we must, then we need only question the premises of such an essay. Perhaps it is sufficient to see and read the originals.

But the last essay in the book is on Thomas Pynchon, and should you get so far, it is exactly what no other part of the book is: lucid, clear, scholarly, informative, and convincing.

Do not call V. *Moby-Dick*. Herbert Stencil is not Captain Ahab, Benny Profane is not Ishmael, the Whole Sick Crew is not the crew of the Pequod. But V., like the white whale, is the illusive object of a human quest which Stencil, like Ahab, makes it his life's occupation to pursue.

That is the beginning. Haskell goes on to build a surprisingly convincing case for the use of Melville, particularly *Moby-Dick, White Jacket*, and *Mardi*, as the source of Pynchon's first novel. Haskell's real point of attack is that

[Pynchon] uses the form of the quest novel to demonstrate the uselessness of that form in contemporary literature, and the characters and substance of a ridiculous quest situation to demonstrate the ineffectuality of their values and attitudes in contemporary life. In this sense, V. is a parody of the quest novel. Pynchon uses Melville's writings, especially Moby-Dick, as his principal referents because Melville's is the extreme position of the questing author in American fiction, and Moby-Dick is the extreme embodiment of the quest theme.

As evidence, Haskell offers a weight of indirect relationships: "Ishmael" approximately anagrammed to "Schlemihl" (Benny Profane); "the devious cruising Rachel" fulfilling the functions Rachel Owlglass fulfills; Cuticle's incorporation of the inanimate (from *White Jacket*) repeated in V.'s incorporation of the inanimate; Queequeg's idol Yojo foreseeing Profane's yo-yoing; Cuticle's surgical methods foreshadowing Shoenmaker's; Ploy honing his teeth as Queequeg honed his harpoon; the story of the golden-screw-in-the-navel recalling Ahab's gold coin, nailed as the navel of the ship; Benny's urinating on the sun growing from Ahab's willingness to strike the sun; Roony, like Pip, going mad into sanity by perceiving too clearly; and on and on. The number of exhibitions is staggering.

Haskell does not offer proof for his thesis: there is none unless Pynchon

226

comes out and says it is correct. But the quantity of evidence he supplies virtually eliminates the need for such proof. Haskell's contention is more than amply justified, and his conclusion is utterly apt:

Pynchon's parody also works back on itself: the concept of V. is finally of as dumb and brutish a thing as the whale; yet, in some form, it is always pursued. It is neither eternal nor ephemeral. It is simply present when Man is present, whether the Seeker looks beyond or within himself.

Why someone capable of this concluding essay should boggle so much other effort is beyond me, unless it was Haskell's intention to juxtapose this essay to the others as a final honor—gadfly or demon—and thereby create an *intimate* respect for some specific literary kind.

What is most depressing about a book like this[4] is that the author really means it: he thinks he is writing good poetry. We might hope for the respect the anti-artist offers form when he attacks it, so that we can look to improvements. But Jack Polk makes no such claims. He does not care for us, and thus owns no ties.

All the poems in *Balls* were written, we are told, during a six-month Merchant Marine stint in 1965. Because this is Polk's first foray into poetry since he "retired" to criticism in 1960, we might hope for some sort of development: we would be disappointed. The childishness he displayed at 21 has not changed a whit. He has only grown five years older, sadder, and lonelier. Unfortunately, emotion alone does not suffice to make poetry. It is also necessary to have skill with words and ideas, which Polk lacks utterly.

> **Lonely. Lonely lonely loneliness**
> **The sea spread beneath the sky is lonely**
> **the boat laying the water lays it lonely**
> **the flock of birds following the boat follows it**
> **lonely as the sun**
> **that beats the backs of my lonely mates.**
> **Everything is so fucking lonely**
> **I can't touch no one.**

This is the beginning of "100th Day" and I leave the reader to imagine the first ninety-nine.

It would be pleasant, somehow, to be able to place Polk with the New Equality writers, whose critical stand is that, according to Mahoum Yenidje, "every production is equally valid; it relies for its Truth on the initial intention, or inspiration." That is: to the degree that the instigative incident (fact, emotion, action, etc.) is of intrinsic artistic value (inspiring), so is the result. On such grounds Polk would be beyond criticism.

4. Jack Polk, *Balls* (University In Your Mail Slot, 1966), $1.45 (paper).

But he does not ally himself to the New Equality critics. In "What Emily Knew" (*Wheels,* Summer, 1964), his cover review of R. W. Campbell's *Drag Doll*, Polk says,

This is a good book. Not because of what Campbell thinks but because of how he thinks it. Think how Jet's meeting with Mitch and his association with the Marlin Modifiers and his trouble with Nick, how these things really build. It makes for real tension and Campbell definitely resolves it at the ending.

Implicitly, he denies the New Equality, since he praises development and resolution, though Polk is too much an emotive poet to force intellectualisms.

What we may have to do in order to either categorize Polk fully, or to understand him fully on his own terms, is to face such questions as he asks himself in his poems:

> **Got to go alone again**
> **next week to Memphis**
> **then to friggin Dallas**
> **then then then.**
> **Always got to go alone.**
> **Crap, who cares, who cares?**

A century ago South Africa, the setting for this novel,[5] would have functioned as the wordly or the universal metaphor against which *plot* would have developed. Mutha, the converted-cannibal turned missionary, would have represented an emerging consciousness, say, striving to relate two opposing cultures, personified by Simba, her lover, and Indio Inque, the Eastern trader-mystic. There would always have been an appropriate one-to-one relationship between the world of the novel and our own world, and however little we learned from the book, we'd have praised its effectiveness.

Today we're still Whitman's children and, we contradict ourselves, very well. Though *None of the Royal Elephants* reads like an allegory, it is rather an embellished story, baroque and gothic, constructed with such infinite care that there is *never* a relationship between what occurs inside the novel and what happens outside it.

"In Johannesburg no one saw us, but at Calcutta— the first day only the throngs already gathered wondered why we took the sacred water of the Ganges; by the second day the bathers brought their families; the third day also their friends; the fourth day their animals—pigs, chickens, sacred cows; after a week even Untouchables and city officials stared as we bathed to be blessed in unimaginably polluted water, where hairs and childrens' turds and the expected assortment of used condoms of touring Europeans and Americans formed bobbing coronae about our hot, wet, emissive bodies. . . ."

We know, by now, that everything *is* possible, once our imaginations

5. Foster Harris, *None of the Royal Elephants* (Baas/Standard, 1967), $3.95.

have acknowledged it, and frequently before. The passage just quoted is from a drug-induced dream sequence: yet every character in the novel, including the third person narrator, assumes the reality of the experience to be true on a tangible plane.

> **"I am lying to you," Popoff said.**
> **"Yes," Mutha said, "you are. I'm sorry you don't know how little."**

What are we to make of this? The end of the end of the novel? We strive in art as in anything else for a balance of power which will check none but the incapacitating extremes. Yet, when the center path and the most innocuous edges have been worn beyond use, we must force new ones in any area that will open to us.

None of the Royal Elephants is, then, a parable in action: a novel which has nothing whatsoever to do with art but which implies, maybe accidentally, by its existence, a Theory of the Novel.

> **"Ha, ha, ha," thought Celine. " I'm glad I have my period," she said.**
> **"You love him?" asked Mutha, surprised.**
> **"My great-grandfather on my father's side was stoned to death for infidelity by the people of his own town; my grandmother was stoned to death for fidelity by some Dutch Southwest Afrikaan fathers who wanted their newly pubic boys initiated; my father was stoned to death for attempting to save a whore from death by stoning on some crazy Grick island; if I stay utterly faithful, avoid, you know, infidelity, I'll be stoned to death."**
> **"Then why not sleep with him?"**
> **"Tradition. No. Challenge. No. Caprice, I guess. To see. Maybe I won't get stoned."**

In a world which has doggedly refused to see itself as anything *but* metaphor for a hundred years, this could be a refreshing throwback in the American idiom. Mutha and Celine and Inque do exist, in literary fact, just as the Calcutta of the dream does: we need not prove it either spatially or temporally.

Once again it is up to novelists to demonstrate the genre and thereby give evidence that the various forms of it are *not* dead. Because despite some popular assertions that this is "an age of prose" it is one of poetry, however prosaic some of the verse might be; and the burden of proof does lie, therefore, with the accused.

Is it Harris's responsibility to teach us the difference between the *all* and the *nothing* of this proof? I think not; we are better than that reason, and only on the specious grounds of a dated concept of responsibility, stemming from the equally dated idea of *fully realized Man,* does Foster Harris's first novel fail.

Now, then, that the Other Victorians have taken over, and Aubrey Beardsley has beaten off even Allan Ginsberg as guru laureate, it seems to have become more important than ever to promote full-scale social evolution; because evidently we are in "danger" of discovering ourselves to be culturally cyclical.

Robert A. Twigge-Chafé would like to *be* Other Victorian: he would like to be hip and hippie; he would like to publish, simultaneously, All Those Books of Every Description which would create, support, and sustain his self-image. But he is human, and, finally, incapable of attaining that God within him; the book he has chosen to publish is *The Bad* Anhänglichkeit.[6]

Perhaps it is as good a book as Rolfe Eigen, in his introduction, says it is:

Twigge-Chafé is an optimist, brave and cheerful; and though it is hard to see such a role, except in contrast to mawkish extremes of pessimism, a modern reader will find him qualified in the ultimate decency of things. He cannot do wrong.

But optimism and decency are ambiguous positions, easy to espouse in someone else after he has attained them.

What Professor Eigen means is that Twigge-Chafé has successfully turned off his mind to nearly all possibilities—particularly those of normalcy —in an effort to demonstrate the possibility of doing so. Perhaps some tragedy lies in the worthlessness of his effort: who ever doubted what he has proved? Or maybe this is not a *tragic* flaw. *The Bad* Anhänglichkeit abounds in it so generously that we might be led to believe it a rampant fact in the current world: three simultaneous generations screaming, "Bad things don't happen except when fools make them happen!" and blowing their minds on *The Little Golden Book of Poetry*.

Which is exactly what happens at the beginning of the book. Ulga, the 60-year-old female Swedish painter, sits on the floor with Evgenii, the 42-year-old Russian painter, and with Walt-Marie, the 19-year-old hermaphroditic American painter, and reads aloud:

> **Johnny go loop the loop**
> **Johnny go loop the light**
> **Johnny go loop the loop**
> **All on a Saturday night**

before the three can have the hysterics which lead to remarkable, if not impossible, sexual endeavors.

The book—note—is written in play form; but its more than 600 pages probably preclude presentation, and the stage directions include such side

6. Robert A. Twigge-Chafé, *The Bad* Anhänglichkeit (L. H. Wotton, 1967), $50.00, Moroccan leather, gold leaf; $7.95, cloth.

comment as render them fictional narrative. Finally the whole—stage directions, dialogue, scene changes—is written in rough blank verse, for no ascertainable reason other than that Twigge-Chafé wanted to demonstrate how *possible* it would be to write a novel in the form of verse-drama.

The little poetry sequence, called "Prologue," devolves into the dream-within-a-dream-within-a-dream which forms Acts I-III of the novel, in order, I gather, to demonstrate a state of occult super-reality beneath the *formal* level of reality. The order goes, as always, (1) reality (the artists into their dream) (2) viewed imaginatively (the dream into the dream's dream) (3) yields the truth behind the tangible (the dream within the dream's dream's dream).

The hideously complicated plot focuses on the imagined ruin of a family, posited by the prodigal son who is dreamed up by the girl at the center of the dream dreamed by all three artists simultaneously. The imagined fall of the family instructs the prodigal son who repents, which causes the girl to *fall* in her life, thereby instructing the artists on a collage upon which they intend to collaborate.

We might hope for linguistic clarification; but look, rather, to *fin de siècle:* in a world of such intellectual structure we find language done in wrought iron baroque, each curlicue a farther level of numb dreaming. Here is a section from the first level, Act I:

> **Ulga:** I think I'm dreaming, sleeping more and dreaming.
>
> **Walt-Marie:** We're always dreaming, Ulga, that is what
> Life's about, and Art, your Canvases,
> Dreams fleshed out to look like what is not.

The quality of the writing does not change into Act II:

> **Inders:** Do you think your nature is so deep
> To see the "something curious" in this?
> The Warmth with which his flushed hand fluttered
> Around her breast was nothing passionate!
>
> **Cello [sic]:** Could *you* distinguish passion in that man?
>
> **Inders:** Of course, my darling; I can see that deep,
> If you can't, into the woof and warp of dreams.
>
> **Cello:** *Dreams* of Dreams. You only know of dreams!
> How far, my dear, can you see into your heart?

Or into Act III:

> **Ionion:** And if our dreams are only dreams of us?
> Then who can extricate himself from life?
>
> **Tonio:** Come, go to sleep and stop your muttering.
> In sleep you'll find the answers to your dreams.

231

The structural shocker apparently comes at the curtain of Act III, when we discover that there is no fourth or fifth act: the play concludes, after telling us what the effects will be, on the innermost dream, never fulfilling the earlier, more external ones.

I think we are intended to see this as a five-act play, which ends in the middle of the third act. The author's intention is to take us out of reality (Act I), carry us through the imagination (Act II), and set us down in the poetic world of Super-reality (Act III). There he wishes to leave us, rather than bringing us all back home, to wander in a *Cocteau-ean* "everness" until we learn to reconstruct the dreams for ourselves, and in that way to escape, with new understandings, back to the real world.

If Twigge-Chafé's writing prevents the book from having any literary or dramatic success, what is still central is the form, the intentions. And if we do overlook the failure—argument's sake, for the moment—what should have been accomplished by these alleged subtleties is what we've been told more tactfully for centuries: that things don't change; that every age and level rediscovers what has always been there; that every new thing is simply a restructuring of something else, primeval, for which we have finally, or again, learned the language. The importance of form is that it be proper for transmitting its message. We already know what we will be told; we only have to learn to say it for ourselves.

New world of will

A black ear crawls on the window. It is
my own, my very own remarkable ear.
I hear little of the original spirit.

A piece of paper caught up in a tree
bearing the stationary marks of you and me.
If you were here in teeth and kisses, in NY.

See these heartless animals, the ants,
how they teem and murder, and they are driven too.
It is time for the pronunciation of the will.

So here among the dull and nightly rocks,
here where we first met, with philosophy,
upon a lake where oarsmen rowed them past—

Receiving the strict letters and in the morning
on this same spot again I hinder you.

DAVID SHAPIRO

Totem

What a tree becomes shyly
waiting for language
            to fall in its mouth:

an eagle, three stars, a buffalo head
—Jesus to some savage eye,
            miracle in a duststorm,

mirage in a mist,
a grain of truth
            to be manhandled, lopped,

pitched on a wagon
and hewed into use.

JAMES HERSH

Veteran's day

Man next to me, little
beer-drinking dart-eyed
work-handed man wearing
a serious though hardly
solemn banty presence,
sits chilling in the
cathoded living color
rain of news, unable
to slip it. Blows of fact
flurry him morose, gut-
puzzled. He has a beer.

Bastogne was where he was,
one time, a porous-bowelled
but truly brave grailer
after sane days, fair days.
Scrunching for a fox-hole
view across the damp bar's
plane, he can't remember
where he earned this match:
Brinkley serves a crimson
siege, Huntley slaps a riot
back, and the volley speeds
to slashing brillance—
Klan/rape/treason/mine
air sea space disasters
followed by serene goodnights
and a (subliminal or WHAT?)
fadeout of the Lady in the
Harbor holding aloft one
long divisional digit.

Man next to me crouches
so sad so empty I can't say
to him in Bastogne's wake
that we've sat beside before:
after Choison and Verdun,
Bull Run and Brandywine,
and before those after
Agincourt and Hastings
and Syracuse and Marathon
and Eden always after Eden.
Man next to me, scarred so
deftly and original, would
not believe that Bastogne
was an end to means; every
day Veteran's Day. I have a beer.

JOHN McEVOY

In madness,
as in utter freedom

I have had a cripple's wish that the rope
That leads the solitary to his cell
Would loosen and his manacles of bone
Be broken and the leg irons of his muscle
That I might dance in the wind like frayed rope.

    Stay. Hold all conversation, like a mute,
    With the muscles. Have your visions here.
    For years your huddled nerves had no mate
    Until led out by the arm by another.
    She spoke into your fingers like a mute.

What could I answer what she told my senses
Before she left? I'd hardly learned love's vowels.
And all I found, in searching for that entrance:
An old rope battering against a wall.
I looked back for myself and found my senses.

    If you had known how casual a touch
    —That you were carrying in your arm all summer—
    Would return to teach your fingers how much,
    I might have made England merry that summer
    And felled the walls of Bedlam with a touch.

TRIM BISSELL

The wound

The air stiffens to a crust.
From bed I watch
Clots of flies, crickets
Frisk and titter. Now
The weather is such grease.
All day I smell the roasts
Like presences. You
Root into your books.
You do your stuff.
In here my bedroom walls
Are paisley, like a plot
Of embryos. I lie here,
Waiting for its kick.
My love. My tenant.
As the shrubs grow
Downy, bloom and seed.
The hedges grow downy
And seed, and moonlight
Burbles through the gauze.
Sticky curtains. Faking scrabble
With the pair next door
I watched you clutch your blank.
They're both on Nembutal,
The killer pill.
And I am fixed. Gone careful,
Begging for the nod,
You quiver loyally
Above my head. I close
My eyes. And now
The prison falls in place:
Ripe things sway in the light,
Parts of plants, leaf
Fragments . . . You are covering the cot
With sheets. I feel
No end. No end. It stalls
In me. It's still alive.

LOUISE GLUCK

Afterthoughts in counterpoint

I

Things have been happening, and I could see
(The magician comes apart, his guise undone)
They were going to happen, and I was helpless
(From his sleeves myriad handkerchiefs) with knowledge
That they had to happen (unfurl and flutter in the wind)
And I watched them happen (a thousand rabbits drain
His leggings) and time passed (three small doves escape
His top hat) and I couldn't stop (tiny gold fish flow
From the aquarium of his cummerbund)
And she couldn't stop and we changed and as expected
(The magician comes apart, his eyes go out)
I was sick for three months afterwards (his heart pops).
I watched myself wandering around sick and concluded
(Each creature flees the prison of his metaphor)
I guess that means I loved her.

II

I'm listening to the Chopin nocturnes, thinking
God I'm a swishy romantic. I remember
Her saying, "Chopin, how hypocritical".
Her hair was shorter than mine, her eyes were so large,
Always dilated. I took it for a sign
Of her passionate nature, but soon it grew
Clear her rapture was lack of glasses.

III

It's funny how one remembers people
(The magician comes apart, his truths forsake him).
I remember best her coming, the feel of her loins
(His innards spill a heap of rags and straw).
Perhaps that means I didn't love her (he falls)
I don't know . . . Well, I'm lucid now, I'm free.
I am not happy (undone upon the fields)
But hell, all told (and crows
Gather on the naked willing earth)
Living's (the crows) pretty good (the crows the crows),
And I (the crows the crows the crows).

ALEXIS VIERECK

Beardsley, Burroughs, decadence, and the poetics of obscenity
PETER MICHELSON

Omne est saccus stercorum.
—the infamous Clodia

Nat King Cole used to sing a calypso song about a homesick Trinidadian comparing the decadent, civilized States with healthy, natural Trinidad. Gringo women, he lamented, were submerged beneath their arty use of padding, cosmetics, and clothes. But with the Trinidad girl, "what you see is what she got." This topical calypso format presents the archetypal problem for all lyrical impulse—the antithesis of art and nature. From Plato to pop this tension permeates the history of art and art theory. Aubrey Beardsley's recent vogue articulates a particularly contemporaneous version of this dilemma.

His artistic elegance—both graphically and literarily—satisfies our desperation for the beautiful, while his blatant pornography adds another raspberry to the popular assault on moral transcendentalism. The dilemma is that poetically we want the beautiful without its constant companion, the ideal good. But the tradition of our aesthetics makes them inseparable. The

238

"decadent" art with which Beardsley was much involved made the first direct hit against the monolith of aesthetic idealism. Beardsley, in keeping with the central principle of Decadence, demonstrated that artistic beauty was not obliged to traditional morality in any way for its being. His two most extreme statements of this are of course the "Lysistrata" illustrations and his unfinished pornographic novel, "The Story of Venus and Tannhauser." Beardsley was one of the first to present pornographic satire in a lyrical guise and make both satire and lyricism convincing. His story of Venus and Tannhauser is at once a rebuttal of the transcendental melodrama of Wagner's libretto, on the one hand, and a parody of pornographic "romance," on the other. Simultaneously it is also a lyrical tour de force celebrating its own purely artistic beauty. Whereas Wagner's libretto is patterned on the morality play—Tannhauser's despair, e.g., is at last resolved in Christian faith and spiritual beauty—Beardsley's treatment denies the artistic potency of moral conflict by simply dismissing it, and thereby he exorcises morality and celebrates style. Wagner's Tannhauser, for instance, is introduced in profound angst—"No more, no more. . . . / how long this nightmare?"; when Venus cloys, his conscience boggles. Not so with Beardsley's dandy, who is introduced thus:

The Chevalier Tannhauser, having lighted off his horse, stood doubtfully for a moment beneath the ombre gateway of the Venusberg, troubled with an exquisite fear lest a day's travel should have too cruelly undone the laboured niceness of his dress. His hand, slim and gracious as La Marquise du Deffand's in the drawing by Carmontelle, played nervously about the gold hair that fell upon his shoulders like a finely curled peruke, and from point to point of a precise toilet, the fingers wandered, quelling the little mutinies of cravat and ruffle.

The Decadent Tannhauser, unlike Wagner's moralistic counterpart, relishes losing himself in the Hill of Venus, and is neatly poised in the face of his ambiguous perdition: "Goodbye, Madonna," he says casually, and then sighs to heaven for "the assurance of a looking glass before I make my debut!" As Socrates says, first things first. In similar manner, Beardsley satirizes pornography and romance (antithetical variations on the same theme): "It is, I know, the custom of all romancers to paint heroes who can give a lady proof of their valliance at least twenty times a night. Now Tannhauser had no such Gargantuan facility, and was rather relieved when, an hour later, Priapusa and Doricourt and some others burst drunkenly into the room and claimed Venus for themselves." Beardsley proves the decadent thesis by creating a pornographic narrative at once denying the necessary connection between either pornography and vulgarity, or immorality and ugliness. Characteristically he casts hard core pornographic images into elegance and wit; for instance,

239

I wish I could be allowed to tell you what occurred round table 15, just at this moment. It would amuse you very much, and would give you a capital idea of the habits of Venus' retinue. Indeed, for deplorable reasons, by far the greater part of what was said and done at this supper must remain unrecorded and even unsuggested.

Venus allowed most of the dishes to pass untasted, she was so engaged with the beauty of Tannhauser. She laid her head many times on his robe, kissing him passionately; and his skin, at once firm and yielding, seemed to those exquisite little teeth of hers, the most incomparable pasture. Her upper lip curled and trembled with excitement, showing the gums. Tannhauser, on his side, was no less devoted. He adored her all over and all the things she had on, and buried his face in the folds and flounces of her linen, and ravished away a score of frills in his excess. He found her exasperating, and crushed her in his arms, and slaked his parched lips at her mouth. He caressed her eyelids softly with his finger tips, and pushed aside the curls from her forehead, and did a thousand gracious things, tuning her body as a violinist tunes his instrument before he plays upon it.

Priapusa snorted like an old war horse at the sniff of powder, and tickled Tannhauser and Venus by turns, and slipped her tongue down their throats, and refused to be quiet at all until she had had a mouthful of the Chevalier. Claude, seizing his chance, dived under the table and came up the other side just under the queen's couch, and before she could say "One!" he was taking his coffee "aux deux colonnes." Clair was furious at his friend's success, and sulked for the rest of the evening.

The appeal of Beardsley's brilliant rhetoric to the literati in an age of fading aristocracy was ironically similar to his appeal for ourselves. To his time Beardsley represented the triumph of an aristocratic, classically oriented aesthetic taste over a modern puritanic, know-nothing moralism. To a contemporary (democratic, middle class) mind he recalls a traditional aesthetic —line, symmetry, and representation highly stylized—without its vestigial moralism. Thus Beardsley is the kind of avant-garde gift the man who has everything can understand and feel comfortable with. His popularity is a pop culture analogue of the now famous "forward-looking return to the past." In short, "The Story of Venus and Tannhauser" is a tour de force carrying formal poetic tradition to extremity and at the same time ridiculing the moral idealism so long concomitant with that poetic tradition.

Of the four major treatments of the Venus and Tannhauser legend that I know in the 19th century, only Beardsley's has artistic potential for us today because his was the only treatment that was in touch with poetic evolution in a really vital way. Not simply because his is pornographic (although a good pornographer is no mean thing), but because he used pornography to make a statement about the nature of art. The others resorted to more acceptable traditions not so dynamic (or pregnant) as pornography. William Morris' "Hill of Venus" (fr. *The Earthly Paradise*), for instance, uses allegory; it is an allegory of psychic despair in which Tannhauser leaves the Hill of Venus, gropes his way to Rome where he is refused absolution by the Pope except if his holy staff should bloom. In despair Tannhauser returns to his venal life. Meanwhile, back at the Vatican, the Pope's staff blooms. Although unknown to him, Tannhauser's salvation exists through the miracle of God's grace. Thus the poem argues allegorically the need for faith. It is a nice poem if you like clean poems, but both its vision and its structure throw us back on tradition, not forward to either a new vision or a new poetic. Wagner's opera libretto is similarly unrewarding. It uses the morality play as vehicle. Morris resolves despair theologically; Wagner resolves it morally, through Tannhauser's repentance. The ending is directly from morality format, with Venus (Knowledge, evil) and Elisabeth (good, Innocence) contending for his will. Naturally Elisabeth's Christian virtues win. Not even Swinburne, from whom we might expect some decay, could get out of the traditional "poetic" bag. His "Laus Veneris" is a good clean poem too. But it articulates a sort of inverted Pascal's Wager in the lyric stoicism with which Tannhauser recognizes that he is doomed, but not doomed until the last Judgment (and there is always the hope that there isn't any judgment to come, in which case he's home free). Swinburne can't seem to figure out if there is a God or not; so he resolves the whole thing by going back to a lyric version of Dryden's "All for Love," on the hunch that the millennium is a long way off.

"The Story of Venus and Tannhauser" did for English pornography what *Tristram Shandy* had done for the English novel, gave it dimensions of artistic possibility hitherto unexplored. And it perhaps lay dormant so many years for about the same reason that *Tristram Shandy* did—because no one quite knew what to do with it. Unlike Sterne, however, by the time Beardsley came back he was artistically obsolete, and however much one may enjoy him he has little now to teach artists. Like the Decadents (and many Liberals since) he gave up everything for classical beauty. Even in his time it was a desperate investment. On the Truth Exchange, the politics and religion markets had already collapsed; science was ominously rising, and artists tried to head off a bull market by pulling everything out of politics and religion and investing in Beauty. It was, despite its brief and glorious success (Beardsley, Beerbohm, Rossetti, Swinburne, Wilde, Symons, Pater, and Yeats in England; Rimbaud, Verlaine, Mallarmé, Gautier, Baudelaire, etc., in France), a strategic failure. The rendezvous between the art of monolithic beauty and the art of analytic exploration was already begun with Claude Bernard and Emile Zola. After that the future lies ahead.

Beardsley's pornographic novel is important because it shows how completely the Decadents were persuaded that, as Oscar Wilde put it in "The Decay of Lying," "Things are because we see them, and what we see, and how we see it, depends on the Arts that have influenced us." The Decadents could produce Beardsley's effete tour de force because it affirmed for them what Zola denied, that art brings reality to man rather than bringing man to reality. But in fact they couldn't really accept it—it is not altogether accidental I think that Beardsley never finished it—because it was the nihilistically logical conclusion of their poetics. For in saying that nothing mattered but artistic beauty they had sooner or later to confront the implication that beauty didn't matter either. One sees Arthur Symons wrestling with this when he says of Zola (1919) that, "He sees the beast in all its transformations, but he sees only the beast. He has never looked at life impartially, he has never seen it as it is. His realism is a distorted idealism . . ." Symons really means that Zola's scientific-poetic formula challenges Symons' own Symbolic-Decadent formula. One must remember that Symons' idea of realism, of "telling it like it is," is Mallarmé's mystical "confidence in the eternal correspondences between the visible and the invisible universe." Symons did not understand that Mallarmé's mysticism, like any mysticism, is simply an idiosyncratic idealism, and that the very idiosyncrasy he so admired was an ominous fissure in his revered edifice of Beauty. For not only did Mallarmé write *prose*-poems, thereby refuting the necessity of artistic convention, but he also located beauty in the perceptions of his mind (in "the horror of the forest, or the silent thunder afloat in the leaves; not the intrinsic, dense wood of the trees"). Such beauty is not in a unified Nature; neither is it in artistic presentation of vision; it is in the vision itself. And the logical conclusion of Mallarmé's theory is that he not write *about* his visions at all, but that he simply *have* them. And, as Symons laments, this is pretty nearly what Mallarmé did. If beauty does not have its own form to control art, and if artistic convention is no authoritative vehicle for conveying the beautiful, then every man is his own artist and every vision has its own beauty. Symons' preference for Mallarmé over Zola is simply a matter of taste, not aesthetic necessity. Beardsley's pornography carried the grand Decadence as far as it could go in creating a cosmos where morality was non-existent, sentiment was merely an ironic rhetorical device, and classical artifice was the nature of being. It is more than a little historically prophetic when Yeats laments that that place where "Fish, flesh, or fowl, commend all summer long whatever is begotten, born, and dies" is no country for old men or monuments of unaging intellect. In recent years art and literature have been much more concerned with those dying generations, their long, hot summer, than with the artifice of eternity.

II

When Schiller noted that the difference between classicism and modernity was in the latter's loss of confidence in a coherent sense of nature, he identified also that component in Romanticism which revolutionized Western poetics. Once such philosophers as Kant and Hume relocated reality from external space and time to perceived space and time it opened poetic possibilities that recreated the imagination. In the poetic tradition evolved from Plato's moral idealism and Aristotle's theory of artistic imitation, art was supposed to imitate nature. Nature was supposed to have an order more or less coherent and comprehensible. Correspondingly, art too was supposed to be ordered, and its truth lay in the rightness with which it represented the correspondence. Thus Dr. Johnson, one of the great products of this tradition, judged that *Tristram Shandy* couldn't last because "nothing odd will do long." Sterne's psychically idiosyncratic novel anticipated the romantic modernity that Dr. Johnson could not be expected to appreciate. Decadence, as I am using it, is a development from romanticism. There was never, of course, a comprehensive romanticism; if Schiller, for example, doubted a coherent natural order, that was certainly not true of Wordsworth. But if one can talk about a generalized and synthetic impression then one can observe that, for all its revolutionary aesthetic potential, romanticism kept to a conventionally unified poetics as an expression of the coherent moral sense which still prevailed. And if we except a tendency to narrative and descriptive impressionism in such Decadents as Gautier, Huysmans, Baudelaire, Swinburne, and Wilde, the structural poetics of Decadence too was conventional enough. Early Decadence manifests itself in subject and imagery rather than form. By introducing the ugly, the grotesque, and the "immoral" as agencies of beauty and "harmony" the early Decadence refuted moral idealism, but maintained the poetic unity so long associated with it. Thus Decadence attempted to "liberate" art from morality, and even life. A later Decadence—beginning perhaps about 1915 (Vorticism, Imagism, Dadaism, etc.), subsiding in the new critical '30s and '40s, and strong again in the '50s and '60s—took the next logical step; having long since accepted the refutation of moral idealism, this "movement" proceeded to repudiate artistic unity and wholeness as necessary poetic principles. In this larger sense, then, Decadence refers to the contemporaneous rejection of complementary moral and artistic unity, the heritage of Western poetics.

A premise of moral unity derives from a univocal metaphysics (e.g., Platonic idealism), or such romantic analogues as Wordsworth's or Coleridge's moral transcendentalism. Decadence denies romantic morality (i.e., the upward good for which Nature is figure) while extending the implications of romantic poetics. Romantic theory (e.g., Shelley's *Defense*) holds that art leads to truth. Oscar Wilde, in "The Decay of Lying", implicitly reverses that with marvelous chop logic: art is lying; art is truth; therefore

243

lying is truth. Thus Decadence confronts romantic poetics with a radical contradiction. The result is the absurd paradox fundamental to Decadence, the paradox that cuts romanticism off from its vestigial idealism. Romantic poets, the popular front for romantic theory, had been unable to do this. They had instead wallowed in elaborate but unconvincing attempts to integrate deep-well psychology with Olympian morality. And in so doing, as Byron says, they "proved unintelligible." It's true that Keats, for example, recognized an incipient Decadence. Negative capability was an unsystematic awareness that dialectical preoccupations like those of Wordsworth, Coleridge, and Shelley were an "irritable reaching after" facts that were clouded by the very presuppositions through which they were to be reached. But Keats unfortunately (though true to Decadent tendency) died young, and doctrinaire Decadence was left for a later generation in England. When Wilde, echoing Gautier, said that art expresses only itself he was articulating the Decadent wish to find a world of beauty that neither the natural nor moral worlds provided. Thus, the Decadents wanted essentially a romantic beauty, but they denied its source in nature. Man, they said, defines nature and not the converse. So art, not nature, is the source of beauty. The later Decadence simply makes the next logical assumption—that if there is no beauty in nature, neither is there any in art. Thus, by our time, the basic generalities of poetic tradition—that art reveals the good and the beautiful—are largely disbelieved. Like the early Decadents, we say that art expresses itself, but that self no longer necessarily implies beauty. Beauty, as an artistic concept, has largely become rhetorical. It was meaningful only when it applied to Creation or formal analogues of Creation. Since the Author of Nature has ceased to exist it is no longer necessary to honor Him by praising His Works. And with His passing so too passed the analogy between His Works and ours. Although the early Decadents tried to grasp beauty a while longer without its metaphysical basis, they had to do so by appealing to an aristocratic sensibility. And that too was doomed. When democracy caught on it swept away the last refuge of monolithic beauty.

The Decadent connection between art and metaphysics is that perception is controlled by the arts (for contemporary Decadence, *art* is expanded to mean something like McLuhan's "media", hence, e.g., pop art) which convey experience to us, and that we can therefore be informed only by what these arts intend or are capable of conveying to us. Thus, we know only what we perceive; our perceptions are controlled by the arts which represent "reality" to our senses; reality therefore depends on the character of the art or medium that represents it; and consequently rather than art imitating Nature (the constant), nature (the relative) imitates or takes on the qualities of art, which has now become the arbiter of reality. Thus Wilde:

Consider the matter from a scientific or a metaphysical point of view . . . For what is Nature? Nature is no great mother who has borne us. She is our creation. It is in our brain that she quickens to life. Things are because we see them, and what we see, and how we see it, depends on the Arts that have influenced us. To look at a thing is very different from seeing a thing. One does not see anything until one sees its beauty. Then, and then only, does it come into existence.

If we substitute "irony" or "absurdity" for Wilde's "beauty" and expand Wilde's use of "Arts" to include popular culture and its "media" we have here a contemporaneous statement of Decadent poetics. Nor is what McLuhan describes, excepting of course his electronic thesis, substantially different from what Wilde observed:

We have all seen in our own day in England how a certain curious and fascinating type of beauty, invented and emphasized by two imaginative painters, has so influenced Life that whenever one goes to a private view, or to an artistic salon, one sees here the mystic eyes of Rossetti's dream, the ivory throat, the strange square-cut jaw, the loosened shadowy hair that he so ardently loved, there the sweet maidenhood of "The Golden Stair," the blossom-like mouth and weary loveliness of the "Laus Amoris," the passion-pale face of Andromeda, the thin hands and lithe beauty of the Vivian in "Merlin's Dream." And it has always been so. A great artist invents a type, and Life tries to copy it, to reproduce it in a popular form, like an enterprising publisher.

In short, to say that life imitates art is to say that artistic media influence our perception and knowledge of complex reality and to that extent control our lives.

The "documentary" or the news film illustrates contemporaneously what I mean. A recent telecast from Vietnam filmed the battle for Hill 888 (or some such number) in which the camera and reporter created a drama from the battle by featuring an interview with one of the young soldiers and using his descriptions to punctuate visual scenes from the battle and battle-field. It was a curious synthesis; the soldier was exhausted and confused about the significance of the victory. What he knew was that he was tired, that he had been afraid, that many friends had been killed, and that he did not want to have to go through it again. What he did not know was why (or perhaps *if*) Hill 888 was so important, or how it was part of a larger view of the war's conduct. He knew only what he had experienced. The reporter (or more likely editors back in the States) bridged the soldier's gaps in information and understanding by reconstructing a *drama* of attack and counterattack, while machine guns, cannons, and medics were playing out the spectacle of war on the screen. The supposition of film and narrative was that Hill 888, being, one guessed, somewhere between Hills 887 and 889 and having an elevation, had specific strategic importance. But that importance of course was not documented nor precisely determined; although it remained an assumption, it was structured to have the dramatic impact of certainty. The important thing here is that the maker of the film (reporter, editor, whoever) wanted some kind of coherence. The soldier's description without the film shots didn't have it. And the film without the soldier didn't have authenticity. So, in the interest far more of art than documentary, the two were brought together to give a view of the war that was neither that of soldier, nor reporter, nor camera. This synthetic artistic view is the one upon which the audience, those of us who have no other data for comparison, has to depend for its knowledge of the battle's reality. So it is that Decadence prevails, and life imitates art. We "see" only what we *can* see through the medial apparatus by which we see.

The next evening's news announced that Hill 888 had been recaptured by the Vietcong. Now what was the reality of that battle? To us at home, its reality was formulated by art. But, at the time we perceived it, we were watching a "victory." Was it a victory then and later a defeat? Was it the same battle? For the soldier it was perhaps a new battle, defined by the rhythm of resting and fighting or advancing and retreating or however he perceived the passage of time. And what if he is killed? From at least one perspective of reality there will be no more battles and no more war. And then our own sense of the battle's reality will have been largely determined by a perspective no longer existing. Where then *is* the reality of the battle? For us it must remain in the realm of art; it must in fact take the shape that the film maker and his art *permit it* to take. And so too for the reality of the war itself. We know its reality only through the artistic representations of it that we perceive. The war takes on the qualities and character of its artistic representation—that is, the war imitates art.

The limitations of perception are clear enough, then. But suppose the artist has some rhetorical purpose beyond even the restrictions of his art. Suppose that the film maker wanted to show the battle so as to make it noble or make it foolish. Then the image of reality that he presented to us would be still more complex because reality would be not only artistically structured but it would be structured so as to persuade us to the artist's purpose. Now reality will have come to us filtered through the art with its limitations *and* the artist with his limitations and peculiar motives. In short, when we add the artist who controls the art to the art which controls our perception, then we must get a very Decadent idea of the reality of the house that Jack built.

The theory that art, as medial purveyor and reflector, controls reality means also—and more significantly—that it controls moral reality. Moral

246

categories, the traditional way of moral knowledge, are consequently absurd. That is, they exist because of faith rather than necessity. Categories have a way of becoming disengaged from experience by way of their own "artistic" (i.e., dialectical) structure and taking on their own intimidating existence. Contemporary Decadents attempt to fight this intimidation by articulating the gap between real moral authority and chimerical moral faith. They assume the stance of an existential Socrates demonstrating that the philistines, like the sophists, are epistemologically dangerous because they believe shadowy categories to be reality. And thus the dominant Decadent motif is, in William S. Burroughs' words, "Let them see what is on the end of that long newspaper spoon."

III

The early Decadence of which Beardsley is representative conceived art as celebration. But, having lost moral faith, it was able to celebrate only its own elegance. The later, or new, Decadence is analytic rather than celebratory, having been for some time convinced that there is nothing under the sun so true or beautiful as to inspire celebration. This contemporary sensibility rejects Art and Beauty because they have, like transcendental morality, proved incapable of the latitude necessary for dealing with a highly fragmented and incoherent reality. Being persuaded that there is nothing to sing about, it is not surprising that it satirizes those who persist in singing. Nor, with the rejection of Beauty as artistic center, is it surprising that its primary imagery draws from the ugly and the obscene. It is possible to employ the poetics of satirical obscenity more than William S. Burroughs, but not much more. So I would like to use his work as a paradigmatic instance of the later Decadence at work.

Excepting the latter's rejection of Beauty and unified form, the artistic premises of the two Decadences are similar—the artistic image is the true reality and its function is to illuminate the ironic falseness of programmatic preconceptions. For instance, it is a culturally programmed generality that drug addiction is evil. Burroughs' *Naked Lunch* "demonstrates" by satiric disposition of images that it is human nature to be addicted, and that drug addiction is in fact the most easily recognized addiction virus. The novel's structure is a dialectical tension of obscene images designed to persuade us that addiction in all its manifestations is man's normal state, and that ignorance of this phenomenon makes us morally absurd.

We are morally absurd when our actions or ideals are dissociated from the moral values authorizing them. Morally abstracted ideals are sure-fire Decadent avenues to absurdity. As Burroughs demonstrates, e.g., our programmed association of addiction with abnormality depends on subsuming human nature into preconceived and simplified moral categories. Burroughs assaults this idol of the mind by counter-asserting that the central issue of addiction is not moral vice at all, but rather the freedom of human will. Then he reconstructs our popular images of freedom through knowledge and order (e.g., the scientist, the jurist, the police agencies, the political parties, the business corporations, and so on) and reveals them to be agencies of control addiction. They are all aspects of the Nova Mob. Thus not only are our cultural ideals cast in criminal context, but we are also shown that complex reality (i.e., the true nature of addiction) is falsified by popular image makers, whose art demands and whose purposes are served by programmatic simplifications of reality. Thus the Decadent thesis. And thus the title *Naked Lunch;* in reference to charges of pornography against his Orgasm-Death gimmick, Burroughs says,

These sections are intended to reveal capital punishment as the obscene, barbaric and disgusting anachronism that it is. As always the lunch is naked. If civilized countries want to return to Druid Hanging Rites in the Sacred Grove or to drink blood with the Aztecs and feed their Gods with blood of human sacrifice, let them see what they actually eat and drink. Let them see what is on the end of that long newspaper spoon.

In short, he conceived both the obscenity and the dialectic as devices to make it possible for men to perceive the reality of cause and effect in such basic cultural addiction syndromes as capital punishment.

Burroughs defines the novel's central metaphor thus:

Junk is the mold of monopoly and possession. The addict stands by while his junk legs carry him straight in on the junk beam to relapse. Junk is quantitative and accurately measurable. The more junk you use the less you have and the more you have the more you use. All the hallucinogen drugs are considered sacred by those who use them—there are Peyote Cults and Bannisteria Cults, Hashish Cults and Mushroom Cults—"the Sacred Mushrooms of Mexico enable a man to see God"—but no one ever suggested that junk is sacred. There are no opium cults. Opium is profane and quantitative like money. I have heard that there was once a beneficent non-habit-forming junk in India. It was called soma and is pictured as a beautiful blue tide. If soma ever existed the Pusher was there to bottle it and monopolize it and sell it and it turned into plain old time JUNK. Junk is the ideal product . . . the ultimate merchandise. No sales talk necessary. The client will crawl through a sewer and beg to buy. . . . The junk merchant does not sell his product to the consumer, he sells the consumer to his product. He does not improve and simplify his merchandise. He degrades and simplifies the client. He pays his staff in junk. Junk yields a basic formula of "evil" virus: *The Algebra of Need.* The face of "evil" is always the face of total need. A dope fiend is a man in total need of dope. Beyond a certain frequency need knows absolutely no limit or control. In the words of total need: "Wouldn't you?" Yes you would. You would lie, cheat, inform on your friends, steal, do anything to satisfy

total need. Because you would be in a state of total sickness, total possession, and not in a position to act in any other way. Dope fiends are sick people who cannot act other than they do. A rabid dog cannot choose but bite. Assuming a self-righteous position is nothing to the purpose unless your purpose be to keep the junk virus in operation. And junk is a big industry. I recall talking to an American who worked for the Aftosa Commission in Mexico. Six hundred a month plus expense account:

"How long will the epidemic last?" I enquired.

"As long as we can keep it going. . . . And yes . . . maybe the aftosa will break out in South America," he said dreamily.

In a world whose chief business is JUNK, the object of man is to profiteer. And in a world where JUNK is the principal industry, its end is to make of man an addiction machine. The Decadent absurdity of such a world is imaged in Bradley the Buyer, the narcotics undercover agent who destroys the institutions he was created to protect because their knowledge of reality has been so categorically deformed that they cannot comprehend or control the monster they have made; Bradley goes beserk, schlupping up the District Supervisor, other agents, junkies, and finally the Narcotics Commissioner himself. Finally he is destroyed by flame thrower, "the court of inquiry ruling that such means were justified in that the Buyer had lost his human citizenship and was, in consequence, a creature without species and a menace to the narcotics industry on all levels."

The Algebra of Need, so central to this deformation, is a Decadent phenomenon too. On its literal level, in reference to drugs, it means being controlled by physiological need. On the larger metaphorical level need is more subtle, more artistic, and so more Decadent. Dr. Benway, himself a control addict, is perhaps the consummate artist at turning man into the soft machine. Benway is a bureaucratic Frankenstein, the bourgeois scientist whose arts of power over human nature and reality describe a massive cultural obscenity. Here is Benway at work:

"I deplore brutality," he said. "It's not efficient. On the other hand, prolonged mistreatment, short of physical violence, gives rise, when skillfully applied, to anxiety and a feeling of special guilt. A few rules or rather guiding principles are to be borne in mind. The subject must not realize that the mistreatment is a deliberate attack of an anti-human enemy on his personal identity. He must be made to feel that he deserves *any* treatment he receives because there is something (never specified) horribly wrong with him. The naked need of the control addicts must be decently covered by an arbitrary and intricate bureaucracy so that the subject cannot contact his enemy direct.

"I digress as usual. Pending more precise knowledge of brain electronics, drugs remain an essential tool of the interrogator in his assault on the subject's personal identity. The barbiturates are, of course, virtually useless. That is, anyone who can be broken down by such means would succumb to the puerile methods used in an American precinct. Scopolamine is often effective in dissolving resistance, but it impairs the

249

memory: an agent might be prepared to reveal his secrets but quite unable to remember them, or cover story and secret life info might be inextricably garbled.

"Many subjects are vulnerable to sexual humiliation. Nakedness, stimulation with aphrodisiacs, constant supervision to embarrass subject and prevent relief of masturbation (erections during sleep automatically turn on an enormous vibrating electric buzzer that throws the subject out of bed into cold water, thus reducing the incidence of wet dreams to a minimum). Kicks to hypnotize a priest and tell him he is about to consummate a hypostatic union with the Lamb—then steer a randy old sheep up his ass. After that the Interrogator can gain complete hypnotic control—the subject will come at his whistle, shit on the floor if he but say Open Sesame. Needless to say, the sex humiliation angle is contraindicated for overt homosexuals. (I mean let's keep our eye on the ball here and remember the old party line . . . never know who's listening in.) I recall this one kid I condition to shit at sight of me. Then I wash his ass and screw him. It was real tasty. And he was lovely fellah too. And sometimes a subject will burst into boyish tears because he can't keep from ejaculate when you screw him. Well, as you can plainly see, the possibilities are endless like meandering paths in a great big beautiful garden. I was just scratching that lovely surface when I am purged by Party Poops. . . . Well, 'son cosas de la vida.' "

Finally, of course, the system produces its logical consequence, a man who becomes the perfectly efficient soft machine—and is then banished as an unnecessary adjunct of the anal aperture: here is part of the story of the "Man who taught his asshole to talk":

"After a while the ass started talking on its own. He would go in without anything prepared and his ass would ad-lib and toss the gags back at him every time.

"Then it developed sort of teeth-like little raspy incurving hooks and started eating. He thought this was cute at first and built an act around it, but the asshole would eat its way through his pants and start talking on the street, shouting out it wanted equal rights. It would get drunk, too, and have crying jags nobody loved it and it wanted to be kissed same as any other mouth. Finally it talked all the time day and night, you could hear him for blocks screaming at it to shut up, and beating it with his fist, and sticking candles up it, but nothing did any good and the asshole said to him: 'It's you who will shut up in the end. Not me. Because we don't need you around here any more. I can talk and eat *and* shit.' "

Human reality has now been subsumed so completely by function, that the functioning parts themselves commandeer Being and exile humanity.

Thus the arts of addiction, the Algebra of Need, define and control complex human reality. We are all the junkie naked in sunlight; we are all the pusher; exploiter and exploited. This is the tension that defines nature. Nature is not, as Wilde saw, our voluptuous mother. Nature is the obscene, the naked reality of our personal being in conflict with impersonal being. Impersonal being, imaged as the Nova Mob, makes it a crime to manifest personality. Benway's arts, the arts of our culture, are designed to redefine identity in "corporate" terms. Thus the crime of separate life:

The black wind sock of death undulates over the land, feeling, smelling for the crime

250

of separate life, movers of the fear-frozen flesh shivering under a vast probability curve. . . .

Population blocks disappear in a checker game of genocide. . . . Any number can play. . . .

The Liberal Press and The Press Not So Liberal and The Press Reactionary scream approval: "Above all the myth of other-level experience must be eradicated. . . ." And speak darkly of certain harsh realities . . . cows with the aftosa . . . prophylaxis. . . .

Power groups of the world frantically cut lines of connection. . . .

The Planet drifts to random insect doom. . . .

Thermodynamics has won at a crawl. . . . Orgone balked at the post. . . . Christ bled. . . . Time ran out.

The center indeed cannot hold. But Yeats was not really persuaded; Burroughs is. The "red shift" is paradigm for both physical and spiritual cosmos. The comprehensive dialectic of Burroughs' whole canon of work articulates the cause of disintegration. In *Naked Lunch* the cultural industry merchandises addiction; Benway programs our interior isolation, dehumanizes us, defines our mechanistic reality for us. *The Soft Machine* explores the destructive human consequences of this reality— ". . . are these experiments really necessary?" *Nova Express* provides an antidote to nova control:

I have said the basic techniques of nova are very simple consist in creating and aggravating conflicts—"No riots like injustice directed between enemies"—At any given time recorders fix nature of absolute need and dictate the use of total weapons— Like this: Collect and record violent Anti-Semitic statements—Now play back to Jews who are after Belsen—Record what they say and play it back to the Anti-Semites —Clip clap—You got it?—Want more? Record white supremacy statements—Play to Negroes—Play back answer—Now The Women and The Men—No riots like injustice directed between "enemies"—At any given time position of recorders fixes nature of absolute need—And dictates the use of total weapons—So leave the recorders running and get your heavy metal ass in a space ship—Did it—Nothing here now but the recordings—Shut the whole thing right off—Silence—When you answer the machine you provide it with more recordings to be played back to your "enemies" keep the whole nova machine running—The Chinese character for "enemy" means to be similar to or to answer—Don't answer the machine—Shut it off—

And *Nova Mob,* by articulating the criminal source and character of nova control, shows nature—the cosmos—in a state of total moral emergency.

We have come a long way, here, from Wilde's or Beardsley's aloof, aristocratic superiority to nature. And we have come still farther from the naive romantic idealizing of nature. But, though "art" and nature have lost coherence in their respective expansions, they still have design. Design is not univocal; it means simply that events happen according to cause and effect, or probability and necessity. The artist's business, that which makes him poet rather than mere artificer, is to locate causality in the events of nature. That is the center of poetic imitation. For Burroughs, as for all contemporary sensibility, cause cannot be referred to such categories as the good or the beautiful. Knowledge of causal reality requires penetrating to those points in time where cause is revealed. Even plot, the long-time poetic agency of showing cause, is a falsification—because it means the artist must superimpose a linear and chronological order on the chaos of his perceptions. The maker of plots is, at least to some degree, the maker of causes rather than the discoverer. Dr. Benway is the dangerous potential of giving life a plot. Our arts work on the premise that knowing requires ordering; Burroughs, realizing that the mind has greater perceptual capacity than we have thought, counters this by showing that superimposed order makes life take the shape we give it, and in so doing it prevents our perception of cause in natural events. Knowledge so derived is a chimerical self-indulgence.

Nakedness is all. Nakedness means images, structured as little as possible—enough structure to show the artist's perception of causal connection, not so much as to give an order that may gratify the mind's ease but which must falsify our knowledge of nature. Thus, direct experience and perception is the aesthetic base of Burroughs' poetic:

I awoke from The Sickness at the age of forty-five, calm and sane, and in reasonably good health except for a weakened liver and the look of borrowed flesh common to all who survive The Sickness. . . . Most survivors do not remember the delirium in detail. I apparently took detailed notes on sickness and delirium. I have no precise memory of writing the notes which have now been published under the title *Naked Lunch*.

There is only one thing a writer can write about: *what is in front of his senses at the moment of writing.* . . . I am a recording instrument. . . . I do not presume to impose "story" "plot" "continuity." . . . Insofar as I succeed in *Direct* recording of certain areas of psychic process I may have limited function. . . . I am not an entertainer.

When he says that he is no entertainer he denies that component of poetic tradition which the earlier Decadents grasped so desperately. When he declines the continuity gambit, he rejects the traditional means by which art was supposed to instruct. How, then, instruct? Through an irregular rhythm of intersecting images which articulate causes and are, in their obscene nakedness, themselves the effects. By forcing us to concentrate on the imagistic connections—connections traditionally made for us by plot—we are kept, as he says, from taking our own pulse. The artist projects his montage, provides editorial control through the ironic inversion of beauty and obscenity, and that serves as catalyst to the reader's imagination rather than the determinant of it. The rhythmic recurrence of coordinated intersecting images acts as objective correlative. Here is Burroughs' own description:

You can cut into *Naked Lunch* at any intersection point. . . . I have written many prefaces. They atrophy and amputate spontaneous like the little toe amputates in a

West African disease confined to the Negro race and the passing blonde shows her brass ankle as a manicured toe bounces across the club terrace, retrieved and laid at her feet by her Afghan Hound....

Naked Lunch is a blueprint, a How-To Book.... Black insect lusts open into vast, other planet landscapes.... Abstract concepts, bare as algebra, narrow down to a black turd or a pair of aging cajones....

How-To extend levels of experience by opening the door at the end of a long hall.... Doors that only open in *Silence*.... *Naked Lunch* demands Silence from The Reader. Otherwise he is taking his own pulse....

The Word is divided into units which be all in one piece and should be so taken, but the pieces can be had in any order being tied up back and forth, in and out fore and aft like an innaresting sex arrangement. This book spill off the page in all directions, kaleidoscope of vistas, medley of tunes and street noises, farts and riot yipes and the slamming steel shutters of commerce, screams of pain and pathos and screams plain pathic, copulating cats and outraged squawk of the displaced bull head, prophetic mutterings of brujo in nutmeg trances, snapping necks and screaming mandrakes, sigh of orgasm, heroin silent as dawn in the thirsty cells, Radio Cairo screaming like a berserk tobacco auction, and flutes of Ramadan fanning the sick junky like a gentle lush worker in the grey subway dawn feeling with delicate fingers for the green folding crackle....

This is Revelation and Prophecy of what I can pick up without FM on my 1920 crystal set with antennae of jissom.... Gentle reader, we see God through our assholes in the flash bulb of orgasm.... Through these orifices transmute your body.... The way OUT is the way IN....

And, given JUNK as existential metaphor, the images are necessarily obscene in character. For we are all junkie analogues, we all share—we all *must* share—his shamelessness and obscenity:

Take a shot in front of D.L. Probing for a vein in my dirty bare foot.... Junkies have no shame. . . . They are impervious to the repugnance of others. It is doubtful if shame can exist in the absence of sexual libido.... The junky's shame disappears with his non-sexual sociability which is also dependent on libido. . . . The addict regards his body impersonally as an instrument to absorb the medium in which he lives, evaluates his tissue with the cold hands of a horse trader. "No use trying to hit here." Dead fish eyes flick over a ravaged vein.

Without that obscene vision of nakedness we know nothing.

But contemporary Decadence is complicated by the peculiar nature of its spiritual vision. Burroughs' doctrine of separate life, that is personality liberated from nova control, is a spiritual doctrine. But it presents spirit in psychic terms, spirit without theological apparatus, radically humanistic spirit. And the form of his fiction is much influenced, though indirectly through Swift, by a homiletic tradition. Swift's own sermons, of course, were far more humanistic than religious. And the tradition that both Swift and Burroughs share is the medieval "Saccus Stercorum" homily. Fundamental to this thinking is the image of the world as compost heap, decadent and obscene in the eyes of God. Burroughs even has his own text; his book of knowledge is his own profound experience of addiction and its obscenity. His novel, like the homily, takes its authority from this book. Specifically it takes the form of his article on drugs in the *British Journal of Addiction*. Though naturalistic and inverted, it is still a "revealed book", and ultimately speaks to the human spirit. It tells us of new demonic gods, the technocrats, and their new arts. It explains their ways to man. Burroughs, like so many contemporary Decadents, is behind all that decadence and obscenity a man of intellectual faith, faith in the rightness of human personality, faith in the possibility of human dignity, faith that man can know if he will look past the demons he has himself constructed. And he brings the Word, in all its fractured complexity of perception. And perhaps most importantly he tells us that the artist, not the dialectician, is king—that his truth and his alone shall make us see.

Poem for a painter

Compare needles to the shrewd injectors of the State:
A poisoned porcupine dead in the road,
Run down by a one-armed night-blinded veteran
Who counts the birds he leaves sprawling behind him;
Not enough living things have fallen from the sky.
Another man who fights wars in his head
Remains aloft. Puncture his spread arms, doctors,—
Mendicants of eighteen years of our lives,—
And he drops with deflated flaps of skin at his sides,
Plummeting to another sky that turns all ice.
May conservationists take him for a murdered bird,
Then turn, faces strung together like beads,
Reach out and make a perfect capture of themselves.
One-armed in your nineteenth year, sit out the sun,
Become an owl flapping through the burnt shape of the moon.
'Soon there will be nothing left alive above ground,'
You say, leaning your body down canyons;
'I paint what it means for a tortoise to live.'

FLOYCE ALEXANDER

254

RON LOEWINSOHN

"The sea, around us"

The sea, around us. The rain
    so steady these past weeks
it's been like a sea around us.
    & a form
of the sea itself, lapping continuously
    at our shores.
               What we might
get from it, were it truly
    familiar
to us: gold, the stories of the drowned,
    war-weary & bound for home
             —what nourishment
from the wine-dark sea.
          Protein.
But these past weeks it's merely
    a medium thru which we move, clumsily,
this rain falling so steadily,
    breathing as best we can.

           (Once with B, fishing the Yuba,
             up to my waist in it, moving
        my feet
          over the rocky
        bottom, I could feel the steady force of it
         roiling around my body,
        down to my flapping pantslegs, the water
         pouring thru my shoes.
        Down in it the supple trout moving &
         the mosses the same brown as their rocks.

Today there's a similar clumsiness.
    Out there the trees rise up into the grey air,
their branches are out in it;
    their deep roots; their heads
pointing to the raining heavens.
    Paradigms.   At times mocking
paradigms.

The dark green flames
        nourished by that grey light & that grey
rain.   Flames.

It may be their subtle movements, but
        like flames there is a space around them
that is still
them.
            In the steady pressure of the Yuba
        I could feel that space around myself,
& the trout too had that space around them, which they
        occupied. Like those trees—

But now, walking into the wet evening
        & seeing them there,
the wet green flame-like trees, the spaces
        around them

—& the spaces between us in-
        habited by falling
specks of water—

        This girl walked past me, her hair
in the light available to me
        falling around her shoulders as yours
does, wet now, & dark. There were those spaces
        between us, too, where you might say,
There, there is a speck of rain, & there.
        —& be wrong every time.

                        Sometimes I step back into myself
                        & there's no one home.

This rain, which I make
        a form of the sea, a sea-form,
& wrestle with it.
        & I'm wrong every time.
It's you: I'm learning that, a space
        between us, all around me like
the sea, or the light that I haven't
        256

wrestled with enough, & so
haven't learned yet.

This rain, those trees
    have been around a long time, familiar
to each other in all their forms,
    in all their changes.   The trees
live off the light, & the rain
    falls day & night.

Summer

As the morning advanced the sun became bright
and warm, cloudless, calm, serene. About nine
an appearance very unusual began to demand our
attention—a shower of cobwebs falling from
very elevated regions, & continuing, without
any interruption, till the close of the day . . .

There is a natural occurrence to be met with upon
the highest part of our down in hot summer days,
and that is a loud audible humming of bees in
the air, though not one insect is to be seen . . .

In a district so diversified as this, so full of
hollow vales and hanging woods, it is no wonder
that echoes should abound. Many we have dis-
covered that return a tunable ring of bells, or
the melody of birds; but we were still at a loss
for a polysyllabical, articulate echo, till a
young gentleman, who had parted from his company
in a summer walk, and was calling after them,
stumbled upon a very curious one in a spot where
it might least be expected . . .

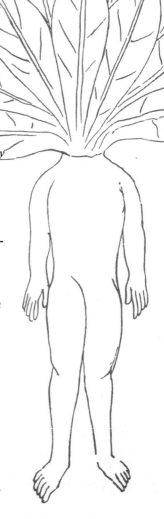

We procured a cuckoo, and cutting open the breast-
bone and exposing the intestines to sight, found
the crop lying as mentioned above. This stomach
was large and round, and stuffed hard, like a
pincushion, with food, which upon nice examination
we found to consist of various insects, such as
small scarabs, spiders, and dragon-flies; the last
of which, as they were just emerging out of the
aurelia state, we have seen cuckoos catching on
the wing. Among this farrago also were to be seen
maggots, and many seeds, which belonged either to
gooseberries, currants, cranberries, or some such
fruit . . .

All nature is so full, that that district produces
the greatest variety which is the most examined . . .

258

1

Upon first opening a cuckoo

I saw the sweet-briar & bon-fire & strawberry wire now

relaxed into intricate thicket.

It was as if seen in strong sunlight, flat

& tapestried, all edge & definition. Here, an airy bone shaped

like a plowshare, there, vibratory membranes within a space

from which the song must come: a syrinx (hollow

pipes of reeds) now silent

in return to the 'Salliter' of earth.

Little more than

a drift of air, brought

into form by plumes.

Mulch to stone.

Yeast of the clouds.

2

What the earth told me

No surface is allowed to be bare,

& nothing to stand still. A man could forever study a pebble

& at last see dilations & expansions of the hills—

to pull the most slender stalk, is to jostle the stars,

& between the bearded grass

& man 'looking in the vegetable glass

of Nature', is a network of roots & suckers

fine as hairs.

I threw a stone upon a pond

& it bounded the surface, its circles interlacing

& radiating out to the most ephemeral edge.

Flint & Mica, Lichened Limestone, Shale & Sarcens, Sandstone, Soil.

259

I saw the wind moving on a meadow

& the meadows moving under wind—

lifting, settling & accumulating.

Flint & Mica, Lichened Limestone,

Shale & Sarcens, Sandstone, Soil.

3
What the air told me

It is breathed into Orpheus' lyre & as rocks & trees & beasts
is divided there. Its original strain

precedes the sound, by as much as echoes follow after:
the quivering of 'cow-quake', a 'loud audible
humming of bees on the down', stresses within the sustaining earth,
clouds of *fleece* & *mare's tail*.

I saw with single eye, the facet of the fly—
the infinitesimal mechanics & all the metallic sheens
of a blue-bottle. In a land where the sun grows fat on cloud
& *summer hasn't come*
till your foot can cover twenty daisies,

she came to the dark, open beak
& laid a myriad of eggs. And in two days' time the dead
bird's body simulated life: maggots in eye-socket &
under feather, in a subtle movement.

The White & The Glistening.

4
What the leaf told me

Today I saw the word written on the poplar leaves.

It was 'dazzle'. *The dazzle of the poplars.*

As a leaf startles out

from an undifferentiated mass of foliage,
so the word did from a leaf—

A Mirage Of The Delicate Polyglot
inventing itself as cipher. But this, in shifts & gyrations,
grew in brightness, so bright

the massy poplars soon outshone the sun . . .

'My light—my dews—my breezes—my bloom'. Reflections

In A Wren's Eye.

5
De vegetabilibus

For there are splendors of flowers called DAY'S EYES in every field.
For one cannot walk but to walk upon sun.
For the sun has also a stem, on which it turns.

For the tree forms sun into leaves, & its branches & saps
are solid & liquid states of sun.
For the sun has many seasons, & all of them summer.

For the carrot & bee both bless with sun,
the carrot beneath the earth & the bee with its dusts & honies.

For sun has stippled the pear & polished the apple.

261

6
De animalibus

For there are owls in the air & moles in the earth
& THEY ALSO have eyes.

For there are shapes of air which are OWL
& shapes of earth which are MOLE,
& the mole brings air to the earth & the owl, earth into air.

For the turtle's back is another firmament & dappled like the cloud.
For there are birds who nest on the earth
& are feathered in its form.
For the rook & the worm are only one cycle out of many.

For man rejoices with rook & worm
& owl & mole & turtle,
& they are only one cycle out of many.

7
Turner, Constable & Stubbs

To see, Turner had himself lashed to the ship's mast
& Constable sat still in the fields
till something came—a bird—'some living thing appropriate to
the place'. He noted the wind's direction, pile
of clouds, the time of day. Stubbs
fixed an iron bar to the ceiling of his room, with hooks
of various sizes & lengths, in order to suspend the body of a horse.
The horse remained for six or seven weeks
'until no longer endurable'.
The form of muscles, blood vessels & nerves was retained
by tallow injections—Stubbs methodically
cutting to the skeleton, making full length drawings
& studies of the ear & nose.
'He was possessed of great physical
strength, being able,
it is said, to carry a dead horse on his back
to a dissecting room,
at the top of a narrow flight of stairs'.

The work was finished in eighteen months.

262

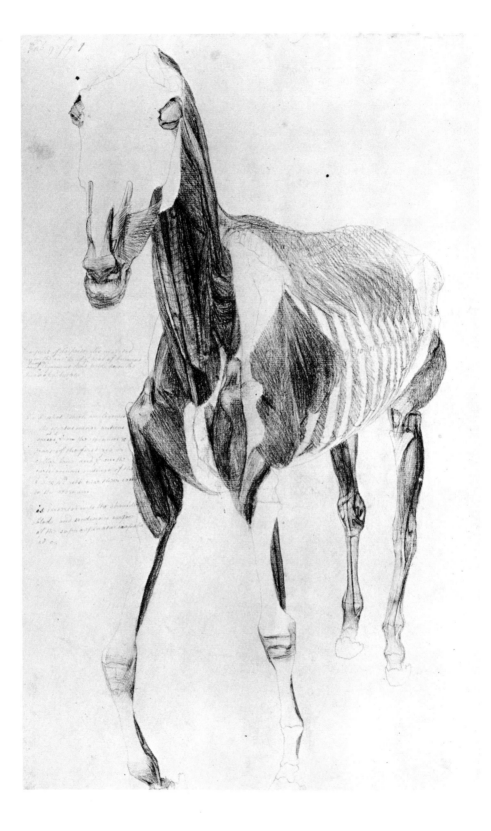

8
Natural productions, occurrences & antiquities

'August is by much the most mute month', yet,

the air may be so strongly electric

that bells may ring & sparks be discharged in their clappers:

'put a bird in motion, *et vera incessu patuit . . .*'

To distinguish a bird by its 'air', to 'hear'

the buoyant owls—woodpeckers rising & falling in curves

—the perpendicularity of skylarks . . .

Gilbert White quotes from the Latin: *He preferred*

the sounds of birds to those of men. The music of men left his mind

disturbed by engaging his attention

with its rise & fall, while the warbling

of birds left no such hold

'to tease my imagination & recur irresistibly

at seasons . . .'

All day the cobweb fell silently

in the air, till whole

baskets-full lay round about, & still

more descending.

9
The leaves of Southwell

Maple & hawthorn & oak. Crow-foot & cinquefoil

(Aubrey's Midsummer Silver?).

Vine & ivy & hops. Rose, bryony (a Mandrake), geranium, mulberry,

wormwood. Fig, bittersweet & blackthorn.

It is an assemblage (a community?) including its dragons with

crisply carved acorns.

264

Two hounds devour a hare. A bird seizes a grape with its
beak. Both green men & the winged

fruit of maple are in hierarchy of accuracy—the ribbed & the delicate
ascending to the general. But here, a throat

come aleaf, there a branch held aloft.
And a kind of greening speech comes from those mouths

all but winged—each leaf
cleft & articulate. Southwell, of the leaves

of limestone: trefoil, quatrefoil, cinquefoil (as *foil* means
leaf): a 'burnisht corall' & geranium

brain: cranesbill, crow-foot: blackthorn & whitehorn,
quickthorn, Jack-in-the-green:

a man cleft, as Mandrakes, the 'man-shaped dragon',
Mandragora: (an agora?).

Exhibit from Frederik Ruysch's Anatomical Museum

A skeleton balances an injected spermatic plexus
in one hand & a coil of viscera
in the other. Minatory assortments

of calculi of all sizes
occupy the foreground. In the rear, a
variety of injected vessels, backed by an inflated & injected

tunica vaginalis,
combine to form a grotesque & arboreal
perspective. Another skeleton,

in extremis, is grasping a skeleton
of that emblem of insect mortality, the mayfly, & a third
is performing

a composition 'expressing the sorrows of mankind'
on a violin, symbolized
by bundles of arteries & a fragment

of necrotic femur.
Bones are arranged to represent
a cemetery—wrists are adorned with organic & injected

frills—& human, comparative
& pathological exhibits
are mingled, as the exigencies of space required.

11

'Unless the humming of a gnat is as the music of the spheres

& the music of the spheres is as the humming
of a gnat . . .' *A spectre came, transparent-winged,*

out of the interstices of light,

& shadow went up like smoke & everywhere
the hills were as clouds over valleys of water, rippling
& reverberating.

And before him the sands of the beach swarmed as insects, close-knit
in electrical flight . . .
'For MATTER is the dust of the Earth,

every atom of which is the life.

For the flames of fire may be blown thro musical pipes'.

And everywhere the hills were as clouds over
valleys of water, rippling

& reverberating.

12
What the light told me

It is now a circle, now a spiral or wheel.

It merges with the eye, with a wing or a sickle-shaped horn.

It takes on the form of beasts—a dragon, fish or bird.

As an orb, at summer solstice,
it balances on the altar-stone at Stonehenge—

& as beam, expands, elongates, twists & 'attenuates
itself into leafen gold
as a covering for the quince'.

With arc & parabolic
& serpent-oblique—'musical in ocular
harmony'. Expanding, elongating, twisting
& attenuating.

An encompassing eye.
Within and out, round as a ball—
With hither and thither, as straight as a line.
Slight as a fox-whisker,
sickled & spiraled as chicory-flower.

Within and out, round as a ball—
With hither and thither, as straight as a line.
With lily, germander
And sops-in-wine. With sweet-briar and
Bon-fire and strawberry wire
And columbine.

---

[1]"De Rerum Naturis", about 1023. Courtesy of The Warburg Institute, London.
[2,3]Nest of Willow Wren and The Shell of Gilbert White's Tortoise from the 1896 edition of *The Natural History and Antiquities of Selborne* by Gilbert White. (Bickers & Son, London).
[4]Courtesy of Royal Academy of Arts, London.
[5]Courtesy of Courtauld Institute of Art, England.
[6]F. Ruysch, "Thesaurus Anatomicus." Courtesy of "The Wellcome Trustees", Wellcome Historical Medical Library.

The dream
of the soldier

Our guns are spiked with a difficult silence

My gun hops round in a circle, re-loading itself

I have wound the steel of it with holly
I have stuck sprigs in the perforated barrel
I have anointed the bullets
I have kissed the stock with tinsel

I have placed my gun in an oxygen tent with intelligent tenderness
and I am keeping watch over it by night

This gun is my beloved father,
in whom I am well pleased

■

All night the great bridges fell,
dripping a green rust of music.
They fell into ravines this country does not possess.
The leader has been negotiating with a foreign power
for some chasms,
to intimidate the people.

And all night the Parachutists fell, like a Pentecost.
For some, it was hours of waiting
at an inter-section of air current,
denied permission to fall further,
jiggling in the night sky, not quite still, a thistle
grim with equipment.

And some fell softly but more fast, like a white
language. Falling
to meet our needs.

269

II

And they are raining on us our mothers, our dead
uncles, sisters we have had, red
Irish dogs long forgotten, orchards, farms, they know
we are in need,
and they have snowed us,
and the enemy will get nowhere near us.

■

The wind was wet
        with the easiest wounds
I tore up the paths
        for difficult bandages

I revolved on a bush
        like a turkey unclothing
I pumped a pullet
    with bullets of milk

I counted the guilty
        I killed in my sleep
Their blood streamed over
        the fences like sheep

■

The soldier comes to me
He is a tenor

He is a shining bullet
in a casing,
a husk of green cloth

Carve my hands
            they are bread
Pack my legs in a flask
            they are coffee
Wrap me up   pour me out
Feed the earth, I wish it
wet with my meaning

Choose me a neighborhood of bullets

III

Set fire to the dog pound
        for my family
Photograph birth
        from a great height
Take stills
        of my breathing
Apply hotels to my temples
        in torture

Unless you put your hands in my wounds
and most surely the wounds of these men,
unless you should so do,
we will not believe you

Wash me in orders
        Read me hot chocolate
Tape up my germs
        Grow me again in a greenhouse
Mount me
        Cut me down

The rains suffer heavy casualties
the rains are raw and new
the rains stiffen

Blow my nose with a battalion
        Chew my gun till it sounds good
Feed me Yugoslavia
        Beget me Hawaii
Christen my children Illinois
        Hang Copenhagen from these branches

Have the whole platoon
washing its weapons in death

271

IV

My wounds excreting silver

The bombs breathing on the water three times
The bombs bleeding on the water

Each bomb is a hermit tortured through and past pain

The bombs exchange shirts on the way down

Now this   and this   easy it is easy   snow as

Call to us   come to us crying
we
will not rise again

■

Orbit a satellite under the earth:
do the dead repose, O tell me,
in radioactive belts,
and will we ever be suited
to travel there, through and beyond
the rings and coils of our dear dead
to the hot moon earth's core?
O you will need special clothing
not to be contaminated
on the lengthy excursion through your dead.

■

I have mailed letters to all my wounds
informing them they are disgusting
I have arranged citations for wild geese
who chose to fly south
I am having my wife enlarged

I have issued weapons to pianos
I have set the cinemas adrift
to float burning and sow panic among
the slow fleets of civilan opinion
I have arranged alarming armadas of sunlight

V

The reservoirs have gone berserk
          and are spilling the beans to the enemy
the city parks have thrown up their green and gold
                    golf courses in horror
the motels are out on their own roofs
watching the night sky for signs

The White House has been holed below the water line
                    and is sinking fast
the archives are shifting dangerously
the hands of thirteen million secretaries
                    are being held as hostages
the skirts of the women of America
                    have been raised to the patriotic maximum
as they wade the sexual waters of war

∎

I am out of the hearing of bleeding

Looking down on the fighting from a great height
I find my mouth filled with moss
which is burning

My tongue has been sent for
my hands are standing by

Clothe my body in the information
                    you have brought back
Read between the lines of the enemy

TAKE MY HANDS AWAY CAREFULLY
I HAVE NO OTHERS
BLOW MY FEET OFF BEAUTIFULLY
THE ONLY I OWN

I HAVE AN EAR FOR LANGUAGE
REMOVE IT GENTLY

273

VI

Sentries are patrolling
  with dogs in their arms
The chaplain has grown a white
  beard in his mind
The orchestras have been anointed
  and are dying

Squirrels are assembling
  helicopters in Montana
The National Guard are learning to fly
  underwater in Mexico
The long-term prisoners are learning to play
  the guitar through the bars

The maimed are sculpting with their noses

■

The throwers of flame, bring them forward

The river melts into equipment,
the hands of the river
are pulled off at the roots;
grass bleeds with the idea of enemies;
the eyes, they seemed to die, in the
eyes of the dead, the eyes.

The throwers of flame, bring them forward

■

Your fingers touching the map
bruise it.
The globe of the world
is eye so veined with countries
it cannot see.
Asia is a cataract.
The Pacific is a rigid tear.
Africa is a scar for ever.
I may not tell you of the shape
of the Americas.

Asia has cut off its ear
and sent it to us.

VII

I stamped on the burning wheat
and the wheat was a child;
the water was living in rings
and the eyes of the water were wild.

Toward evening we sat in the willows and village
        drinking our guns

I hanged a gnat from the roof
        of a hut with my belt

This is a child
This is a pig
This is foam

Obey it

■

A great wind
crawls through the wounds of these children
green limbs of them
green hair of them

I hear the groves of wounds at the water's edge

Unless you put your hands in such wounds
and most surely the wounds of these children,
unless you should so do
we will not believe you

No wound has a still center

Each wound has a liquid eye, watching
Each wound has doors that will not heal

The trees see fit to wither

275

VIII

I have seen the planes come,
and the tall hands of their commanders.

But most of all did I see, as their long loads fell,
Age, in search of his lost sons, climbing there,
mounting with fevered eyes through those falling stairs,
seeking, in the dark that is newly come to light,
Hope, Belief, Expectation and Love,
his maimed irretrievable children.

MICHAEL DENNIS BROWNE

Beyond the baroque: *the role of the audience in the modern theater*

LESLIE EPSTEIN

It is a commonplace of aesthetics that the baroque imagination—an uneasiness with formal limitations; an acute self-consciousness about what one is doing; an all-pervasive doubt about the worth, even the reality, of the work of art—is a regularly reoccurring phenomenon in the plastic and literary arts. Heinrich Wölfflin has defined the differences between Renaissance and 17th-century Italian architecture in terms that illuminate the entire baroque sensibility:

In place of the perfect, the completed—the restless, the becoming; in place of the limited, the conceivable—the limitless, the colossal. The idea of beautiful proportion vanishes, interest concentrates not on being, but on happening.

Yet beneath this periodicity of styles, the regular alternation between the classical conception of the work of art as a finished, fixed, and bounded object, and the baroque idea that it is never finished but rather part of a

277

process crying for completion, an unbounded subject, there has been a steady and hardly wavering, and indeed quite obvious, growth of artistic subjectivity. It is not my purpose here to discover the precise origins of this trend. After all, from the primitive tattooing his own body to Fellini doing much the same thing in a film like *8½*, the artist's real interest and one masterpiece has always been, to one degree or another, himself. Moreover, even in the classical eras, the subject matter of music, painting, and literature has remained, though deviously, music, painting, and literature. Be that as it may, through the emphasis upon individual creativity in the Renaissance; through the turning of the artist into a god in the 17th-century and art into a religion in the 18th; through the hero worship not of the character but of the author, and the author's complementary histrionics in the 19th-century; and through such modern movements as impressionism, surrealism, expressionism and abstract art (in which the personality of the artist is the totality of the work: in other words, the return to tattooing), the stress has been continually and increasingly away from the objective depiction of the artist's relations to nature and society, and toward the subjective realization of the artist's relations with himself. It is no longer the work's "proximity to reality that proves its value," Ernst Kris has remarked, "but its nearness to the artist's psychic life."

In the history of almost all the arts since the eighteenth century the trend to an increased insistence on inspiration seems to be detectable—dominant in certain phases, more submerged in others, and yet clearly continuous as a movement that gained increasing strength, to the point where dream and fantasy could be painted and put into words, where relation to stringencies became less important, and where finally the work of art became a document of the process of creation. *(Psychoanalytic Explorations in Art.)*

Now what has happened in contemporary art can only be described as a triumph of what Wölfflin calls "the will to alienate the picture from the frame." For it is only through the exercise of that will that, on the one hand, the boundary between the creator and his creation dissolves and, on the other, the lines separating the work and its public are loosed, so that the spectator not only experiences but participates in what he sees or hears. I take this to be the single most important characteristic of the baroque: the identification, the merging, of art, artist, and audience. The three become indistinguishable parts of a single creative experience. My thesis is that these elements, nicely balanced and equally emphasized in baroque art, have fallen into desperate disarray in contemporary, or post-baroque, art.

Before inspecting that disarray, and the role the modern audience plays in it, I think it would be best to define more clearly the attitude of baroque art toward reality, and most specifically toward the spectator, by examining a traditional masterpiece of the genre, Velazquez' *Las Meninas* (1656, The Prado). In a large rectangular room, Velazquez has portrayed himself before his easel, while nearby the Infanta stands surrounded by her retinue. The rear and right side walls of the chamber are visible, and they are covered by a single mirror and a group of large, dim paintings. The formal organization of the work seems, at first glance, clear and strict. There are three receding planes, in the first of which, arranged like props and actors on a stage, are the back of Velazquez' canvas, the two maids of honor, two dwarfs, a dog, and, of course, the Infanta, with her stiff starched skirt and dazzling hair. In the second plane, which forms the middle ground, are Velazquez, palate and brush in hand, a nun, and a middle-aged man, perhaps a tutor. The final plane consists of the rear wall of the room, and a courtier who stands in an open, brightly-lit doorway. The painting is tied together by a jungle-gym of rectangles: Velazquez' canvas and the struts of its stretcher, the doorway and the door and the twenty-two panels set into it, the frames of the paintings on the walls and the spaces between the frames, and so on.

Yet the more rigid the structure seems, the more resoundingly it disintegrates when we look more closely. For the central rectangle, and in many ways the second focus of *Las Meninas* (competing as it does with the Infanta's hair), is the mirror on the back wall, the mirror in which we suddenly see the formal, posed, and posing faces of the King and Queen. Immediately the space in the painting, so elaborately delineated and controlled, collapses. The rear wall leaps forward, even out of the painting, to where the royal couple stand—an area roughly corresponding to our vantage-point in the museum—heads slightly tilted, waiting for posterity. What can be made out of their expression reveals they have little idea of the joke that Velazquez is in the act of playing upon them. For it is clear that the canvas the painter is working upon is meant to be a royal portrait. The artist leans backward, staring at his invisible subjects. Five of the other people in the room do likewise; they are there not to have their pictures painted, but to accompany the sitting of the King and Queen.

But instead of the faces of the royal couple, Velazquez has painted a portrait of the artistic process itself. The King and Queen, who are meant to be immortalized, are caught only fleetingly in a mirror, the seat of all illusion, while the bystanders, the spectators, are made the permanent subject of the work (particularly the Infanta, in whom, of course, the King's posterity *does* reside). But Velazquez has also captured those other bystanders, the viewers of the painting, we ourselves, who stand—physically and aesthetically—in the same relation to the work as the missing King and Queen; and we too age, while *Las Meninas* remains resplendent.

There are two other elements which further undermine the reality, the solidity, the *composure,* of the work. The paintings that surround the mirror on the back wall have been identified: they are all rather poor copies of Flemish originals—in other words, reproductions of fakes of paintings of distant realities, paintings within paintings within paintings, barbershop mirrors. (In the Prado, the viewer is caught between the large mirror set up by sly museum officials, and the painting, in which he is similarly reflected.) Moreover, these are not the only framed works in the painting. There is the Infanta framed by her maids of honor, the courtier in the frame of the doorway, the formal faces of the King and Queen framed by the molding of the mirror, and the frame on the back of the canvas on which Velazquez is working. Each interior image tends to undermine the reality of the frame that surrounds it, until the largest, most ornate, and most substantial frame of all—that surrounding *Las Meninas*—dissolves altogether, and the viewer trembles to say where life ends and art begins.

Even more important is Velazquez' quasi-impressionist style, which emphasizes the tenuousness of the connection between what Velazquez has painted and what we see, object and image. If the spectator moves closer to the canvas—that is, if he violates his role as the true subject of the painting, the object of the Spaniards' gaze, stand-ins for the King and Queen—everything breaks apart, vanishes before the eyes. The Infanta's hair does not resolve itself into separate strands, but dissolves into a shining haze; the patterns on the ladies' dresses do not maintain any recognizable geometry, but shatter into a series of incomprehensible brush strokes. The whole painting, up close, falls into dissolution, becomes haphazard patches of color and disorganized motes of light. The organization of *Las Meninas* is only in the beholder's eye—and only when he retreats to where the artist has already placed him, posing for his portrait. In short, *Las Meninas* is a very witty painting whose statement is not limited to the nature of longevity, the artistic process, the relationship of appearance and reality, but includes, as well, a commentary upon the subtle tensions of remaining for thirty-five years the official painter to a court ruled by a man as ugly as Philip IV.

In a recent issue of this journal, Charles Newman wrote, "Do we ask whether we *trust* a composer, a painter?" The answer, of course, is that we'd better: Velazquez, at any rate, knew how to put his tongue in his cheek. I have spent so much time with *Las Meninas* because we are most accustomed to speaking of baroque in connection with the plastic arts, and this is an acknowledged masterpiece of the genre. But the tendency to merge art, artist, and audience that is the hallmark of the baroque sensibility is by no means limited to any one form of expression, and in what follows I should like to suggest that it is the drama to which, of all the arts, the baroque is most congenial—and this despite the presence of the proscenium arch which, for drama critics no less than the general public, has done for the theatre what the frame has done for painting; distanced the very illusion it helped to create.

Ironically enough, the drama is not, at least in the technical sense, a proscenium art. The word proscenium itself originally meant only the stage —that is, the area in front of the dressing room upon which the actors performed. In the Elizabethan theater it meant the forestage, the apron where most of the action took place; this apron was thrust directly into the crowd, which stood on three sides of it, in direct, almost intimate contact with the actors, without hindrance of border or frame. This has been the nature of the theater during the periods of its greatness. Indeed, one could tabulate the theater's decline or health by the extent to which it is framed or free, classical or baroque. The particular kind of doubt, the reflecting mirrors effect, generated by *Las Meninas,* has permeated a drama—as how could it not?—designed for a stage that was itself (the Globe is the most famous example) a metaphor for reality. Lionel Abel's term for the kind of drama which erases all distinctions between the play and the world around it, is metatheater, which "assumes there is no world except that created by human striving, human imagination," and that that "world is a projection of human consciousness"; or, as Oberon put it, "The poet's pen . . . gives to airy nothing / A local habitation and a name." Abel believes the origins of metatheater to be Elizabethan. While he is wrong to deny the extent to which a writer like Euripides conceived the whole tragic superstructure as a projection of the human psyche ("O Artemis," cries Iphigenia at Tauris, "these people, being murderers themselves, / Are charging Thee with their own wickedness"), and to ignore that large percentage of Euripidean action which takes place under spells, charms, bewitchment, and trickery, he is nonetheless correct to emphasize the tremendous influence of Shakespeare upon the baroque theater.

For what remains a strain in Euripides becomes an obsession with Shakespeare, whose entire career is marked by an increasing and at times compulsive concern with doubles and replicas and reflections, the disguises, plays-within-plays, and hidden manipulators that serve to substitute fabrication for reality. Running through these devices, and eventually taking them over, is the metaphor of life as sleep and existence as dream. And within that metaphor there is another image, which ultimately (in the last plays) becomes coterminous with it—that of creation as a work of art. We are such stuff as dreams are made on is joined to all the world's a stage, so that the dreamer is a creator, the chief actor an artist. Or, as Strindberg put it in the preface to *A Dream Play,* "There is, however, one single-minded consciousness that exercises a dominance over the characters: the dreamer's."

That dreamer, of course, is Prospero, hardly a man one would trust without question. For on his island no event is real. The shipwreck—with all its realistic dialogue and detail—is a show, the very weather so much sleight of hand. Every action, however innocent, is only a trick, which itself is the mechanism of a larger plot, which in turn is part of an even more elaborate design. No man in *The Tempest* is what he seems to be, no behavior is straightforward, the smallest gesture immediately gnarls, tangles into scheme and counterscheme; Sebastian and Antonio connive Alonso's murder; Caliban, Trinculo, and Stephano plan to usurp Prospero's rule; and Ariel is everywhere to hidden music, arranging a series of revelations and terrors, spells and entertainments for the visitors to the island. Prospero's accomplishment, finally, is the dissolution of our sense of, trust in, reality. Should any circumstance be taken at its face, or even its imagined, value, he immediately undercuts it by shifting its context, like a magician pulling the cloth from a carefully set table. The hidden hand behind the action, the manipulator behind every movement, overturn natural law. The characters are denied that coefficient of experience by which they might check what is happening to them, by which they might measure the decline of their stature to puppets, the receding of the circumstances in which they are caught into an image within a reflection, a play-within-a-play-within-a-play.

Shakespeare used the play-within-the-play as the dramatic equivalent to Velazquez' reproductions of the Spanish copies of the Rubens works that Philip IV evidently admired. And so, however imperfectly, do all plays-within-plays function for us, undermining the credibility of the surrounding action. If we know that the innermost action is a fake, "only a play," then what about those other actors whose gestures are so similar? And what, indeed, about that largest action, life itself, to which the drama holds so many mirrors? A second function of the play-within-a-play is to dramatize the situation and the powers of the artist, as Velazquez did in *Las Meninas,* or as Shakespeare did when he restaged a traditional playlet for the diversion of the King and Queen at Elsinore. That scene, of course, epitomizes the functional relation of the work of art to its audience. "The play's the thing / Wherein I'll catch the conscience of the King!" Claudius starts from the chamber, as if from a nightmare, calling for light, and while the stress of the scene is upon the relationship of the King to his entertainment, it would be foolish to ignore that of the playwright to his work (staging and rewriting is, for Hamlet, symbolic action, standing for and clearing the way for the real movement he is not yet ready to make); or that of the playwright to his society (Hamlet has exposed, revealed, and endangered himself as much as Claudius by transforming *The Murder of Gonzago* into *The Mousetrap*). The scene, then, exposes in miniature the varying relationships of designer and design, of artist, art, and audience.

In Shakespeare's work, as in Velazquez', there is an equal emphasis upon the work, the man who made it, and upon those for whom it was made. Yet no sooner did Shakespeare create and perfect the baroque theater than it begins to pass into a new, and post-baroque, phase. The crucial difference between his plays and those of the modern theater is the absence of that "one single-minded consciousness," Prospero busy with his plans, Hamlet carefully calculating the effect of his craftsmanship upon his intended audience. What has happened to the baroque in modern times is that the delicate inter-relatedness of art, artist, and audience (a nexus perfectly expressed at the end of *The Tempest*, when the omnipotent magician gives himself up —in symbolic prostration—to the spells and mercy of the audience) has been violated by the abdication of the artist, especially from that Prosperine exercise of intelligence and control, with the consequent running amok of the audience. This disruption of balance, this abdication of the artist, is exemplified best by what is in many ways the first modern play, Pirandello's *Six Characters in Search of an Author*.

In this work, the artist, a playwright, having conceived a set of characters, proceeds to abandon them, to withdraw from their lives and to leave the stage entirely to them. One of the many ironies that spring from this abandonment is that the author's absence, instead of freeing the characters, burdens them intolerably. That burden is the crushing weight of non-fulfillment. Each of these characters is bound, to an almost Aeschylean degree, by a sense of destiny. Each (rather, the Father and Step-daughter, who drag the others behind them) feels it his destiny to realize somehow the character and the situation he has been given. If that is not—in the Greek sense—their fate, it is, in the Father's terms, their sole "raison d'être," their one purpose in elbowing their way onto the stage. Each exists, in short, to become a playwright.

None quite makes it. All their attempts to bring their story to what they conceive to be its noble, tragic conclusion—or just to enact a simple scene, to impose *any* degree of order upon their unformed experience— dissolve into chaos and, more significantly, laughter. That is to say, none of the characters is capable of being an author, though each seems to have been delegated a portion of Pirandello's powers. Hence the characters act as their own muse: the sight of one another compels them to speak. Those characters most deeply involved in the miasma of their common experience seem to have the most creative power. The Father magically conjures Madame Pace and keeps declaring, "The drama consists in this . . ."; while the Step-daughter goes about acting like a director, telling characters when and how to make their entrances and deliver their lines. She, in particular, has the ability to act as a muse, especially when she goes into a trance in order to inspire, tempt, invoke the missing author and draw him onto the stage:

It's true. I too have sought to tempt him, many, many times, when he has been sitting at his writing table, feeling a bit melancholy, at the twilight hour. He would sit in his armchair too lazy to switch on the light, and all the shadows that crept into his room were full of our presence coming to tempt him . . . (Makes a sudden movement as if in the vision she has of herself illuminating those shadows she wanted to seize hold of herself.) Ah! my life! my life! Oh, what scenes we proposed to him—and I tempted him more than any of the others!

In production this monologue is often moved to the beginning of the play, so that throughout the action the author's chair, and hence the author, are present at the side of the stage. The monologue only underlines what is perhaps the most acute irony in the author's abdication: that his withdrawal is really an intrusion. In no other play are we so aware, not only of the functions of the author, but of his work and the intricate workings of his mind. The Step-daughter apostrophizes him, the Manager discusses his ideas, the actors start off with a parody of his work. Pirandello is not only present, he is omnipresent—as a personality and as, in a fashion, an activity, and further, in a strict formal sense, as the missing character of the play, the antagonist whose own action (or lack of it) is the obstacle to the self-realization of every other character. It is difficult to avoid the impression that at times he is the protagonist as well, that the struggle in *Six Characters* is between the artist's unconscious and conscious, fantasy and form, and that the play is a portrait not so much of Pirandello as a man, or even as an artist, but of the creative components, in action, in flux, of his mind.

As each attempt by the characters to become an author, to invoke *the* author, fails, they come to rely more and more heavily upon the authority of their audience, the Manager and his company, who in turn also start to behave like authors ("Oh," says the Manager airily at one point, "we'll cut him out"). Yet this second delegation of artistic responsibility takes the characters still further from fulfillment, from the release of expression, and still closer to comedy. In *Six Characters,* the theatrical company represents life, society, the world—and ultimately that audience for whom a work of art must always justify itself. The misfortune for the six characters is not that the author and the company use each other, but that they *cannot* make use of each other. The world has its rules and conventions ("It says so in the Book") and must necessarily distort what it represents. This is nicely illustrated in the opening scene. The play-within-a-play *(Il giuoco delle parti)* is stiff and rigid, with fixed entrances and exits and stereotyped movements. Its inflexibility is so extreme that the action is a parody of what it is supposed to represent, in this instance a play of Pirandello:

Dialogue: "The empty form of reason without the fullness of instinct, which is blind." —You stand for reason, your wife is instinct. It's a mixing up of the parts, according to which you act your own part and become a puppet of yourself. Do you understand?

In exactly the same way, when the acting company attempts to perform the scenes they have just seen the six characters relive, the results are either unrecognizable or also a parody, and the family breaks into laughter.

The effect of this is characteristically subtle. Life, society, the responses of the audience, distort a work of art. But here the onlookers are represented by an artistic company, and the work of art, the unfinished play, is really a slice of life. Thus the acting of the family is true, "real," while the style of the company is artificial and false. "You're not going to pretend you can act!" says art to life. Madame Pace, to give another instance, is a real character; yet she moves naturally, "in a manner impossible for the stage." The family are characters in a play and real people; the stage company are real people, but actors. When the actors perform the characters laugh; when the characters relive their experience, the actors are bored. The trouble is that the two groups touch always in the wrong places, with the result that a kind of blocking out, a censorship, takes place, and neither group can help the other. Each destroys the value of the other group, though it needs it to realize itself. The form, then, is exactly what Pirandello called it, a comedy in the making.

Because the six characters wander onto a stage (they might have tried to convince a group of factory workers, for example; they *would* have if the play had been by Brecht) baroque doubt is intense. The stage company acts a play-within-a-play, and the company's attempts to enact what they see the family do is a further recession from reality—instead of, of course, the attempt to come to grips with it the characters desired. As in *The Tempest,* art frames actuality, and one loses one's grip on what is true. The pull of the company is always away from the tragic, from the fulfillment, the catharsis the characters require, and toward the trivial and the comic— either in outright parody, or in the kind of visual punning that occurs when the real curtain is accidentally substituted for the word "curtain," or when at the end of the play the Manager trivializes the action by making it an incident, a cause not for pity or fear but for annoyance, the loss of a day's work: "Pretense? Reality? To hell with it all!"

I have said earlier that the identification of art, artist, and audience is the hallmark of the baroque. What Pirandello has done, in this work as elsewhere, is to see that set of relationships in terms of conflict. Here is an excerpt from his "Premise" to *Six Characters, Each in His Own Way,* and *Tonight We Improvise:*

In the first [play] the conflict is between the Characters and the Actors and the Actor-Manager; in the second, between the Spectators and the Author and the Actors; in the third, between the Actors become Characters and their Director.

Similarly, compare Wölfflin's original definition of the baroque with Pirandello's description of *Six Characters* in his Preface:

Nothing in this play exists as given and preconceived. Everything is in the making, is in motion, is a sudden experiment: even the place in which this unformed life, reaching after its own form, changes and changes again contrives to shift position organically.

The concepts are virtually identical, except that what is "in the making" here is not a comedy but an audience, an audience which no longer shares, but has started to take over the function of the work of art and its creator. It is the audience which—in the role of the stage company, a chorus that stands for the "real" audience in the theater—immobilizes and then swallows up the characters and their story, reducing them to the level of spectators at their own drama, forcing even the playwright to become a passive witness of his own processes of creation. This is a transitional work. The abdication of the author is not complete, and the ending (the final gunshot acts like the mirror in *Las Meninas,* shattering all frames, confounding image and reality) is a baroque tour de force. Nevertheless, the audience, no longer consciously controlled and manipulated with a magic wand and a secret book, has had a taste of freedom: in the modern, entirely post-baroque theater it will become hungry and ubiquitous.

The passivity of the artist, his extraordinary abasement before the audience, is carried further in the work of Brecht. (Brecht's technique would seem a negation and not an extension of the baroque sensibility. That is, the *Verfremdung* effect appears to drive a wedge between the audience and the work of art, to separate, not join the two. In fact, its purpose is typically baroque: the audience is raised to the intellectual level, given the awareness and the fervor of the hero, becomes the hero, and hence, hopefully, capable of finishing the drama, carrying out his program, *in the world,* on the stage

286

of history.) An early play like *Baal* is a good example of what has happened to artist and audience in modern drama.

The extraordinary thing about Baal is not his criminality. After all, the murderer, the sodomite, the thief, the seducer, the betrayer, the madman, the diseased, the alcoholic are all variations on what has always been the artist's traditional role. What is remarkable about Baal is that he should be all these things not because he is a poet but because he is not a poet, because he abandons, turns over to his audience, his poetry. I mean to say that Baal despises his art because it demands that he be conscious. The whole action of the play is his attempt to escape awareness, and with it guilt and thought and creativity. Baal is a weird parody of the artist manquée—for what he lacks is not talent, or even genius, but the will to use it for anything other than oblivion. He is the caricature of the archetypal frenzied poet, and the symbol of what must become of the possessed who give over the function of exorcism to the crowd—the artist as psychopath.

Without a conscience, simply unaware of evil, Baal is able to act out his most perverse fantasies of incest, rape, murder, self-mutilation, and self-gratification. What emerges from the context of his activity is that the poet's deepest wish is the narcissistic desire to be acted upon, to have inflicted upon himself the fantasies of the group (instead of, traditionally, vice-versa), to be made entirely an object, to be destroyed as a solitary self, to escape consciousness and avoid any kind of movement, any quickness—in short, to be obliterated.

Each scene of the play is arranged in such a way that some form of activity is exchanged for a mode of passivity—health for sickness, day for night, wakefulness for sleep, the independent action of the initiator for the dependent reaction of the victim, the one for the many. Thus the spectacle of the bulls which Baal arranges is really designed to make him the victim of the cheated farmers, just as his behavior with the lumberjacks, or with the friends he betrays, is meant to turn them, in fury, against himself. The best illustration of the way activity is turned toward passivity and eventually quiescence is the series of seductions and rapes that Baal works upon innocent girls and experienced women. For as his sexual history unfolds it becomes clear that Baal is in reality violating himself—not so much because whatever guilt he incurs is debilitating (that hardly seems to matter), but because the act itself is decimating. Baal is perhaps the only lover in literature to use intercourse to bring about impotence, to screw himself to death.

I dwell upon the sexuality of Baal because it is characteristically through the medium of sexual fantasy that—as we shall see in *The Balcony* and *Gorilla Queen*—the audience has tyrannized the art of our times. In

Brecht's play, poetry and sexuality are not opposed; both are perverted in the service of oblivion, in the process of transforming activity into passivity. The proof of this is Baal *at work,* as a poet and singer of songs before an audience. In the rare instances when Baal practices his art in public, he is typically surrounded by a group of large, strong men (teamsters, lumber-jacks), whose passions he deliberately seeks to arouse and turn against himself. The clearest indication of what is going on during his performances is Scene 7 of the play, which is set in a "nightspot," between the toilet and the stage. Baal, drunk, "half-naked," starts to sing about a child who "played with its body so soft and white." The stage directions read as follows:

Applause in the cafe, with some cries of protest. Baal continues to sing. The turmoil increases, as the song becomes more and more shameless. Finally, there is an immense row in the cafe.

Baal has to run from the stage and escape the crowd through the toilet. The art he practices is clearly that of enticement and incitement. He touches the audience's fantasies and then invites them to act them out—that is, to become their own artists and victims. In a sense he does not so much incite them as inspire them, act as a muse for them, provoke them over and over into wishing to tear him, like the ancient victim in a tragic rite, apart. Scene 7 ends with a great, rhythmic shouting of many voices, "Baal! Baal! Baal!" It is the artist's audience out for blood, frustrated lovers, a chorus of Cory-bantes about to fall upon and rend their god, who has just skipped out the window. In this scene, as whenever Baal sings or stages some event, the artist gives up to the audience the completion of his act: he becomes the passive victim of their responses. At one point he even gives them his name, a name that the audience of our time—always stimulated, never satisfied—rightly deserves: Baal, god of insatiability.

Those few writers who have continued to produce dramatic literature since Pirandello and Brecht have been sensitive to the audience's increasing usurpation of the functions of the work of art and the role of the artist. Occasionally a work like Beckett's *Krapp's Last Tape* will assert, though in a shrunken, almost surreptitious way, the traditional baroque relation-ship. At some point in Krapp's life, for example, when expectation, promise became experience, memory, he withdrew into a bare room and became muse, actor, audience, artist—even critic, since, indeed, his new tapes are almost entirely comments upon the old ones. But while there is great pathos in this portrait of a man whose great task was to make his life memorable, and who finds he is living it altogether in retrospect, there is not much rele-vancy. A more acute account of the artist-audience relationship is that in Ionesco's *Chairs,* where the invisible spectators have more reality than the

288

concrete figures of the Old Man and Old Woman, who exist only in order to give them a vacuous message and offer them their lives. Even this description has been superseded. There have been plays in New York in which the audience jumps onto the stage, hatchet in hand, and destroys the theater. It is this audience, on the loose, invading the frame, shattering it, turning upon itself, self-rending, self-devouring, which Genet depicts in *The Balcony*.

In this play, as a direct result of the disappearance of the author, each man is left to create his own fantasies. Genet's theater becomes a brothel in which the separate citizen becomes his own playwright, in which "each individual, when he rings the bell and enters, brings his own scenario, perfectly thought out." The script is always the same *idée fixe,* the same boring narcissistic drama, the same masturbatory fantasy; yet because it is performed before the gilt reflecting mirrors of the Grand Balcony, it does manage to cast and maintain a genuine theatrical doubt about the nature of reality. Gazing at his own reflection, the playwright/pornographer becomes his own actor and audience, his own hero. Genet indicates that the individual seeks to relieve himself in a traditional dramatic mode, through catharsis, by giving each client of the Balcony a "tragedian's cothurni" and padding, so that the gas-man becomes not only a Bishop but a classical hero, Oedipus of Consolidated Edison. (Thus Roger's castration, the logical and inevitable anti-climax of such fantasies, may be taken as a faint echo of Oedipus' retribution.) To a limited degree this catharsis works; the hero does step back through the frame to his everyday, workaday world:

You miss the entire point. When it's over, their minds are clear. I can tell from their eyes. Suddenly they understand mathematics. They love their children and their country. Like you.

The difference between the gas-man and Oedipus is that the applause following his performance sounds like machine-gun fire. His drama has remained a *private* fantasy, and the outside world, the larger audience, without means of vicarious release, revolts. The clients exercise control over their own instincts by acting out the parts of authority figures, a Bishop, a Judge, a General; but because they can forgive, condemn, and command only themselves, the society at large seeks to overthrow precisely the clergy, the army, the magistracy, along with every other ineffectual symbol of hierarchy and order, including, most especially, the seat of all illusions, the Grand Balcony, the stage itself. "The rebellion is an epidemic," Irma declares, "it has the same fatal sacred character." And most dangerous to the proprietress of the Grand Balcony, the revolution is led by men who are unable to fantasize:

289

That's precisely the difference. Those gentlemen—and this seems a new phenomenon —aren't playing, or rather, don't realize they're playing. They calculate. Their faces are pale and sad, their gestures sharp and precise, their speech exact. They don't cheat. They have tremendous power over people. They want to save them.

The central irony of *The Balcony,* and what saves the brothel from the revolution, is that the rebels, no less than the clients, act out a role, play a game. It is only that they do not realize this until they approach the Grand Balcony, and absolute reality falls from their hands. The closer the rebels come to this intricate network of stages, the more they begin to doubt their cause; the easier they find it to fantasize, the more they begin to act like clients instead of citizens. By the time the brothel is surrounded, the reality of the revolt is so ambiguous that it seems but one more charade performed in front of the golden mirrors. The solitary actor and the social rebellion become identical. Thus Irma can say, "The more killing there is in the working-class districts, the more the men roll into my studios." The revolt, like the pornographic dream, is a game, a game in which "there's always the false detail"–black lace beneath the homespun of a saint–"that reminds them that at a certain moment, at a certain point in the drama, they have to stop, even to withdraw." The streets of the city become the brothel: the rebels fight "one hand on the trigger, the other on the fly." The rebellion is a ritual, a "carnival," a replica or "mockery" of the life within the brothel it now surrounds. All the world's a stage.

The revolt is lost when the pale, sad leaders no longer calculate but begin to dream. They build up the whore Chantal into an image of their struggle, a fantasy martyr, a mental embodiment of the revolution. The citizenry begins to fight for her, lets her suffer vicariously for them; and at that point it is a comparatively easy matter for the masters of fantasy to destroy Chantal and substitute their own mock-ups of authority (Bishop, Judge, General, Queen) to quell the revolution. When the doors of the Grand Balcony fly open, the rebels are blinded by the images in the outward-turned mirrors. They *believe in* the stuffed figures on their high wooden shoes. The revolutionaries are so lost in their role-playing that the leaders now gratify themselves within Irma's studio.

The play ends as it began, to private performances and the distant applause of machine-guns. But before it does, the leader of the revolt, Roger, makes a last attempt to remove the source of all fantasy. But his castration has come too late. By turning off all the lights, one by one, all the while explaining to the audience the details of her craft, Irma fits the episode into the general scheme of a day's work (rather like the Manager dealing with

290

the final gunshot in *Six Characters*), as if she controlled not only Roger's act, but the revolution itself, and even the private lives of the theater audience: "You must now go home, where everything—you can be sure—will be even falser than here." It is also a speech closely analogous to the epilogue of the great manipulator in *The Tempest*: weary Prospero, jaded proprietress; the help of the audience's good hands, a final burst of gunfire. The significant difference is that where Prospero breaks his charms and frees his audience from fantasy, Irma delivers hers, spellbound, to it. The magician's audience returns home; the madam's steps through an even more ornate frame into further illusion, of which, once again, they are the authors and the participants.

The problem has been—how to get them back again? As the play suggests, society can be turned into a hall of mirrors, one's life can become the home ground of fantasy. The result is that *The Balcony* has been the last great new play produced in New York, and that was eight years ago. No one goes to the theater any more, or to the concerts, or the galleries. As a kind of enticement, every form has been forced to open up frantically, to clear the way for audience participation. Music is written around stretches of silence, during which the listeners improvise the melodic line. Paintings are left blank, or are arranged so as to act as frames for the casual spectator, backgrounds for the living viewers who stroll before them and become their real subject. Tinguely and Niki de Saint-Phalle's "Hon." rested with legs asunder, waiting for the spectator to become a violator, to possess, in every sense of the word, the work of art. Plays draw characters from the audience, spew actors into the auditorium. The marbled page has come back to publishing, and cardboard cut-outs with crenellated walls thrust upward at what was once the reader. The film, based as it is upon the psychic identification of spectator and star, has always been a baroque medium, and lately it, too, has lost control of its audience. Godard, an inept director, has been praised for introducing accident into the film (as if it were not the artist's pride to leave *nothing* to chance), and into the breech step interviews with "typical" or "representative" citizens, or interminable shots of people eating in cafeterias. In the best of *cinema-verité*, and even in such a superb work as Pasolini's *Gospel According to Saint Matthew,* the real subject matter is the faces of the crowd. Hence, the phenomenon of the bystander as hero, and that concomitant catastrophe, the hero as bystander, as the passive spectator to real events *(Blow Up)* or catatonic mute *(Persona)*. It has all been a dismal failure, something on the level of an Art Linkletter radio show, or one of those long-playing records where the viola part has been left out of the quartet, so that the enthusiast may play along at home.

291

The reason for the irrelevancy of art can be seen on any street corner of San Francisco or New York. The city has been turned into the Grand Balcony. In a place like the Electric Circus in Greenwich Village, or at any multi-media discotheque, the dancers flicker in the stroboscopic lights like actors on a faded screen. As Peter Michelson remarked of the Dom, the "patrons are themselves both part of the art (as discotheque dancers) and its audience. The audience and artistic form are made one." In fact, at one club, Salvation, the audience, on entering, picks a costume and plays a role. But even the Electric Circus is too specialized, has, like the already defunct happenings, too much form. Instead, there are half a dozen places in New York where you can have your photograph blown up into a poster, Belmondo-size. Even in Flushing, students wear fantastic costumes on the streets. "Tattoo" is a trademark, and on Macdougal Street, as at the Circus, you can get your body painted by a professional in the full psyche-delic spectrum. The wits don't read; they make their own statements with buttons, some of them a full eight inches across, Tolstois of the industry. The ultimate work of art, of course, is the trip, and like a playwright arrang-ing the props for a public performance, the artist meticulously orders his environment—dims the lights, sets the color wheel spinning, puts on the acid-rock (*all* music is folk music now)—to prepare the stage for a private viewing.

Every Man an Artist! The execution of that slogan has not only de-stroyed art, it has disarmed criticism. This is not only true of the essentially private phenomena I have mentioned above, but also of the pathetic rem-nants of public communication that make up the bulk of the avant-garde. For in no contemporary work is it possible to detect any aesthetic distance, either of the artist from his work or the work from the audience. The collapse of an internal point of view makes it impossible to maintain one from with-out. The result is what one would predict: the popular critics remain uptown and the academic ones—confusing the prostration of the underground before chance and accident with a new insight into reality and its flat, absolute amorality with social criticism—hop on the bandwagon. Those few critics who remain, and who practice their craft, seem stricken with a terrible uneasiness, which has not stopped them from seeing what is happening. (The two most intelligent critics of underground theater are, it seems to me, Ross Wetzsteon and Peter Michelson. Here is an excerpt from the former, writing about the most interesting dramatist at work in New York, Sam Shepard:

Shepard's plays are not "about" what takes place on stage, but "about" what takes place in the audience—their subjects are actually the emotions they create in those who witness them . . .

292

I shall have more to say about Michelson later on, but I would like to offer this quotation from his piece on Ronald Tavel's *Juanita Castro,* because it illustrates his sensitivity to the same process: "The cast is as much 'audience' as is the viewer," he remarks, and then goes on; "this new esthetic, with its almost exclusive focus on the audience," is entirely without commitment to form. One could multiply the examples.) Inasmuch as the underground theater has any program at all, it is to subvert the exercise of independent judgment—not, that is, to convert the audience (that has already been accomplished) but to force the critic to participate in its way of life.

Perhaps the most relentless and illuminating example of that program in action is Tavel's *Gorilla Queen,* whose success should be measured not by its thrust halfway to Broadway, but by the enthusiastic study Michelson gave it in *The New Republic* (Sept. 9, 1967). [See also his discussion of "The Theatre of the Ridiculous" in *TriQuarterly* #6.] This play, like so many underground or avant-garde works, especially films but not excluding fiction, is based upon material from, and the structure of, fairy tales. In some cases the fairy tale material takes the form of science fiction (the foreground of Burroughs) or exotica and *Chinoiserie* (the background of, say, Robbe-Grillet's *La Maison de Rendez-vous*); in others, of straightforward stories about animals; and in still others, as here, of pop reworkings of grade-B films, newspaper cartoons, or advertising. In each case, the work moves along a similar fairy tale framework, from intense peril to miraculous rescue, to happy ending, from which it dares not deviate. (Thus, trying to marry off Claudette Colbert, Clyde, in *Gorilla Queen,* says, "But let me look around the set: we do have to find someone for you before curtain call." The reason, of course, is that that's the way the movie ended.) The importance of the fairy tale structure is in the first place its irrationality, its magical, random leaps in thought and situation. The destruction of Cartesian logic in favor of "the thinking patterns and non-syllogistic links subliminal reasoning feels along" (Tavel), the substitution of purely associative punning in place of "the trap of words," is high on the formal agenda of the underground. An even more important function of fairy tales (as Freud noted in "The Occurrence in Dreams of Material from Fairy Tales") is to replace the private fantasy with the public myth, the individual, separate childhood with the group experience. Lastly, and as a closely related function, *Gorilla Queen* uses pop fairy tales in order to reach the child in the man, to circumvent adult defenses and reach the creature who once sat in the darkened moviehouse, taking infantilism seriously.

For it is the adult, particularly the adult critic who must remain to some degree aloof from the material he judges, that remains the enemy of the baroque and particularly the post-baroque sensibility. It is he, with his cultivated privacy, his sense of necessary separation, his college-bred dedication to logic, and even his struggle through the psychosexual zones of orality, anality, latency, and his entrance into a glowing, if precarious, genitality, who is the antagonist of the theater of the ridiculous. The purpose of *Gorilla Queen* is not only to dissolve the boundaries that separate men from mob, but also to collapse the individual into himself, to turn the spectator inside out, transforming the repressed trivia, as well as the savage strength, of his unconscious into waking reality. Whereas tragedy tended to seek therapeutic strategies, to replace, in Freud's terms, id with ego, or, in Aristotle's, to lighten and delight the soul, the underground is anti-cathartic: it would flood us with our own fantasies. In tragedy the chorus is composed of average, rational men. In this play we are meant to recognize ourselves in the Glitz Ionas, a horde of concupiscent baboons.

Gorilla Queen goes about its attack upon the critical faculties with, as I have indicated, an assault upon logic and form. The play is filled with parodies of traditional, Western thought:

Because someone always knows where someone else is, such is pure Cartesian logic; because anyone always knows where everyone is, as follows in undiluted Carthusian logic based on the well-known specimen theory of the sample that's amply the whole; and because we are all really one and, being one, are some and, being some, are none and so actually one and since one knows none of two, therefore one specimen knows one of one and therefore one of you knows where one another of you is right now, which is authentic cartographic logic so whoever it is, etcetera, etcetera.

As a substitute for what Tavel takes to be a vestigial tradition, we get some sly references to Yin and Yang, an honest to goodness Indian Mandala ("a mystic symbol that tells you where It's at"), and more delicate references to the superiority of Eastern intuition than you are liable to find this side of Doctor Suzuki. Far more effective is the obsessional punning that makes up the greater part of the play's dialogue: "If I can make her to the altar," says the Chimney Sweep, "I'll be sable to shit the degrating job of chimney sweep and be King for a lay!" Or consider this rather typical exchange:

Karma: Ho-ho; I perceef you are not only wise, but witty, my dear detectif; haf a slug.
Carries: I prefer a hug.
Karma: But a drink in time safes nine—nine months. I should be quite offended if you decline my bar-maid art.
Clyde: Full many a maid by the bar was made.

Contrary to Karma's perception, there is nothing witty in this, nor, probably, was any wit intended. What *is* intended is, on the one hand, the destruction of language, its reduction to nonsense rhyme and monosyllable, and on the other its sexualization, and through that, the eroticization of all thought.

Which brings me to the question of sexuality in this work. Tavel— and a good many other underground film-makers and playwrights—uses sex in two ways, for precisely the two goals I have mentioned: first, horizontally, to force the individual man, the separate critic, into a group, an audience; second, vertically, to collapse the internal borders dividing the individual from his own past and the desires of his infancy. That the sexuality in *Gorilla Queen* and most other underground art is irredeemably homosexual is not so important, it seems to me, as that it is public. We never see lovers alone. There is never, on the small stages and the 16 mm screens, time or room for endearment. Usually there are as many characters crowded about as there are orifices to fill, and whatever the exigencies of the plot, or the particular yearnings of the characters, we are never far from the practice and mentality of the orgy. Again, the celebrated homosexuality of *Gorilla Queen* is less significant than its sexual regressiveness, its inability to make distinctions among sexual objects, its polymorphous perversity. Indeed, the sexual message of Tavel's play reads at times like a gloss of the paradise of Norman O. Brown ("O, gregarious Glitz Ionas! Cease off your Edenish-innocent frolicking and licking!"). Its attitude toward adult genitality runs from the lofty patronization of the dedication—"With patience, to the unpracticing, we dedicate the natural thing"—to the more typical contempt of the Venus Fly Trap:

> Cheeky he to whom is aught
> Alien in an'mal thought;
> Sim'lar he who beastly instinct
> Thinks mere love of licking sin-stink.

The "natural thing" knows no more boundaries than the primitive id, of which it is a manifestation, nor is it capable of making any finer distinctions:

> Male! man! female! king! queen! human! animal!
> ape!
> —what are these terms except expedient, comforting
> designations.

The doctrine, in short, is sexual nihilism, and it is sung out, in all its an'mal thought and beastly instinct, loud and clear by the entire cast at the end of the play:

> Soooooooooooooooooo:
> If it's got a mind, stump it.
> If it stands too high, slump it.
> If it willn't budge, bump it.
> If ya don't like it, lump it.
> But if it's got a hole, hump it!

295

This credo is delivered in the midst of the spectators, and it is because Tavel feels sure of his audience ("Please, tight patrons, bend right over!") that he can indulge in a series of baroque clichés: lines like "the four corners of the stage are the far corners of the earth," or "show cause why theez show shouldn't be closed down," or "I seen this play before"; and references to the program credits, the wings, the difficulties of exposition. One of the stock devices of the play is for a character to be asked the time, look at his watch, and deliver the exact hour in the theater. The fact that stage time and audience time are identical only underlines the audience's submergence in the material. Ultimately, there *are* no characters, no plot, to *Gorilla Queen;* there is only a series of variations on the audience's recognition of its own past, the childhood response to the Hollywood epic. As one of the actors remarks, "We're but the go-between / In this forties' flick routine." Or, as the chorus of Glitz Ionas sings at the start of the play: "We be all a single corps!"

Though it is true that Tavel and his audience keep the same time, that *Gorilla Queen* is, in a sense, a dream of its spectators, it is also true that the play is aimed—as its dedication makes clear—at the hold-out in the crowd, the separate viewer who refuses to go along with the religion, the critic who must, if only for professional reasons, keep his distance. I used the phrase, "go along with the religion," deliberately: the fact is, the conflict in this play is essentially a recapitulation of that between Dionysus and Pentheus in Euripides' *The Bacchae*. In *Gorilla Queen*, Pentheus, he who would resist the new, wild, orgiastic, ecstatic religion, is represented by Clyde Batty, while Dionysus, the perverse, the bringer of "sleep" and "oblivion," the god with a woman's curls, is represented by Queen Kong. In his appreciation of this play, Michelson incorrectly calls Batty the hero, and confuses his values with those of the theater of the ridiculous. It is a fundamental error. Batty, no less than Pentheus, is the antagonist, the civilized man who impedes the spread of the faith, the colonialist in the jungle of the instincts (Pentheus is a hunter, Batty a lion-tamer, both professional curbers of animal thought and passion). Above all, Batty is the non-believer. "All that mumbu-jumbo bloodthirsty juju is over," he announces to the disappointed Glitz Ionas, "gone with the Dark Ages to which it belongs." He is not the hero of the play, but of that small remnant of an earlier audience, whom Tavel has set out to convert, the "hetero-hero" that the savages have sworn to "homogenize." He is also a man committed to rationality, a pataphysician who insists on making just those distinctions, in both thought and sex, that the theater of the ridiculous calls madness (hence the name Batty) and has sworn to obliterate:

I am Clyde Batty, the *great* Clyde Batty, by Hollywood given the jurisdiction to corner, capture, and round up all—to cage, categorize, and define!

. . . you see, where I come from, animals as well as people are taught to keep their place. For beast is beast and nest is nest and never the sane shall invest in the twain. A line is a line and division division and woe be to he [who] holds derision toward either. And neither shall lessen but both find a blessin', if brute in the junkel stays and man goeth separate ways.

Batty's sin, then, is identical to Pentheus's. He is unable to accept. He must assert his critical judgment, his sense of discrimination; he refuses to give up his heterosexual genitality; and he rejects the religion of the underground:

Cause it's a cult grounded on pain, on banal anal mass masochism and shady sadyism. Isn't it funny, honey, that in two thousand years of worship it shouldn't have occurred to you that pleasure can also be fun?

In the world of *Gorilla Queen,* this is heresy indeed. Yet, for a time, his criticism, his anti-heroics, succeed. As Pentheus was able to round up the Corybantes and jail their leader, Batty manages to interrupt the sacrificial rites of the new religion, to attack and kill the emasculating Venus Fly Trap, and even to tame Queen Kong, incarcerate it, and shoot it between the eyes. But the triumph of reason, or if you will repression, is short-lived. Just as Dionysus changed himself into a bull and broke down the prison walls behind which Pentheus had thrust him, so the caging of Queen Kong is the signal for a series of startling transformations whose effect is to undo, in every sense of the word, Batty, both as a critic and a man.

That collapse begins when Kong is transformed ("like a omnivorous prince from a frugivorous frog") into Taharahnugi White Woman, who has been pursuing Clyde, in "her" inverted way, throughout the play. Batty loses, first, his reason ("I'm stark raving nuts") and then, when it turns out his toes are webbed, his lofty position on the cultural scale ("Not so high up on de tree of efolution himself, is he, theez Mr. Muskelar Half-Back!"). This is the beginning of Clyde's psychic and sexual and even evolutionary collapse. In his confusion, Clyde, still asking his irrelevant, logical questions ("Which do you prefer: screwing men or screwing women?") is raped by the Corpse of Kong and, thus impregnated, gives birth to himself as Clyde as Kong. Lest this imagery of incest and hermaphroditism seem too abstruse, this is how Taharahnugi, herself the offspring of the first Queen Kong, and blushing bride of the resurrected Clyde, explains it:

Clyde shot Kong, and I resulted. Kong-Shot raped Clyde, and he resulted. I am Kong-as-Kong-Shot; he is Kong-as-Kong-Shot's-Load-Shot.

The fairy tale structure dictates a marriage at the end, and since "we be all single corps," the ceremony sounds like this:

And now, with the power invested in me by the Union of Witch Doctresses, I pronounce you man and wife, or man and man, or ape and man, or queen and woman, or queen and man, or queen and queen, or ape and ape up and up.

The marriage is ultimately between the mass fantasy of *Gorilla Queen* and the last member of the audience, represented by Clyde. Torn asunder, it is the critic that stains the sheets. This is why, at the end of the play, Brute comes forward and throws a rose, which throughout has acted as a symbol of perfect consummation, into the audience of savages, and why he can say, with horrible truth, "Art ain't never 'bout life, but life *is* only 'bout art."

When I saw *Gorilla Queen* a few months ago I inadvertently happened, while digging through my pockets for something to read, to elbow the spectator on my right, who turned out to be a boy of about eight.

"What are *you* doing here?" I asked.

"Oh, I come every night," he replied, without taking his eyes from the stage. I was dumfounded enough to ask him why.

"Because my mother is in the show. She's on the stage now."

"Where?" I asked.

"There!" he answered, and pointed to where a hollow-cheeked woman, a member of the chorus, was fornicating with an ape. That child was the same age as the Boy in *Six Characters,* and in a sense their functions were the same. When, in Pirandello's play, the Boy shoots himself, the last barrier between the stage and the audience, appearance and reality, art and life, is whisked away; so here he sat, his eyes glazed with future fantasies, far more a part of the chorus than the audience, which in truth was filled with corpses, mindless homunculi, corrupted no less than that child for the lack of a babysitter, the absence of a critical consciousness. "If it's got a mind, stump it," sing the savages, to the echo of their own laughter, their own applause. It is a sound like death, and it is everywhere in the air.

298

Contributors:

Stephen Koch teaches at the State University of New York at Stony Brook. **Ron Loewinsohn's** latest books were *L'Autre* (Black Sparrow Press, 1967) and *The Step* (Black Sparrow Press, 1968).   **Faye Kicknosway** is a past editor of *Wayne Review*.   **Andrew Field** is currently at work on two books and a cottage in Palm Beach, Australia. His recent critical study, *Nabokov —His Life in Art,* appeared as a paperback in 1968. The chapter herein is from a novel-in-progress, *Fractions.*   **C. G. Hanzlicek** teaches at Fresno State College.   **Dennis Schmitz,** also from California, is included in the first Swallow Poetry Series anthology.   **Karen Hanson** is a graduate of Cornell. **T. Voss** was born between D-Day and V-E Day. His first novel is yet to be published. In spite of this, he still has one great ambition.   **Mitchell Sisskind** is a graduate of Columbia University, and has published previously in *Arts and Literature.*   **Eugenia Macer** has designed public relations material for the Riverside Church Theatre, and handled the thunder sheet for Ghelderhode's *Chronicles of Hell.*   **Jack Anderson** is news editor of *Dance Magazine* and a New York correspondent for *Ballet Today* (London). His book of poetry, *The Invention of New Jersey,* was published in 1969 by the University of Pittsburgh Press.   **Andrea Pfeiffenberger** attended Vassar. She spends summers in Turkey working in Byzantine archaelogoy.   **John Perreault** is art critic for *The Village Voice* and associate editor of *Art News.* **Marvin Bell,** author of *Things We Dreamt We Died For* (Stone Wall Press), edits poetry for *North American Review* and for *Midland II.* He teaches in the Writer's Workshop at the University of Iowa.   **David Shapiro's** collection of poems, *January,* was published in 1965 by Holt, Rinehart and Winston.   **James Tate's** first book, *The Lost Pilot,* was published in the Yale Series of Younger Poets. His second book, *The Notes of Woe,* was published by Stone Wall Press.   **Mark Malkas** resides in New York State with his husband and wife. He graduated from, his hobbies are, and when he grows up he wants to be.   **Jonathan Penner** lives in New York. His novel-in-progress, *Three Children,* is under option to Scribners.   **Jonathan Strong** lives in Cambridge, Massachusetts. The entire *Tyke's Days* will appear in a collection of his work from Little, Brown.   **Louise Gluck** lives in New York, where she teaches poetry to dropouts. Her first collection of poems, *First-born*, was published by the New American Library.   **Walter Hall's** first book, *Spider Poems,* was published in 1967 by Walter Hamady's Perishable

Press Limited. He is now producing and directing educational radio programs for WDET-FM in Detroit. **Alexis Viereck** is a graduate of Harvard University. **John McEvoy** is a former college English teacher now employed as a feature writer for the *Daily Racing Form.* **Joyce Carol Oates's** latest book is *Expensive People* (Vanguard). She is now teaching at the University of Windsor, Ontario. **Keith Abbott's** first book, *Dumptruck,* was published by the Polygon Press. **James Crenner** is the author of *The Aging Ghost* (Golden Quill Press, 1964). He teaches at Hobart and William Smith Colleges in Geneva, New York. **Susan Whitney** is an art student at the University of Montana. **David Lunde** teaches at the State University at Fredonia. **St. Geraud,** also known as William Knott, reportedly perpetrated suicide in 1966. Their affairs are currently being handled by David Carellis, of the same address. His first book, *The Naomi Poems,* will be published by Follett. **James Hersh** teaches in Atlanta, where he is at work on a book of poems. **Tom Clark** is the author of *The Sand Burg* (Ferry Press, London) and *Stories* (Harper and Row). **Jon Anderson's** first book, *Looking for Jonathan,* will be published by the University of Pittsburgh. **Jim Harrison** is the author of *Plain Song* (Norton). He teaches at the State University of New York at Stony Brook, and co-edits *Sumac.* **R. J. Wilson** is not R. J. Wilson, except when writing poems. Otherwise he is Walter Burckhard, currently serving a California prison sentence on a drug charge. **Trim Bissell** teaches at Wayne State University in Detroit. **Daryl Hine** is editor of *Poetry Magazine.* His most recent books are *The Wooden Horse* and *Minutes*, both published by Atheneum. **William A. Henkin, Jr.,** is the author of *Toward Skiles,* a collection of poetry. **Charles Newman's** first novel, *New Axis,* was published by Houghton-Mifflin Co. in 1966. He is currently at work on a second novel, *The Promisekeeper.* **Michael Dennis Browne** was a Fulbright scholar from England at the University of Iowa Writer's Workshop. He has written a children's cantata and a song cycle, with the English composer, David Lord. **Sylvia Wilkinson** is a painter, tennis champion, and sports car enthusiast. Her first novel, *Moss on the North Side,* was published in 1966 by Houghton-Mifflin Co., which also published *A Killing Frost,* from which this is an excerpt. **Danny Lyon** is a member of SNCC, the Chicago Outlaws, and Magnum. His first book, *The Bikeriders,* was published by MacMillan. **Ronald Johnson** has published two books of poetry: *A Line of Poetry, A Row of Trees* (Jargon Books, 1965), and *The Book of the Green Man* (Norton, 1967). **Leslie Epstein** has published fiction and criticism in the *New American Review* and the *Yale Review.* He teaches at Queens College in New York City. **Peter Michelson** is a former editor of *Chicago Review,* and now teaches at Notre Dame. He is at work on a study of pornography for Herder and Herder.